HOME BUTCHERING
AND
MEAT
PRESERVATION

To the animals . . . I dedicate this book.

No. 2713
$24.95

HOME BUTCHERING
AND
MEAT PRESERVATION

GEETA DARDICK
ILLUSTRATIONS BY SAM DARDICK

TAB BOOKS Inc.
Blue Ridge Summit, PA 17214

FIRST EDITION
FIRST PRINTING

Copyright © 1986 by Geeta Dardick
Printed in the United States of America

Library of Congress Cataloging in Publication Data

Dardick, Geeta.
Home butchering and meat preservation.

Includes index.
1. Slaughtering and slaughter-houses. 2. Meat
cutting. 3. Meat—Preservation. 4. Livestock.
I. Title.
TS1962.D27 1986   641.3′6   86-5856
ISBN 0-8306-0513-4
ISBN 0-8306-2713-8 (pbk.)

Contents

Acknowledgments   ix

Introduction   x

1 Why Raise Your Own Meat-Producing Animals?   1

Health Benefits—Dangers in Commercial Meat—The Link with Eggs, Milk, and Manure—Animals Work for You

2 Which Animals Should You Raise for Meat?   6

How Many Pounds of Meat Does Each Animal Give?—How Much Fencing and Housing Do You Need?—At What Age Do You Slaughter Animals?—What Will Feed Cost?—What Are Your Family's Taste Preferences?

3 Tips on Raising Meat Animals   13

Chickens—Ducks—Turkeys—Geese—Rabbits—Pigs—Goats—Lamb—Beef

4 Are You Ready to Slaughter?   33

The Knives You Will Need—Sharpening Knives—Basic Equipment—Is the Carcass Healthy?

5 Poultry: Killing, Cleaning, Cooking   44

Slaughtering Poultry—Removing Feathers—Evisceration—Geeta's Poultry Recipes

6 Can You Skin a Rabbit?   59

Killing Rabbit—Evisceration—Rabbit Recipes

7 Butchering Goats, Sheep, and Venison   **72**

Preparations for Slaughter—Slaughtering Goats/Lambs—Skinning the Goat/Sheep—Eviscerating Goats and Lambs—Slaughtering, Skinning, and Eviscerating Venison—Chilling the Carcass—Cutting the Lamb/Goat Carcass into Primary Pieces—Cutting Up Deer—General Instructions for Jerky—Recipes for Lamb, Goat, Venison

8 Pigs: Slaughtering and Cutting Up   **99**

Pre-Slaughter Considerations—Killing the Pig—To Scald or to Skin—Scalding and Scraping—Skinning—Evisceration—Cutting Up the Pig—Recipes for Fresh Pork

9 Veal and Beef: Slaughtering and Cutting Up   **128**

Gathering Your Equipment—Stunning and Bleeding the Beef Animal—Skinning the Calf/Steer—Hoisting, Eviscerating, and Splitting the Calf/Steer—First Lessons in Cutting Up Beef—Cutting Up Beef—Recipes for Beef

10 Making Your Living as a Home Butcher   **181**

The Building—Getting Started—Equipment—The Work Load—Is Home Meat Cutting for You?

11 Professional Slaughtering   **200**

Bill Dowling: Local Professional Slaughterer—Equipment for Ranch Slaughtering—The Business of Slaughtering—Customer Relations

12 Freezing   **209**

Before You Freeze Your Meat—How to Freeze Meats—Freezer Shelf Life of Meats—Additional Benefits of Freezing

13 Canning   **216**

Why Can Meat?—Home Canning Precautions—Pressure Canning Basics—Creatively Canning Meat—Canning Times for Meats

14 Curing   **224**

The Curing Controversy—Nitrates and Nitrites in Home Curing—Ham Basics—Country-Style Hams—Brine-Cured Hams and Bacons—Brine-Curing Hams and Bacons at Home—How to Make Salami and Other Cured Meats—Recipes—Building a Smokehouse—How to Smoke Meat

15 Meat By-Products   **248**

Saving Rabbit Skins—Tanning Hides at Home—Tanning with the Fur On—Tanning with the Fur Off—Rendering Animal Fats—Making Soap—Blood and Feathers, and Other Odds and Ends—Back to the Land

Appendix   **265**

Index   **269**

HOME BUTCHERING
AND
MEAT
PRESERVATION

Acknowledgments

I WANT TO THANK MY HUSBAND SAM DARDICK FOR suggesting that I write an article on our neighbor, John Taylor, the meat cutter; Lynn Acrizzi for running the article in *Farmstead Magazine*; Leslie Wenger, from TAB BOOKS Inc., for asking me to turn the article into a full length book; and Kim Tabor from TAB BOOKS Inc., for her keen interest and helpful assistance during the writing process.

Special respects to all the people of the San Juan Ridge and Nevada County, California, whose ideas contributed to this book, especially John and Julie Taylor, Dennis and Natalie Atkinson, Bill Dowling and Regie McDaniel.

Thanks also to the government and agency officials who helped me, and kudos to Caleb, Joshua, and Samantha Dardick for the many, many years you did all those animal chores.

Introduction

THIS BOOK IS FOR PEOPLE WHO WANT TO LEARN how to raise, slaughter, cut up, and preserve their own meat. For those of you who have been reared in the country, this book will review skills you most likely learned from your parents and grandparents. For those of you who have moved to the country from urban upbringings, this book will offer an introduction to the art of butchering and meat preservation.

I fall into the urban category. Before my husband Sam and I moved back-to-the-land in 1973, I had never raised a farm animal—and had never killed anything larger than an insect. But urbane as I was, I soon learned how to slaughter and cut up our meat animals, and so can you. Not that it was easy.

As enthusiastic new homesteaders, we brought animals onto the land from the start: goats for milk, chickens for eggs, ducks to swim on our 4-acre lake. We planted orchards and vegetable gardens and used all that great animal manure to make our crops flourish. As for killing animals—no way. We decided we'd only eat fruits, vegetables, milk, eggs, and grains.

For a year this vegetarian animal rearing worked quite well. Our animals were very alive and happy, and come springtime, like all good animals, they reproduced. Soon we were overwhelmed with excess animals, especially excess males which gave us neither eggs nor milk. We bought more and more bags of animal feed, and put off solving our dilemma.

Then one day our healthy crew of male ducks killed one of their favorite female friends in an overzealous round of love-making on the lake. The message was clear. Either we thinned out our male duck population, or they were going to thin out our females.

That night we had duck a l'orange for dinner. And we haven't been vegetarians since. We still view animals as the beautiful, living creatures that they are, but we also use them for meat . . . healthy, home-raised meat.

You also might have moved back-to-the-land with high ideals, but very little practical knowledge about raising and slaughtering animals. And like me, perhaps you also feel a little guilty about killing animals. After all, those of us who have left behind the conveniences of life in the eighties to sweat it out on the farm wish to be close to nature, not kill it. Yet killing (harvesting) animals is an intrinsic part of the back-to-the-land movement. And even if you know nothing about slaughtering and cutting up animals, if I could learn how, you can learn how as well.

This book is for all of my fellow back-to-the-land friends who keep animals on their farms. Please enjoy your animals fully while they are alive. Always raise your animals healthfully and treat them humanely. When their time on your farm has come to its end, follow my directions for killing your animals, cutting them up, and preserving and cooking their meat. I have tried to make all explanations clear yet simple. I have assumed you are intelligent, but basically unknowledgeable concerning how to get a live animal from the field to the table.

Thus the heart of the book includes how-to chapters on poultry, rabbits, goats, sheep, venison, pigs, and cows—how to kill them and how to cut them up. Initial chapters help you decide what animals to raise, detail methods for raising animals, and describe equipment you will need for butchering the animals. Later chapters deal with methods of processing and preserving animals and their by-products. You can read the book straight through from start to finish, or you can use the index to look up the specific animal or subject that concerns you.

Of special interest are two chapters giving directions for readers who might want to go into business slaughtering other peoples' farm animals or cutting them up. Rural people are always looking for ways to make extra money. Free-lance slaughtering and butchering are viable home business opportunities that could help support your back-to-the-land habit. As you become more proficient at home butchering you never know where your skills might take you.

Above all, this entire book is about eating. I hope the information will help you put many delicious meals on your country table. How many times have I come to the dinner table in my overalls and muddy boots, to sit down to a meal that would only be served at the finest gourmet restaurant. A back-to-the-land lifestyle might contain many examples of voluntary simplicity, but the food on the table most often resembles a gastronomic extravaganza. If you enjoy eating meat, there's nothing quite like growing your own. Bon appetit!

Chapter 1
Why Raise Your Own Meat-Producing Animals?

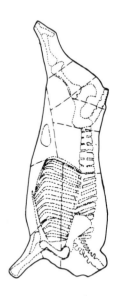

CARNIVOROUS APPETITES NOTWITHSTANDING, raising some domestic animals on the land is like raising some tomato plants—your homestead wouldn't look quite like a proper farm without them.

Farm animals contribute to that basic farm scene depicted on so many country calendars. From the human viewpoint, they please the eye. I never fail to gaze at my neighbor Regie McDaniel's yard as I drive by on my occasional trips to town. Last night at dusk his peacocks, sheep, geese, and cow were all grazing contentedly in the same small field, while a full moon inched its way up over the horizon. Contented farm animals have a beautiful aura that pleases the human soul.

Although I am not aware of any scientifically-controlled psychological studies on the effect of farm animals on people's attitudes toward life, it is obvious that domestic animals make people feel good. (I am not talking about the chores here—we'll deal with that later.) I am talking about looking at the animals, touching them, talking to them, hanging out with them. Children always go into ecstasy when they visit my farm. "See the ducks, see the rabbit, see the chickens, see the goats," they scream, running from cage to cage, pointing wildly. "Can I go into the cage? Can I play with them?" they ask hopefully, enthusiastically.

Modern zoos are a case in point. They all contain these marvelous "touchy, feely" areas full of what? Animals, of course. Children love them. Farm animals help adults feel good about themselves, too. I can't tell you how many times I have walked outside depressed, bummed out, negative (I am the emotional type), only to feel cheered up by the presence of my contingent of domestic animals. Is it trite to say that in a fast-paced world, contact with calm, undemanding animals refreshes the human spirit?

Sighting wild animals also gives people a big lift. Every time I see the great blue heron land on my lake, I feel blissful, like I have just received a special gift, a visual thrill, a good omen. But I cannot guarantee how often Mother Nature will bless me with a heron, a school of red-winged blackbirds, a bittern, a flock of wild mallards. So I keep my own duck flock to grace the pond. On my farm, I am "Mother Nature," raising animals to give my land the look that pleases. Animals are my own private therapists.

HEALTH BENEFITS

Besides giving your land a wonderfully pleasing appearance, farm animals provide you with a source of food. Isn't that why we all farm—to raise food for the table? And delicious food at that.

I cannot tell you the right amount of meat to eat. Meat definitely provides needed protein, as well as vitamins and minerals in the diet. It is a highly nutritional food.

Today, eating huge portions of red meat at every meal is a bit out of style. Many people prefer oriental-style cooking, stir-frying smaller portions of meat along with vegetables, rather than gorging nightly on a pound of flesh. How much meat to eat is a subject for you and your health consultants to consider. Every book and every expert will tell you something different. It is also possible that there is actually no such thing as an optimum diet; the diet that is right for one person might not be right for another.

Assuming that you have decided to eat some meat, there are definite benefits in growing your own animals for slaughter. If you raise your own animals, you know everything about them—what they are eating, the type of care they are getting, their immunizations, their health, the condition of their cages, the method of slaughter, the appearance of the carcass.

I killed two baby goats yesterday. I know they were milk-fed by their mothers for four months, and then let out to browse on plentiful brush, plus fed a daily ration of barley-corn for the two final months of their life. I know they were healthy, well-loved animals. I know they were never given hormones, antibiotics, or chemicals of any kind. I know I killed them as mercifully as I possibly could. I enjoy knowing what I am eating.

DANGERS IN COMMERCIAL MEAT

The meat available in supermarkets comes from commercially-raised animals. Today commercially-raised animals are given hormones and fed antibiotics and other drugs. These practices increase growth and prevent illness. In the competitive business arena, the use of chemical additives assures the farmer a profit on hogs, steers, or poultry. Unfortunately, these same additives can leave unsafe residues in the meat we eat. They are a mixed blessing—helping the farmer raise plump, healthy animals, yet endangering the health of the consumer.

The concern about drug residues in our meat supply is not merely the worry of a few food faddists. On the contrary, it has become a major public health concern, with Congressional committees currently investigating the degree of risk to consumers.

Antibiotics kill off many disease-causing bacteria in animals; however, they let the strongest drug-resistant bacteria flourish. When these drug-resistant bacteria are passed on to humans in meats, they increase the risk of serious illness or death because they don't respond to antibiotics treatment.

Hormones used in commercial meat production have also caused serious problems in human health. In 1979, the controversial animal hormone DES was finally banned after it was linked to cancer in human beings. Many other hormones are still being implanted in animals today, and even DES is still being used illegally.

Besides the link with cancer and the growth of resistant bacteria, animal drugs can cause birth defects, anemia, and allergies. Some of these drugs such as arsenic and sulfonamides, are legal; some such as albendazole and choloramphenicol are used illegally.

The United States Department of Agriculture, Food Safety and Inspection Service, sets safe residue levels for all chemical additives in animals, and monitors slaughtered animals by checking a percentage of them to make sure they do not contain dangerous residue levels.

In a telephone interview, Dr. Gerald R. Snyder, Acting Director, Slaughter Division, Food Safety and Inspection Service, told me that the government inspection program provides protection to the consumer from dangerous levels of antibiotics, hormones, and other chemicals. He added, however: "That's not to say some doesn't get in there." Dr. Snyder definitely supported the idea of raising your own meat at home. "I think most anyone would feel better eating an animal that they knew how it was raised."

I agree with him. Raising and eating homegrown meat avoids the residue problem completely. When you raise your own animals, you don't have to get caught up in the debate whether or not routine use of hormones, antibiotics, and arsenic is dangerous; you just don't use them. When an animal gets sick—as will happen occasionally—if you give chemical medicines you can be certain not to slaughter the animal until the approved time, as stated on the label.

Raising animals at home takes work and costs money. It takes no effort to buy meat at the store, and if you buy sale items, you often find real bargains. But if you want to know exactly what you are eating, if you want the meat on your table to be as organic and natural as possible, growing your own meat should appeal to you.

At the bottom line, in this highly industrialized and advanced society, growing your own meat links you with your primitive roots. How exciting that we still have the knowledge how to raise meat healthfully down on the farm. Tending animals and killing them connects us with the collective past. As the civilization marches toward an agribusiness mentality based on making money at all costs, perhaps it is fitting that a few of us still remember and practice the old ways.

THE LINK WITH EGGS, MILK, AND MANURE

Many people who raise animals to supply meat for their families simultaneously receive eggs, milk, and manure. Producing your own eggs is very desirable. You can see the difference between farm fresh eggs and most commercially-produced eggs in the color of the yolk. Chickens allowed to range (or fed a varied diet in their cages) produce rich, tasty eggs. You might want to raise poultry primarily for these eggs, and then eat the excess roosters that hatch every year, as well as stew the older hens as their egg production falls. If you produce eggs, chances are you will also eat poultry.

Raising dairy animals gives the same sort of meat dividends. For milk production, you breed your animals annually. The animal uses its milk to feed its young. Every spring, with gamblers' luck, your farm will be blessed with several baby boys—non-milkers. Even though their economic value is often negligible, if you give these male animals away, you are depriving your own family of savory meat.

My neighbor Dennis Atkinson recently slaughtered a male baby Jersey calf. Jersey males are known to grow up mean and boney. Dennis had no desire to keep the animal. Although the animal weighed 100 pounds at 2 months, Dennis couldn't have gotten $15.00 for it alive (a female baby would have been worth $2000.00). However, by killing the animal rather than selling it, the Atkinson family will enjoy veal, a delicacy worth $6.00 to $7.00 per pound. That's the type of meat most people can't afford to buy, but the Atkinson's eat veal regularly in their ultra-simple, back-to-the-land lifestyle, as one of the by-products of milk production.

In my first years of raising milk goats, I took several baby boy goats to auction and received only $6.00 each for them. The people who bought these little billies took them home, raised them on milk, and resold them for meat. My $6.00 fee didn't even cover the gasoline needed to drive to auction. In later years I learned to enjoy chevon (goat meat), and now would never sell cheap or give away babies. I raise them and slaughter at five or six months. Believe me— young goat meat has an excellent flavor. It is easy to acquire a taste for it.

Fig. 1-1. An ideal small farm.

One of the joys of back-to-the-land living is being involved in every aspect of the life cycle. You grow a tomato plant, eat the tomato, save the seed for more plants, compost the spent vines into fertilizer to sidedress more tomato plants.

Animals fit in well with this natural process called "permaculture." At nearby Pike Apple Orchard, sheep graze among the organically grown trees. The sheep nibble the groundcover (clover) and leave their manure to fertilize it. The clover enriches the orchard. Clover . . . sheep . . . manure . . . apples . . . people: do you see how they intertwine?

My neighbor Sharon Umphress raises goats for milk and apple trees for apples. She also raises a pig and feeds it her excess milk and whey (from cheesemaking) and her apple culls. She uses her pig manure to fertilize the apple trees. In permaculture, all farming practices interconnect.

Figure 1-1 is an artist's conception of a farm where permaculture is practiced. The farmhouse sits centrally to the orchard, garden, barn, fields, and pond. All aspects of the small homestead are interconnected.

The manure you receive from your animals links them directly to your garden. In our area, green thumbs notwithstanding, the success of a garden is directly related to the amount of manure put into it. The more animals, the more manure, the more productive the garden.

With the costs of manure going up and the cost of trucking equally high, producing manure at home is a compelling reason for raising animals. I am probably safe in saying that farmers do not raise animals for their manure and then eat the animals as a secondary by-product. But the value of manure to the homesteader cannot be underrated.

ANIMALS WORK FOR YOU

Besides giving you meat, milk, eggs, and manure, domestic farm animals will even work for you. At our farm we use goats to control our brush. (We often joke that we bought 34 acres of brush rather than 34 acres of land.) People are always looking for a goat to keep their lawns mowed or the blackberry patch under control. The brush keeps the animal well fed, and the animal holds down the risk of fire and keeps the place cleaned up.

We use ducks to keep the waterweeds on our lake from multiplying so rapidly. Chinese geese are also excellent weeders, especially on land. Many folks buy them to hold down weeds in strawberry patches. Geese are also effective watchdogs (watchgeese). If you feel comfortable running chickens in your garden, they definitely help with bug control.

It's hard to imagine a back-to-the-land farm without animals. Their appearance, their sounds, their by-products, and their ability to work for you link them strongly to any attempt toward self-sufficiency. Although the subject of this text is how to kill and cut up your animals, raising animals on the farm has many more dimensions than their ultimate appearance on your plate as a piece of meat. The killing and cutting will take only a few hours or days of your time, yet you will spend many months with your various animals. You will feed them and care for them. They, in turn, will give you a vital connection with the world of nature.

Today many people know animals only from picture books, if at all. Their sole contact with animal life is as a dead hunk of meat, packaged under plastic wrap in the supermarket showcase. These people have no idea what knowledge and experiences they are missing. As a back-to-the-land farmer, you know animals firsthand. How fortunate.

5

Chapter 2
Which Animals Should You Raise for Meat?

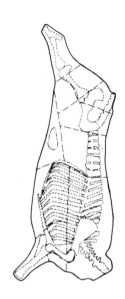

YOU HAVE DECIDED YOU WANT TO RAISE ANIMALS for meat. How can you determine which animals are right for you and your family? Should you choose cattle, sheep, goats, pigs, turkeys, chickens, ducks, geese, or rabbits? All of them? Some of them? One of them?

Some back-to-the-land people seem to prefer the "buy now, learn later" approach. They will spontaneously purchase an animal because it is cute or a bargain. They also take home every free animal that is offered to them. In my opinion, this philosophy of animal-rearing can prove costly on many levels.

I firmly recommend the "think now, buy later" method of animal raising. If you can answer five basic questions before you bring home any animals, I believe you will be much more successful at raising delicious, affordable meat.

Here are the questions I want you to ask yourself:

☐ How many pounds of meat does each animal give?

☐ How much fencing/caging/housing will I need for each of the animals I raise?

☐ How long will I raise these animals, and how many months does it take to reach killing weight?

☐ What will it cost me to feed each animal for this amount of time, and how well does the animal convert feed into flesh?

☐ What are my family's taste preferences in meat?

Please don't let these questions scare you away from raising animals. Their only purpose is to help you make wise decisions. And if you still want to take in every "freebie" animal that your neighbors toss at you, you can do that. But at least you will know what you are doing.

HOW MANY POUNDS OF MEAT DOES EACH ANIMAL GIVE?

Even small children can tell you that cows are big and ducks are little. But how big and how

6

little? The following figures aren't absolutes, but they should help you think about which animals you might grow.

Do you really want to raise beef? "Oh, I love the taste of T-bone steaks," you think to yourself. But I ask you, do you want to raise a 1000-pound animal, that will dress out at about 600 pounds? Or would a lamb (115 pounds live weight and 60 pounds dressed weight) be more practical for you? You could supplement it with about a dozen ducks at 2 or 3 pounds each. Is that more realistic?

Only you can determine approximately how many pounds of meat your family consumes in a year. If you only want to eat a little meat, be cautious when your neighbor tries to sell you a baby pig. They might seem small at first, and the price might seem ultra-reasonable, but pigs grow up to weight about 225 pounds, and give 150 pounds of meat. Is that what you really want? A young goat, which would give you about 35 pounds of meat for the freezer, might be a wiser choice.

On the other hand, if you have a big family that enjoys meat, raising only a couple of chickens could prove frustrating. The year we raised ten meat chickens (White Rocks), their flavor was wonderful, but they didn't last us past Christmas. They whetted our appetites rather than satisfied them. By January, we were buying chicken at the supermarket, and it didn't taste nearly as good.

While you consider which animals to buy in terms of weight, you must be clear that certain animals are awesome breeders. For example, if you learn to raise rabbits successfully, you can get 70 pounds of edible meat per year from one doe. Does, of course, don't weight 70 pounds, but each doe can have four births (kindlings) of eight baby rabbits per delivery. You need to look into reproductive potential as you think about various animals.

In Table 2-1 I estimate how many pounds of meat you will get from each animal you raise. Please realize that these figures are meant as general guidelines; the breed you raise, the feed you use, and the age of death will cause weight variations. Also, different people butcher their animals at different weights because of personal preference.

As you read the table, please remember that live weight and dressed weight are not the same thing. And if you are considering some of the larger animals, or a large number of smaller ones, be sure and ask yourself: How will I store the meat I raise? If you can't eat it all in one sitting, you will need adequate freezer space.

After studying Table 2-1, try to do the following simple math problem. If your family wants to freeze 300 pounds of meat, which combination of animals should you raise?

☐ 5 rabbits, 10 ducks, 5 geese, 2 lambs, 3 goats, 1 hog.

Table 2-1. Live Weights and Dressed Weights* of Meat Animals.

ANIMAL	LIVE WEIGHT	DRESSED WEIGHT
beef	1000 lbs.	600 lbs.
hog	225 lbs.	150 lbs.
veal	150 lbs.	90 lbs.
lamb	115 lbs.	60 lbs.
goat	60 lbs.	35 lbs.
turkey	25 lbs.	20 lbs.
goose	12 lbs.	10 lbs.
duck	5 lbs.	3 lbs.
chicken	5 lbs.	3 lbs.
rabbit	4 lbs.	2 lbs.

*After removal of head, skin, innards.

☐ 1 hog, 1 veal, 1 turkey, 20 rabbits.

Did you get the right answer? Knowing approximate weights of dressed animals should help you make your own decisions.

HOW MUCH FENCING AND HOUSING DO YOU NEED?

You will want to have your fencing, caging, housing, and barns completed before you bring home your animals. Therefore, you will need to know the type of shelter your animals require. In some climates (like mine) you can get by with relatively simple shelters. In others, you will need to keep your animals in more complex buildings. To protect them thoroughly from too much cold or too much heat.

Unless you intend to let your animals range freely, you will have to fence them. How much fencing will you need? What will it cost you? Will you be raising your animals on pasture or will you keep them in small pens and feed them once or twice a day? Will you need to build super-strong fencing, or will you be able to get by with moderately-strong (less expensive) fences? Do you have facilities to run commercial electric fencing, or solar electric fencing?

You need to know something about the methods of containing various animals before you even get started, or else you could make costly mistakes. Bill Helphinstine, who just retired after 40 years as a farm advisor, puts it this way: "If a person is asking me whether or not they can raise meat, the first question I ask them is: Do they have facilities?" So ask yourself, do you have facilities for the animals you are thinking of raising? If not, how much fencing, caging, and housing will you need to buy and to build?

Let's think about fencing first. Nothing causes worse community relationships than having your animals get into other peoples' gardens. The people out here on Robinson Road are still talking about how Mr. X.'s cattle always got out and trampled their gardens. And Mr. X. moved away almost 10 years ago!

Country people have long memories, so it's best to treat them as you want to be treated. You feel secure when your neighbors' animals are well-fenced, and vice versa. Even if you are positive that your animals can range freely without causing disturbances to your neighbors, you will undoubtedly want to fence them out of your own gardens.

My neighbor, Arlo Acton, lets his goats run free, but he has fenced them out of the acres he uses for his gardens and orchards. On the other hand, my neighbor Sharon Umphress built a 2-acre corral for her goats, surrounded by a strong, high fence. Sharon wants to keep a closer tab on her goats than Arlo does; she wouldn't be comfortable having them range freely. Other people keep goats on chains. This method cuts out fencing costs, but adds a labor cost. You have to move the animals around, and keep a close watch on them if you don't want to find them tangled up. Personally, I don't like keeping animals tethered.

When you consider fencing for goats, please realize that they are like deer; they can get over and under many fences. Your cattle fences need to be equally strong, but you can get by with a lower fence. Sheep fences can be low like cattle fences, but they must be strong at the bottom, or the sheep will crawl underneath. And electric fences can't contain sheep because they don't feel the shock through their wool.

When you are thinking of fencing several acres, you should be prepared to spend money. One square acre requires almost 850 feet of fence and over 100 fence posts. Call the store and price this out.

According to Bill Helphinstine, it takes 10 acres of dry, brush-free land to feed a cow for six months. If you have 10 acres, it looks like you can definitely lower your costs by ranging your cattle. But have you considered today's costs of fencing those 10 acres? Perhaps fencing 1 acre and irrigating it is a cheaper way for you to go?

Pigs take up only a small area, but you will need an escape-proof cage. Pigs use their snouts to dig under cages. Don't underestimate them.

One summer, one of my neighbors must have come over weekly searching for his pig. His cage was inadequate, and the clever creature kept escaping. The owner would find the pig, make some small improvement in the pen, yet the pig would escape again and again. Finally, he lost the pig completely. That was an expensive mistake.

Your poultry will also need adequate caging. You might be able to let them range during the day, but you certainly will have to put them away at night, in a closed area—sides and top. Predators love poultry as much as you do. You'll have to protect them.

You really need to know the predators in your area. If you have active bobcats, coyote, or neighborhood dogs, you might not want to let your birds out even in the daytime. One sunny afternoon I watched a bobcat boldly nab my favorite Muscovy duck. My initial reaction was anger, but over the years I've changed my philosophy. I no longer think that domestic animals take precedence over wild animals.

I feel that it's an owner's responsibility to protect his domestic animals. Instead of running around with a gun in your hand and feeling angry over all your losses, spend your time fencing your animals securely. In the long run, that's the easiest method. If a wild animal breaks into your well-constructed pens, that's another story.

If you do let your birds out, you can train them to come back to their cages at feeding time. Rabbits can't be trained in this manner. If they get out, they might run away. You'll need secure rabbit cages held off the ground, and you will want to keep your rabbits in them at all times. Location of your cages is extremely important, too. Damp, drafty locations can cause deaths. Animals can also die of heat exhaustion.

It is impossible for me to estimate your costs of housing various animals. Costs will vary depending on your climate, your land, your predators.

As you attempt to decide whether to raise chickens or pigs or cattle, or all three, learn about their housing/fencing needs in your locality. What will the chicken coop cost? How much time will it take you to build the pig pen? What's involved in fencing an acre for cattle?

In my area we can still buy slab-wood (the outside cuts from the lumbermills) for only $5.00 a truckload. We make many of our animals houses and pens out of this wood. They don't win beauty contests, but the price is right and the wood is still sturdy.

Saving money can have its drawbacks. When pricing fencing, I'd encourage you not to consider 2-inch poultry wire. From my experience, it doesn't hold up. Many animals can jump right through it. Of course, sometimes economy is more important than quality, and an inexpensive cage is definitely better than no cage at all.

Whatever type of materials you choose, I encourage you to have your facilities set up before the arrival of your animals. You'll save yourself and your animals a lot of problems.

AT WHAT AGE DO YOU SLAUGHTER ANIMALS?

More people eat tough meat because they don't know the proper time to kill an animal. They waste money buying feed for a year, when they could have killed the animal at four months. If you really want to raise animals for meat (and not for pets), you will want to kill them when they are quite young.

If you aren't interested in breeding animals, you can often buy them in the spring and kill them in the fall. That way you aren't tied down by animals all year. You can even take a vacation.

Table 2-2 gives an approximate list of the ages at which various animals should be killed for meat. Of course, if the animal hasn't reached the proper weight, you might want to feed it a little longer, but not too much longer. And if it is fully grown sooner than expected, don't wait. After all, what you want is tender meat. Tough, stringy meat or overfat meat—who needs it?

Table 2-2. Approximate Age at Slaughter.

ANIMAL	AGE AT SLAUGHTER
beef	18 months
hogs	6 months
sheep	6 months
goats	6 months
turkey	5 months
geese	5 months
ducks	4 months
veal	3 months
chicken	2-3 months
rabbit	2-3 months

WHAT WILL FEED COST?

I think it is wise to know the costs of feeding animals before you purchase them. Most failures in raising meat at home come from underfeeding your animals. If the price of feed shocks you, don't react by giving your animals less food; this approach will only give you skinny animals. Your animals probably won't die—they are remarkably resilient—but they also won't grow properly.

You want your meat animals to grow rapidly so that you can kill them when they are young and tender. If you kill a young animal that is underweight, you won't get any meat. If you wait for the animal to grow, which takes several extra months, you might have tough meat. Keeping the animal longer than necessary might cost you more money. Your best technique is to feed the animal properly from the start.

Although people will tell you that you can feed animals for free on leftovers, I think this is extremely misleading. Yes, you can feed animals on leftovers, but I'm not at all convinced you can grow animals this way. Like people, animals need protein for optimum growth. Thus, the effectiveness of leftovers is directly related to the protein content of the garbage. When determining cost, consider the following:

☐ Do you have pasture for your animal?
☐ Is it irrigated or dry?
☐ Do you have free sources of supplemental feeds, like whey from cheesemaking, or other high-protein leftovers?

☐ What is the current price of commercial feed in your area? Can you buy wholesale or with a group?
☐ Are you close to feed sources? Can you buy alfalfa by the ton at a good price?
☐ Can you grow some of your own feed?
☐ Can you let your animals loose to forage freely?
☐ Will your animals be able to nurse on their mothers, and for how long?

All of these considerations will affect the costs of your home meat production. At the bottom line, you can always run through one season of raising a particular animal and keep accurate records of everything you feed and all of your costs. You should also record the weight of the animal at slaughter, and your evaluation of the meat. Then you will be able to say exactly how much it costs you to feed pigs. It might cost me quite a bit more, or quite a bit less.

Bob Lester raises sheep. He keeps the lambs on the mothers and also lets them graze in his irrigated pastures. Because sheep don't need any grain to make a choice carcass, Bob can raise his sheep "for free" because he has grass and mother's milk available. On the other hand, a person who raises a lamb in dry-lot (no grazing), will have to consider grain costs. Without knowing about your land and your preferred technique of raising animals, an estimate of feeding costs can't be made.

However, there is a method of comparing costs of feeding animals that might help you decide which animals to buy. It is called the "feed-meat conversion ratio." How well does a particular animal convert grain into flesh? How many pounds of grain must you feed the animal to produce 1 pound of gain?

I worked with farm advisor Harry Dasher to develop Table 2-3, giving approximate feed-meat conversion ratios for domestic animals in a dry-lot situation. Pigs and poultry do a fine job converting their grain into weight. If you had to keep animals penned 100 percent of the time—buying all their feed—pigs and poultry would give you the most return for your dollar.

Chapter 3
Tips On
Raising Meat Animals

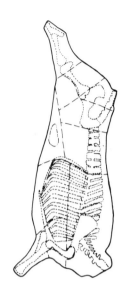

BEFORE YOU CAN ENJOY HOME-RAISED MEAT ON your table, you must raise your meat animals successfully. You can't butcher meat until you've grown it properly. And over the years I've learned a few tips I'd like to pass on to you.

If you are new to raising meat animals, my first advise is to find yourself one or more animal "gurus." By gurus I mean people who are really knowledgeable about animals. Your guru will teach you, commiserate with you, and talk to you at any hour of the day or night about your animals. I suppose your gurus could be your country agricultural agent and veterinarian, and certainly you will want to consult these people. However, I think the ideal animal gurus are folks actually doing what you want to do, under similar climactic conditions. By that I mean neighbors with many years of experience raising animals.

You can read all the animal-raising books and manuals you want—and I strongly advise you to read, read, read,—but at the bottom line, knowledge of animals comes from experience.

If you haven't any personal experiences with meat animals, find neighbors who do.

By asking around at the local store or post office, you can find out which of your neighbors raises the animals you have decided to raise. Call them and ask to drop by for a visit. Tell them that you have heard they raise excellent lamb and you want to learn more about it. I guarantee you they will share their knowledge with you. They'll feel complimented that you are interested in what they have to say.

How can you tell if your chosen gurus are experts? Look at the environment they keep their animals in and look at the animals themselves. Does the environment appeal to you? Do the animals look healthy? Does the farmer seem interested and enthusiastic about the animals? It's easy to spot an animal guru. Trust your intuition.

Don't feel embarrassed to ask questions of your neighbors, your county agricultural agent, your feed store operator, and your veterinarian. As you raise your animals, you will assuredly see things that you have never seen before. If the behavior of one of your animals concerns you, ask someone about it. As one of my college professors used to say, "No matter how dumb you think a question is, you're only dumb if you don't ask it."

Raising animals is an exciting task and I am sure you will be highly successful. As far as your animals are concerned, you are the expert who takes care of them. Enjoy your role as barnyard supervisor.

There's an old saying: "The eye of the master fattens the calf." Your interest in your animals will be the key ingredient in helping them grow. If you take good care of them, they will give you back scrumptious meals for your table.

CHICKENS

You will want to buy day-old chickens. You might be able to find them at your feed store, and this has several advantages. First, you can see they are all alive when you buy them. Don't accept any that look sickly. Second, sometimes these chicks are actually several days or a week or two old, yet still sold at the day-old rate. These older chicks are slightly stronger. Buy them if you can.

If your feed store doesn't stock chickens, you can send for them through catalogues. I've listed a couple of catalogues in the appendix. But I always buy mine at the store.

You will want to buy meat chickens. My favorite breeds are called White Rocks or White Rock Crosses. That's what everyone raises around here. They can grow to weigh 8 pounds. If you want smaller chickens, you must kill them promptly, when they reach the weight you like.

I like growing a big chicken and then serving it roasted. A big chicken can feed my family. If I use small chickens, I need two. White Rocks are like an ultra-small turkey. Two other breeds of large chickens are Jersey Giants and Light Brahmas.

You can also grow dual-purpose breeds for meat. These chickens do well producing either eggs or meat. Try Plymouth Rocks, Rhode Island Reds, New Hampshires, or Sex-Links. Per-haps you can buy only cockerels (males) from these breeds and raise them as fryers. Or you can buy straight run, keep the females for your egg layers, and kill the roosters for meat.

The problem with that method is trying to figure out which chickens are the roosters. It is not always that easy to tell on a young chick. If you want to butcher them at 8 to 10 weeks, you could make a mistake and butcher the hen you intended to save for egg laying.

For my serious meat raising, I prefer buying White Rocks and killing off the entire lot. That way I know exactly how many chickens I plan to raise. And as we said in earlier chapters, planning is an important aspect of home meat-raising.

When you get your chickens, you will want to keep them warm until they have feathered out completely. You can keep them indoors in a large cardboard box with an electric light or outdoors under lights in a more elaborate brooder house. The proper temperature for day-old chicks is 95 degrees Fahrenheit. You can lower the temperature 5 degrees each week until you reach 70 degrees Fahrenheit.

Remember, too much heat isn't good for chickens either. Don't suffocate them. If they are too hot they will try to keep away from the heat; if they are too cold, they will huddle together. Keep your eye on them, and they should do fine.

Because you are growing your chickens for meat, you will want them to be able to eat all the time. You achieve this by keeping food in front of them constantly, and also keeping the lights on 24 hours a day. Of course, if you have no light source, you can't do the latter, but do keep the food available.

Your chickens should weigh about 4 pounds in eight weeks, that is if you raise them on commercial high protein feed. This is called broiler feed. You will want to use broiler starter for the first six weeks, and then broiler finisher from seven weeks to the time you kill the bird. Put the feed in containers that the chickens can't walk in. Don't feed egg maker to young birds. The calcium in it can damage their kidneys.

As an organic gardener, I have often felt perplexed raising meat chickens, because I would ask myself, "Are they really organic?" As an admirer of natural foods, raising chickens on store-bought bagged feed feels somewhat awkward. So one year I tried a new approach. I fed my White Rocks whey from my cheesemaking, compost from the kitchen, garden scraps from the garden, plus barley-corn.

My White Rocks grew very poorly. Several of them even developed a condition called perosis, which is a weird-looking leg deformity. They became crippled with splayed legs and couldn't walk to the feed container.

Since then I have learned that heavy, fast-growing chickens (and turkeys) have a congenital predisposition to perosis when there are nutritional lacks in their diets. Consequently, I chose not to experiment with their diet again. It didn't seem worth it.

In a sense we naturalists are caught in a difficult situation with raising some animals for meat. When the animals have been bred for rapid growth, it seems like we are forced to give them the type of food that aids this type of accelerated growth. Unfortunately, this is not always feed we grew ourselves.

I stick with commercial feed (22 to 24 percent protein) for my meat chickens and I do not supplement with household wastes. I suggest you use the same approach. However, If you do want to deviate, I have an idea.

Divide your baby chicks into two batches. Keep them separated, but grow them under the same type of conditions. Feed one group on commercial broiler rations, and feed the other your own experimental broiler mix. You'll want your chick formula to contain proteins for growth, carbohydrates for energy, and vitamins, minerals and fat. Be sure you provide grit for your experimental birds as well. Keep accurate records. Then you can judge your own results. If you like how they turn out, that's what counts. You are the one eating them.

You will want to keep fresh water in front of your chickens at all times. Clean the water container everyday so that no slime builds up in it. (Don't use any containers that the chicks could drown in.)

I suggest you keep your birds confined. You don't want them to run around a lot and get tough. However, give them enough space. Make sure that they all can get to feed or water at the same time. Provide at least 4 square feet per bird. Some people claim 1 or 2 square feet is adequate. I think that is too tight (Fig. 3-1).

You can decide when you want to kill your birds. At 2 to 3 pounds they are called broilers. At 3 to 4 pounds they are fryers. Over 4 pounds they are called roasters. If you wait too long to kill them, they will all be stewing chickens.

One final reminder: Keep your meat chickens separated from your other poultry—ducks, geese, turkeys, and even your laying hens. Separate confinement is very important. Mixing birds invites disease. If you buy healthy stock, keep your cages clean, give your birds plenty of room, feed them well and keep fresh water in front of them, you probably will never experience disease.

These five rules—healthy stock, clean cages, ample room, good food, and fresh water—apply to every animal you will ever raise. I might not repeat these rules nine times (this chapter deals with nine different domestic animals), but you should commit them to memory. They are the key to successful animal rearing.

If you do get a sick bird, and you don't know what the problem is, separate it immediately and get expert advice. Birds can carry some highly infectious diseases, and you don't want to mess around with them at all. If the bird dies, burn it.

DUCKS

We keep two batches of ducks: our pet ducks who swim on the lake and give us eggs in the spring, and our ducks we raise for meat. We like duck meat and I know many interesting ways to cook it. However, before you get started raising ducks for meat, you might want to be sure you like the taste of duck. It tends to be expensive

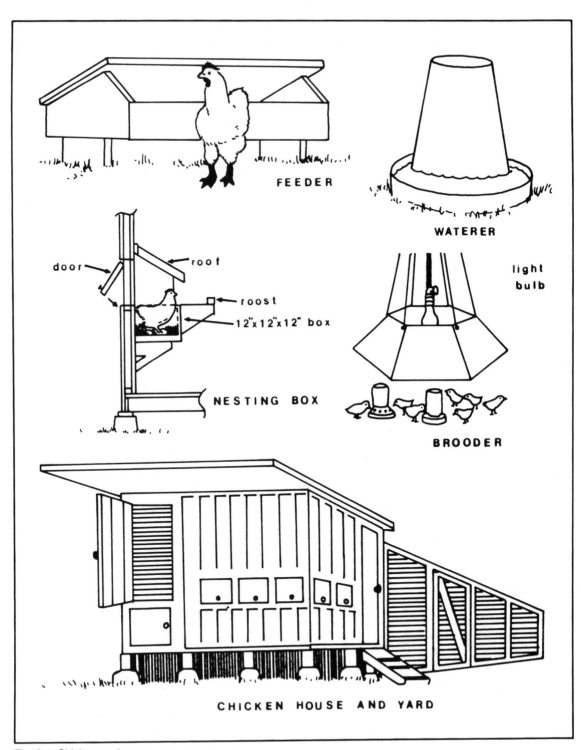

FEEDER

WATERER

door

roof

roost

12"x12"x12" box

NESTING BOX

light bulb

BROODER

CHICKEN HOUSE AND YARD

Fig. 3-1. Chicken equipment.

at restaurants, but take the splurge before you go to the trouble of raising your own ducks. In case you don't already know, duck meat is 100 percent dark meat.

Because you will be raising ducks for meat, if possible you should have one of these four breeds: Aylesbury, Muscovy, Pekin, or Rouen. Whenever I see baby ducks at my local feedstore, no one seems to know what breed they are. Therefore, if you want to be sure you purchase one of the meat breeds, you could buy them from one of the duck hatcheries listed in the appendix.

Muscovy ducks grow the largest. Mature males can weigh up to 16 pounds. They are excellent foragers and can be raised on pasture with a grain supplement. They have an unusual appearance; their faces are covered with a mask of red skin. They also don't quack; they hiss.

Muscovy ducks do very little swimming because their feathers are less water repellent than other ducks. If you don't have a pond, that's fine by them.

Muscovy ducks originally came from South America. Some authorities say they aren't truly ducks. It is a fact that you can't cross Muscovies with other ducks—the eggs come out sterile. However, when bred to one of its own kind, Muscovies reproduce most efficiently. I'd suggest raising Muscovies just because they are so unusual. You'd have to see them to believe them. People either love them or hate them.

You might have never seen a Muscovy duck before, but you've undoubtedly seen a Pekin. These are your basic orange-billed white ducks, and also the fastest growing meat duck available. They can average 7 pounds in seven weeks on high-protein feed. When raised this way, they are called green ducklings.

It only takes 20 pounds of feed to raise green duckling, but you must keep their high-protein feed (20 percent) in front of them at all times under full lights. However, if you don't butcher at seven weeks, this excellent feed conversion ratio drops very quickly.

Another breed of meat duck is the Rouen.

Rouens look like Mallards but they are larger. They grow more slowly than Pekins. You can raise them on forage with a supplement of grain. If you want to keep your ducks on the place for a longer time, you might want to raise Rouens. They should weigh about 8 pounds at slaughter.

Aylesburies are also white ducks, but they look different than Pekins because their chests almost touch the ground. After they are plucked, their skin is white rather than yellow. Aylesburies aren't as commonly available as the other three breeds. If you can find them, they make fine roasting ducks, also weighing about 8 pounds at slaughter.

Regardless of the breed you select, you will want what is called production-bred stock. Some ducks are bred for show and they are called standard-bred. Don't buy these; they cost more.

After you receive your baby ducks, you will need to brood them, just like your baby chicks. They will need slightly less heat than chicks. Ducklings require 90 degrees Fahrenheit the first week, 85 degrees Fahrenheit the second week, 80 degrees Fahrenheit the third week—a drop of 5 degrees per week. You can tell if you have them at the right temperature. They will sleep happily, and when awake they will move around drinking and eating.

You should have fresh drinking water available for your ducks at all times. And because you are growing them for meat, you will want to feed them a diet of 20 to 22 percent protein for the first two weeks, and then 16 to 18 percent protein until butchering.

You will have two opportunities for butchering. The first comes when they feather out at about eight to ten weeks old. At this point they are called ducklings. Then they will molt, and you will have to wait until they are about four months or more to kill them. At this point they are called ducks. If you keep them too long, watch out. They will turn into pet ducks, not meat ducks.

Most ducks are excellent foragers and if you can let yours range, your feed costs will be cut considerably. However, I have only been suc-

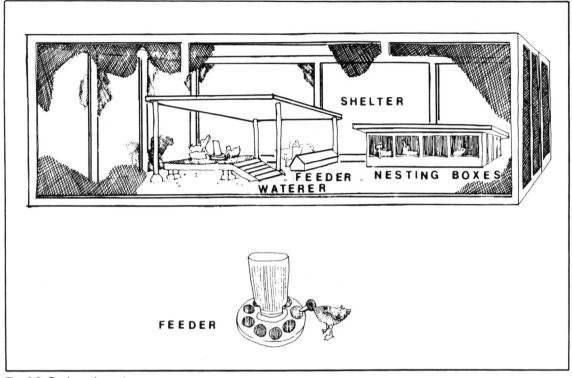

Fig. 3-2. Duck equipment.

cessful raising eating ducks in closed quarters (Fig. 3-2).

We have a lovely, natural 4-acre pond, and my grown ducks flourish there; but predators make it impossible for baby ducks to survive the environment of the pond. Wide mouth bass and bullfrogs are two predators. Even in the company of their mothers, my baby ducks seem unable to survive the wilds.

Consequently, I have chosen the safe approach, permanent caging. I bring them food and water, and they lead a relatively boring life until slaughter. If I let them out, they will run straight for the lake, so I really have no choice. Ducks do not need to swim. If you do put a swimming pool in their pen, make sure they can get out of it easily. Ducks can drown in water or get overwet and die of being chilled. Please beware.

You can raise ducks very successfully on commercial chicken feed. Some duck experts recommend fortifying the chicken feed with ad-

ditional niacin. You may mix the chick feed with water at first, so that it is easier for the ducks to eat. Look for a grower feed with the approximate protein content you want, but avoid egg-maker with young birds.

Make sure your ducks have plenty of water so that they can get their bills totally submerged. Bring them cuttings of greens. They will eat them enthusiastically.

If you let your ducks range in your orchard, eating insects and leaving manure, be sure to lock them up securely at night. Otherwise you might loose your entire flock. You should also watch out for predators in the daytime.

About three weeks before you plan to butcher ducks kept on pasture, you can confine them, feed them heavily, and restrict their movement. They should flesh out quite well.

As you probably know, ducks fed high-protein feed tend to have a high fat content. By letting your homestead ducks forage for part of their food, you can grow leaner ducks. You might prefer duckling raised the natural way.

As always, you are the one doing the eating. As you grow ducks, you might want to experiment with different growing methods, as well as different breeds.

Ducks are a fun animal to have on the homestead. Save a few of your meat ducks, and keep them as breeders the following year. You'll enjoy watching them. If they provide you with a dozen or more meat ducklings, who can complain?

TURKEYS

Sooner or later most back-to-land people want to try their luck raising turkeys. Although rumor has it that raising turkeys is difficult, they are really quite easy to raise.

In all your phases of poultry rearing, you will probably experience some losses with your babies. That's the nature of this home enterprise. In the wild, birds loose their babies, also. When you buy 24 chicks and lose a couple, that's hardly noticeable. But if you buy just one turkey and lose it, that's a disaster. Buying two is risky also, because if you loose one, the other turkey will be raised alone and turkeys prefer being with a group.

If you can afford it and have the space, buy three, or four, or even a half dozen turkeys. If all six make it, don't complain. You will have especially nice presents to give people to whom you owe a favor or two.

Every year Becky Burton raises about a dozen turkeys for friends. The only stipulation is that the recipients must come over the Sunday before Thanksgiving and kill, pluck, and clean their own turkeys. "They have to pluck it themselves and eat it fresh on Thanksgiving," says Becky. "It's kind of a tradition. If they froze it and ate it any old time, it just wouldn't be the same." Perhaps some of you will want to adopt Becky's traditional turkey plucking party on your farms.

Of course, before you can be in the position to give turkeys away, you must get them raised. As with chickens and ducks, you will want to brood your baby turkeys for about four weeks in warm weather or six weeks in cooler weather. The temperature in the brooder is the same as for chickens, 95 degrees Fahrenheit the first week, diminishing weekly at 5-degree intervals.

You will probably find turkeys at your local feedstore. If not, you can order them early from one of the catalogues listed in the appendix. But buying them locally seems preferable. That way, they might already be six or eight weeks old, and no longer even require brooding. It doesn't hurt to have someone else get them over the hump.

When you shop for turkeys, you will see two basic types: white or bronze. You can choose the color you like. Each group has strong advocates. Both should reach the same weight in five months: 25 pounds for the males (toms) and 16 pounds for the females (hens).

You will want to start them on turkey starter. This is an ultra-high protein feed: 28 percent protein. Help them find their feed if they seem to have trouble knowing where it is. And dip their beaks in water to help them to learn to drink. Some growers claim they have to put colored marbles in the feed or water so the turkeys can find it. Whatever it takes, just make sure they get off to a good start.

The safest way to raise your turkeys is to keep them confined in a large, open pen and raise them on bagged, commercially processed feed. From weeks four through eight use a feed with 26 percent protein, gradually reducing this to 22 percent for weeks eight through 12, 19 percent for weeks 12 through 16, and about 16 or 14 percent until slaughter at 20 weeks. You can probably find these feeds bagged as starter, grower, and finisher. If you have left-over grower, and it is time to switch to finisher, you can lower its protein percentage by adding grain. (If you are good at mathematics, you can make accurate calculations for mixing different products together.) Be careful not to dilute the feed too much. These rapid-growing birds do best on the suggested percentages of protein.

It takes approximately 70 pounds of high-protein turkey feed to raise one of these large turkeys. If grown this way, your homegrown turkey might end up costing you far more than the supermarket price for frozen turkeys around Thanksgiving. Don't even make comparisons.

A less costly, and more natural, method to raise your turkey is to let it range for some of its feed. If you have excellent fenced pasture, your turkeys will enjoy nibbling bugs and live grains. Arlo Acton starts his turkeys on turkey starter. At about six weeks old, he pastures them and supplements their diet with chicken scratch. He is satisfied with his results. "They didn't grow the huge white breasts of commercially raised turkeys," says Arlo's wife Robyn Martin, "but they were quite edible." Of course, Arlo has high-quality fenced pasture that he always keeps watered. Only you can judge your own situation.

Every case is different. Personally, I always stick with the high-protein, store-bought feed. I like the convenience. I'm less concerned about total self-sufficiency than I used to be. I no longer attempt to have everything I do come off the land. But I can certainly respect those who want to grow 100 percent of their feed to make sure it is totally organic and natural. More power to them. And I do think it is wise to read the labels on all bagged feeds so that you know exactly what is in them. If you don't want feed with antibiotics in it, look for more natural brands.

My turkeys come out costing about the same as the "natural" turkeys in the store. And I have had the fun of raising them myself. At the bottom line, I think that fun is what raising your own meat is all about. It feels right to raise your own turkey. If I skip a year, I always regret it at Thanksgiving time.

Turkeys can really be quite personable. But be forewarned that your male turkeys can fall in love with you and exhibit pretty bizarre behavior, spreading their tails wide and doing a little dance at your feet. They can also scare children, and even attack them. (So can geese.) If you don't like their behavior, keep them locked up.

As I said before, keep your different types of birds separated from each other. This definitely refers to turkeys. Even if everyone else you know is raising their chickens and turkeys together, don't do it. It is a bad practice that can endanger the health of your turkeys.

And don't forget cleanliness. Keep the pen clean, the waterers clean, the feed dishes clean. Sometimes it really seems that my animal pens get better care than my house. But truly, cleanliness is ultra-important. Keep your eyes open.

GEESE

You might want to follow your Thanksgiving turkey with a Christmas goose. You can raise geese like ducks; in fact, they are really easier to keep because they can make extremely good use of green pasture.

For meat I'd suggest that you purchase Toulouse geese, which are the large gray ones. Another large breed are Emdens, which are white. Because Chinese geese (the ones with the humps on their heads) grow to only half the size of the Toulouse, I don't suggest raising them for meat. I'd also keep away from the African. Their honking might drive you crazy.

I'd suggest you buy your baby geese in the spring, and eat them the following fall or winter. By that time your Toulouse should weigh 20 pounds, an Emden 15 pounds. If you keep geese longer than that, they will pair up. Geese pair for life, and if you kill one of a happily married twosome, the remaining goose can actually go into a depression and even starve itself to death. I've seen it happen. Of course, you can always raise these animals to maturity and let them lay eggs and raise their own babies, but then you are in the business of breeding geese.

If your main interest is one or two geese for dinner, raise your babies for consumption as soon as they reach the weight you want. Also, if you wait too long they will be terribly tough. I, for one, hate tough meat. I think chewing too hard takes the fun out of eating. One time I gave away a three-year-old pet goose to a friend (it had been attacking people). I wouldn't have thought of eating that bird. My friend said he liked it just fine. Maybe he enjoys shoe leather.

Unfortunately, baby geese are quite expensive. You might consider them something of a luxury item—perfect for a holiday meal.

After you buy your baby geese, keep them warm—following the rules for ducks. Even though they are a larger baby, they seem to have a high casuality rate. Be attentive.

Many people make their own baby goose feed with things like hard boiled or scrambled eggs, wet oatmeal, bread soaked in milk, and chopped tender greens. (You could start baby ducks on this type of diet as well.) You also can use chick starter, but.keep it very wet.

When you raise baby geese without their natural mother, they will decide that you are the mother. This is called imprinting. They will follow you, go swimming with you, nestle next to you. Enjoy their adoration.

At about six or eight weeks if the weather is good, you can let your geese out on pasture. You might still want to give them a supplemental feeding at night. Feeding them grain will help to keep them trained to come in to their cage. Before time to slaughter, you should put them on a fattening diet, but switch to this gradually. Eventually their diet should consist of 70 percent grain.

In terms of feed, you'll need 2 pounds of starting feed per gosling, some excellent forage over the summer, and then about 20 pounds of corn to fatten up your goose in the fall. Keep geese out of the reach of predators. It seems that there are lots of creatures besides humans who relish goose.

RABBITS

Raising rabbits for meat is a little different than raising any other farm animals. In this case, you are going to be involved with breeding whether you like it or not. Actually, another way to think about this is that the mother rabbit will be doing some of your work for you. And you won't need to worry about brooders!

You will want to start your foray into rabbit production by purchasing at least two females (does) and one male (buck). These will be your breeding stock.

Because you are raising your rabbits for meat, you will want to buy one of the fast-growing, medium-sized breeds, like New Zealand White, Californian, or Champagne d'Argent. Or you might want to raise one of the giant varieties like Checkered Giant or Flemish Giant. Although these giant breeds might seem appealing because of their size, they are less efficient than the medium breeds in converting feed into flesh. Moreover, much of their larger size is actually big bones.

If your feed store has no breeding stock available, you could check with your county agricultural agent for the names of reputable breeders in your nearby area. You will want to pick out your rabbits and check that they are well-built and healthy. Check the breeder's records. You want does that will have babies easily and take care of them adequately. Most important, you want the babies to be equal to or better than the parent stock. Buy carefully.

Before you bring your rabbits home, you should have their cages ready. You'll want a hutch for each rabbit. You can buy these or build your own. They should have wire bottoms (not chickenwire) so the droppings can fall through. Most people use all-wire cages, but you can also use some wood; in fact, for the giant breeds you might want some of the floor space made out of wood to protect their feet. You can put some kind of matting on this part (Fig. 3-3).

Cages should measure about 3 feet × 3 feet and stand 1 1/2 feet high. Make the doors large enough so you can take nest boxes in and out. For giant breeds make your cages a little larger. The mature giant rabbits can weigh about 14 pounds.

You can start breeding does at five to seven months old. You'll breed your doe by taking her to the buck's cage and leaving her there for a minute until he breeds her. Watch to be sure. Keep a record of the breeding date. Don't bring him to her cage. She may attack him and kill him.

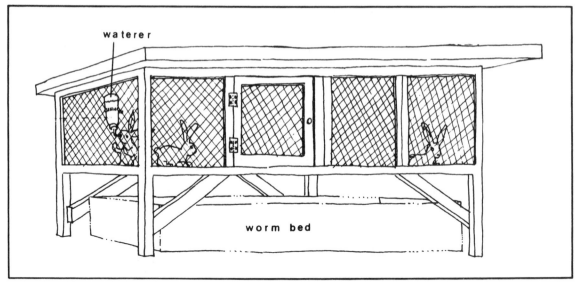

Fig. 3-3. Rabbit cages.

About 25 days after breeding, put a nesting box in the cage with your doe. The box (it has a bottom, top, and sides) should have its entrance cut several inches above the bottom of the box so that the babies couldn't possibly fall out. Fill the box with good nesting materials, about 5 inches in cool weather and 2 inches in warm weather. The doe will mix her own fur in with the nest.

You want her to have her babies in the nest, so they will stay warm and not fall through the wire. Hopefully she will oblige you. She will have them somewhere between day 28 through 32. When born they are hairless, blind, and deaf.

About 24 hours after birth, count her babies. Take out any deformed or dead babies, and reduce the litter to seven to nine babies. Your rabbit can feed about nine babies, but not more.

At about four weeks old, the babies will start coming out of the nest. At this point you can remove the nesting box, but still keep the babies with the doe until weaning age at eight weeks. At this age you can butcher them. They should dress out at two pounds.

If you want to save some of them to be more breeders (perhaps you are really getting into this rabbit trip), you can sex them at this point. Eat the males as well as any females that don't have perfect features. At ten weeks old, house any remaining rabbits in separate cages. You can keep harvesting them for meat up to six months old, but your feed conversion ratio will definitely go up the longer you keep them.

Rabbits eat greens, grain, and hay. You can go with commercial or home-raised feed or a combination. The feed should be about 15 percent protein. Buy a commercially prepared rabbit feed, which is a pellet with a combination of grain and hay in it. Or you can feed grain to your rabbits, supplemented with roughage cuttings from your own farm. Rabbits like all the green feeds from your garden also, but if you feed them too much of your garden products (which actually contain a lot of water), the rabbits might not consume enough of their other feed to make adequate weight gain. Too much wet feed can give the rabbits diarrhea.

If you use a pelleted feed, you can keep it in front of the rabbits at all times. However, you must be watchful that your breeders do not get overweight. If they get too fat and sluggish, they might not breed. Also, the doe can actually produce too much milk which can cause breast problems.

Feedstores carry a number of different rabbit feeds. One company produces six different types of rabbit feed for different purposes. I strongly urge you to read labels carefully. If you get into raising quite a number of rabbits, you will need to study their feeding needs more thoroughly.

One interesting note about rabbits is that they practice coprophagy, which means they eat some of their soft, partially digested fecal pellets. Don't be shocked if you see them do this. It's normal.

Of course, I know you will keep water in the cage at all times. If you use those upside down waterers that rabbits suck, you won't have to worry about them spilling their water.

Here's what you will have to worry about: chilling, overheating, and over-excitement. Rabbits can take a lot of cold, but not drafts. Don't place the cages where the wind can blow through them. A man I know lost all of his rabbits from locating his cages poorly, and it happened in one night.

Overheating can also be a serious problem. Too much heat will kill them equally fast. If you see they are overheating, try putting ice cubes to their ears. Or better yet, locate your hutches where your rabbits can't overheat, even in super-hot weather.

Try not to excite your rabbits. Strange noises scare them. Some growers keep a radio playing so that the rabbits become used to a noisy environment. If by chance your rabbit gets so excited that she doesn't care for her young, give her another chance or two to breed. If she continues letting her young die, cull her.

The main problem with raising rabbits is that you can't just be into it from spring until fall, stick your meat in the freezer and tend to other business. You will be caring for your rabbits on a year-round basis, and it might be more than you bargained for.

Each of your does can give you about 32 rabbits per year. If you don't eat this many, you could end up saving some as additional breeders, and even expanding your operation.

But be careful, you could get too big too soon!

A positive note that I haven't mentioned is that you can actually raise earthworms right under your rabbit cages on straight rabbit manure. This is a real plus for the serious back-to-the-land farmer. So rabbits may have a definite role to play on your homestead after all. And of course, their skins have commercial value as well.

Before getting started, I'd make sure your family likes the taste of rabbit meat. People like to say it tastes just like the white meat of chicken, but I think it tastes just like rabbit, with a flavor all its own. You can probably buy some rabbit meat from one of the local farmers. Check it out before you decide to raise them.

PIGS

If you want to raise a pig on your homestead, you do not need to bother with breeding. You can leave that task to another farmer. All you have to do is purchase a weaner pig, either a castrated male or a female. Don't confuse weaner with wiener or hot dogs. A weaner pig is a pig, six to eight weeks old, that has been weaned from its mother. Shoat is another term for weaner pig.

You will want to buy a healthy animal from good meat stock. Try to find stock from a purebred boar (male pig). Duroc, Poland-China, and Hampshire are some breeds of meat pigs. Durocs are red; Poland-Chinas are black with white on the feet, tail, and face; Hampshires are black with a band of white around the front shoulders and legs.

If the bacon is your favorite part of the pig, you might want to choose one of the bacon-type breeds, such as American Landrace or Yorkshire. Both of these are white breeds that have the typical pink piggy look.

A six-week-old weaner pig should weigh about 25 pounds; at eight weeks it should weigh 35 to 40 pounds. Try to avoid buying a lard-type hog. These are short-legged and overly plump. They are called chuffy pigs. Also avoid a pig that is overly long-legged and thin. These are called rangy pigs. What you want is a top feeder pig, graded either choice or fancy. Try to pick a pig that is of good size for its age group. Don't fall in love with the runt of the litter, it probably will not fatten up so well. When you buy your pig, if you can get vaccination and health certificates, so much the better. Also, try to find out what your baby pig has been eating. It should already be on a starter ration, but make sure about its exact diet. Because rapid dietary changes can upset or even kill a pig, you will want to feed the same diet, and then gradually take three to five days to switch over to whatever diet you choose.

Your first concern will be housing for your baby pig. A 200-square-foot pen can house from one to three pigs. The pen must provide a feeding area, a sheltered area, a shaded area and a toilet area. Whatever type of pen you build, it must be strong enough so the pig can't escape. Also, make the doors large enough so that you can easily haul out all that precious manure. Pigs are actually clean animals if you house them properly and keep their toilet area shoveled out (Fig. 3-4).

If you can build the pen in a shaded location, that is best. Pigs cannot sweat so they have a real problem with overheating. It can kill them. If you can't provide them with enough shade, or if your weather is quite hot, you will have to give them a bathtub or wallowing pond so they can cool off.

You'll want to build your pen on a high, slanted location for good drainage. You can build the pen out of panels or hog wire. If you use hog wire, leave room at the bottom for several strands of barb wire. You want to make sure that the pig can't root under the fence. Because you also want to make sure the pig can't jump out, make the fence about 42 inches high. Some farmers have had trouble containing pigs with hog wire. Eventually the pigs managed to break through it. You might want to use a stronger woven wire, called diamond mesh. Another option is to build your pen from wooden panels or even steel panels.

This problem of escaping pigs is a serious one. Once they have learned they can get out,

they can really give you a fit. And they are hard to catch. Luckily, you can usually coax them back in with their slop bucket. Because you have been bringing them their wet food—slop—every day, they will recognize you and their wonderful slop bucket. That way, if they do escape, you can go up to them with the slop bucket, and they should follow you right back into their cage. But it is better if you can build a strong escape-proof cage.

Your pig's shelter can be a simple roof, about 8 feet × 8 feet, slanted so that any rain will run out of the pen. You can put a wood or cement floor under the shelter, so that you have one area the pig can't churn up with its snout. However, you would never want your entire pig pen on cement. This could hurt the pig's legs.

You will want to have fresh water in front of your pig at all times. This is very important. Some people use automatic waterers. Or you can use a large watering trough. Mount it so the pig can't turn it over.

You can build your own feed trough out of wood, or you can buy one. Self feeders are also popular, as they allow the pig to eat to its heart's content. If not using a self feeder, feed your pig three times a day, all it can eat without wasting any feed. As long as you aren't introducing new feedstuffs, don't worry about bloating your pig. They know when they are full.

Your 35-pound weaner pig should reach 200 to 225 pounds in 4 months if you feed it properly. At that point, you will want to slaughter it. Growing it larger will give you a larger proportion of lard. Because you are looking for lean meat, more weight is not desirable. You only want about 1 1/2 inches of back fat. If you have more fat than that, your pork will be too marbled. That's one of the big advantages of raising pork at home—you can really control the fat content. I think all people who grow pork on the homestead will agree with me that its flavor is superlative. Store-bought pork doesn't compare.

There are several alternative methods for feeding. If you have adequate fenced pasture,

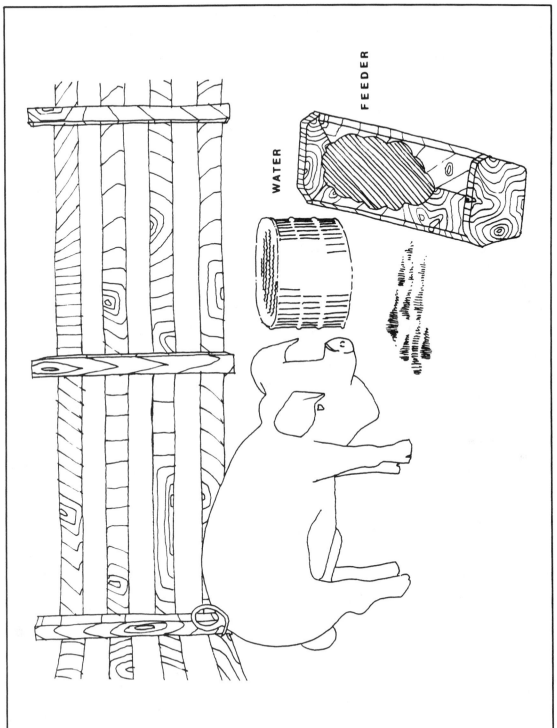

WATER

FEEDER

Fig. 3-4. Pig pen.

25

you can pasture your pigs and supplement their diet with grain and minerals. Historically, pigs were raised in a pasture setting. Confinement is a relatively recent trend. If you aren't pushing for record-breaking gains in weight, use your pasture, but be sure the pig doesn't eat it down below 4 inches. This would mean it wasn't getting enough feed.

Pigs need a balanced diet containing water, carbohydrates, protein, minerals, and vitamins. If you are able to grow your own corn, barley, milo, or wheat, you might want to buy a protein-mineral concentrate and mix your own feed. You will want to grind all grain before you feed it.

You can also buy commercially produced ready-mixed feeds. These are classified as starter, grower, and finisher. Buying ready mixes and supplementing with your excess farm product is probably the easiest method for the beginner. But read the labels carefully. Some commercial pig feeds contain antibiotics, and if you don't want these, you might have to search for an antibiotic-free brand. Insist on this. Healthy pigs grown under sanitary conditions do not need antibiotics in their rations. Just keep your pens, feed troughs, and waterers clean. If you avoid sloppy conditions, you won't have problems. You can throw lime in your pens to control odors and hold down flies.

On the other hand, I do advise you to worm your pigs. Worm them when you get them and again during their growth period. Do not worm near slaughtering time. Check the label for the number of weeks required between worming and slaughter. If pigs have worms they won't grow properly. Precautions here seem warranted.

As for raising your pigs for free on garbage, I don't think you should even consider it. Supplementing their feed with healthful apple culls or whey is one thing, but trying to grow them on 100 percent garbage is another question entirely. First of all, garbage isn't necessarily safe. If you are hauling it from restaurants or supermarkets, you must check it carefully for non-food

items like bits of metal and glass and plastic. Also, the law actually requires hog growers to boil all garbage before using it as a precaution against trichinosis. But do you want to boil garbage?—I doubt it. Finally, as my animal guru, Deanna Jones, puts it: "A pig grown on garbage tastes like garbage." Need I say more?

A pig has the best feed conversion ratio of all the farm animals we are discussing. If you are going to purchase all your feed, you will get the largest return raising a pig. Feed your animal well, and it will grow rapidly for you. In just four months you will have a 225-pound animal that can give you 150 pounds of meat for the table. If you like ham, bacon, and pork chops, this one's for you.

GOATS

Many people don't think of goats as meat animals, but to my taste their meat is absolutely delicious. Young goat is even more tender than beef. When it is cooked rare, it is very juicy and flavorful. The next time someone offers you a baby goat, take it. I bet you will also become a chevon (goat meat) fan.

I still can't figure out why goat meat isn't more popular here. Goat milk brings a high price, but people often give away baby male goats as if they had no value. And sometimes, when you tell people you eat goats, they think you're crazy.

Of course, the positive side to this lack of appreciation for goat meat, is that it is easy to pick up young billies for almost nothing. You can raise them on pasture and by fall you will have excellent meat. You can also stake them out, moving them from one brushy location to the next. They thrive on many plants that other animals won't even touch.

When I lived in a Mexican village in the Isthumus of Tehuantepec, I realized that there are still places where the goat is extremely important. In this particular village, people measured their wealth by the number of goats they owned. The more goats, the higher the family's social status in the village.

These villagers didn't ever milk their goats. (Actually, when I told them I drank goat's milk, I think they thought I was demented.) These folks only kept goats for meat. Everyday the village herdsman took the goats out into the brush and let them browse for about six hours. Then he drove them to the watering hole where they drank. After that they were penned up (without water!) until the next day. The adult goats were smaller animals than my milk goats, but their meat tasted great.

Raising meat goats on your homestead is equally easy and inexpensive. If you have milk goats, you will want to castrate their baby boys and raise them for meat. Castrated goats are called wethers.

To castrate them, you use an elastrator. This is an instrument resembling a pair of pliers. You want to place a special rubber ring on the tip end of the elastrator and expand it. You will then put this ring around the goat's testicles.

The rubber ring is like a super-heavy rubber band, and you put it on by stretching it out with the elastrator and just popping it around the testicles. Have someone hold the goat for you while you perform this task. It's a simple, 30-second, bloodless operation. In a month or two, the testicles just dry up and disappear. You probably won't even see this happen.

The reason you want to castrate the baby boys is that they can breed females at a very tender age. It's safer keeping them around the farm if they have been neutered. It also assures you more tender, tasty meat.

You will want to feed your baby goat some type of milk—goat's milk, cow's milk, or milk replacer—until it is able to browse. It will actually start nibbling alfalfa at a week old. At three weeks, you can add some grain to its diet. At about six weeks, you can wean it if it is eating well, or you can feed it milk for a longer period. If you have the spare milk, let it go longer, of course. You can leave it on the mother, bottle feed it, or train it to drink from a pan. Serious dairy goat people always remove their babies from the mothers immediately after birth. The mama goat cries over this separation, but it's better for her udder if the babies don't nurse.

Keep your newly born baby goats in a box in the house (or a warm location) and bottle feed them every few hours. You will want to make sure they get the colustrum or first milk from their mother. Feed this for three or four days, and then you can switch gradually to cow's milk or milk replacer if you wish. Always warm the milk or milk substitute to about 103 degrees Fahrenheit before feeding. Keep the bottles or pans clean. Feed about 2 pints of milk a day, in three to five feedings. At about three weeks, you can gradually add in a good calf starter to the milk.

As you goats grow older, they will browse on all sorts of brush. They also eat your rose bushes and young fruit trees, so be sure and keep them fenced out of your gardens. They are very hardy animals, and will only need a shelter to keep them out of the rain.

Goats have different nutritional needs than pigs or poultry. Like sheep and cows, goats are ruminants, which means they are a cud-chewing animal with a four-compartment stomach. Ruminant animals can utilize a diet that is 80 percent roughage and actually synthesize additional proteins and vitamins from it. Thus, ruminants can do very well on pasture.

I keep my goats penned at night, and let them run on my brushy land during the day. I feed them some grain in their cage so they know where home is. I also have a mineral salt block available in their pen, plus plenty of fresh water. They always return home in the evenings. Goats are extremely people-oriented. If I go for a walk, they will always come along with me.

Because I don't dehorn my goats (they can defend themselves better with horns), I keep them penned in a cage made of wooden slats. If I used hog wire, they could catch their horns in it. The only problem with a wood cage, is that baby goats can often find a spot to crawl through. You'd be amazed how they can squeeze themselves through the smallest openings. Like pigs, goats are superb escape artists. They can even open hook and eye closures on doors. Use hooks with locking springs (Fig. 3-5).

Goat feed is divided into two categories: roughages and concentrates. Roughages consist of the whole plant and are higher in fiber than concentrates, which are mainly cereal grains. If your brush is of good quality, your meat goats can do quite well on this 100 percent roughage diet. In bad weather, or on days when you don't want to let your goats graze, you can feed them alfalfa in their pen. Supplement that diet with grain during the last month or two, and you should have a superb-tasting animal.

If you don't browse your goat, you can raise it dry lot on alfalfa and grain. The goat will thrive. Be careful not to switch a goat's diet too rapidly. They can bloat and die if they overeat green pasture or get into an open grain bag in the feed shed.

I recommend slaughtering your baby goat at about five months. Of course, you can wait longer, even a year or two. But baby goat has the excellent flavor I am raving about. If you wait for the animal to grow larger, you might lose that luscious tenderness.

LAMB

Lamb is another one of those meats that people seem to either love or hate. (I love it.) It's an excellent meat for the homestead because, like goat, lamb can be raised to a choice carcass on mother's milk and pasture.

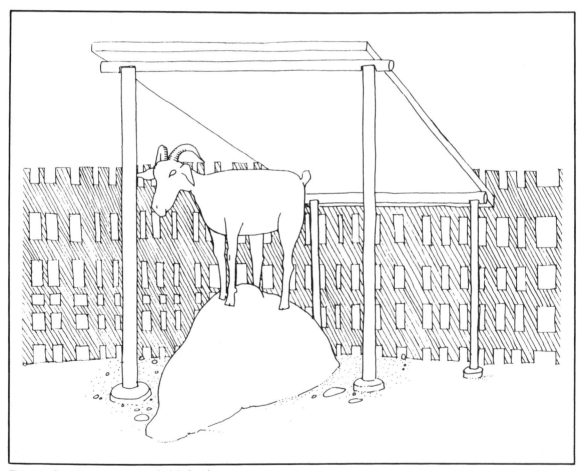

Fig. 3-5. Goat shelter and wood slab fencing.

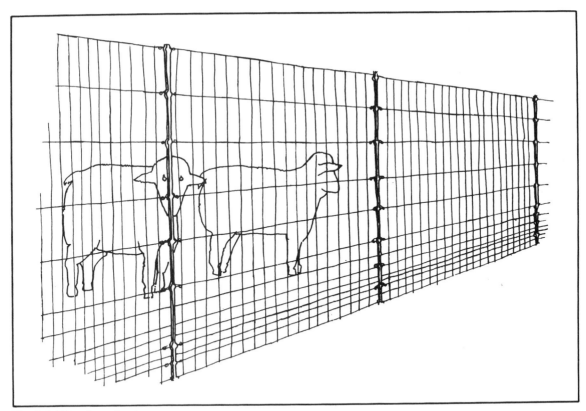

Fig. 3-6. Wire sheep fencing.

Of course, this means that you might decide to raise ewes (mature sheep) in order to produce lambs. In buying ewes, avoid ones which are lame, have unsound udders, have mastitis , (an udder disease) or have missing teeth (a sign of old age). Another way to put this is: make sure you buy healthy, young ewes.

Lambing time can have its complications, and you will want to watch this closely. One local breeder, Bob Lester, keeps a walkie-talkie connected between his barn and his home, so that he can hear when his lambs begin "mothering their water after it breaks." Bob listens for the moment of birth, and then runs down to the barn to help out. That way he doesn't risk losing his baby lambs. Ewes tend to have only one baby. It's smart to be attentive, if you want to eat lamb the following fall.

Like goats, lambs are hardy and you won't need expensive housing; a simple shelter from the elements should do fine. However, you will want to have fencing, both to keep the lambs in and the dogs out. Unfortunately, dogs and coyotes also have a penchant for young lamb (Fig. 3-6).

Sheep eat pasture, especially the short, fine grasses. Your baby lambs will be out on pasture with their mothers, but you can also feed them a little ground grain in a creep feeder after they are about a week old. A creep feeder is a cage that the babies can get into, but the mothers can't. However, the main proportion of their diet will be simply mother's milk and pasture. Be sure and rotate pastures to avoid over-grazing, as well as parasite problems.

You will want to castrate baby rams with an elastrator, the same as for male goats. You will also want to worm your lambs monthly, as they are very susceptible to parasitic infestations. Just make sure not to slaughter your animals

29

within a certain number of weeks after worming. The directions are on the particular product you use.

If good spring and summer range is available, lambs can reach market weight from grazing alone. If the pasture is marginal, then you will definitely need to supplement their diet using a creep feeder as described above.

If the lambs haven't reached slaughter weight by weaning time, you might want to dry-lot them until they are fat enough. You might also follow this practice if you bought a baby lamb that was weaned early (or a bummer lamb that was orphaned), and are fattening it up on your own. In either case, you could feed a ration that contains about 14 percent protein. This should make your animal grow.

To determine if your lamb is ready for slaughter, don't look at its belly. Instead, look from the backside around the hip bones to see if the animal is adequately fat. A lamb is ready in about six months, when it weighs 100 to 110 pounds on the hoof. It will dress out to 50 or 60 pounds. Don't keep it longer than this, or try to grow it larger. At about eight months it will turn into mutton, and this meat is strong flavored, and not what you are trying to raise.

BEEF

Beef are big, but they are really no more difficult to raise than any other domestic animal. And for very little trouble, you can end up with 600 pounds of meat in your freezer, a large percent of it delicious steaks. Who said growing beef was too difficult? In terms of effort per pound, a beef is your easiest meat animal to raise.

If you are raising cows for milk, you will end up with your own baby calves that you can kill young for veal. Or you can continue feeding them and raise them for beef.

You'll want to castrate your baby bull calves. The reasons you need to castrate are twofold: bulls, like male goats, become sexually active at a young age. They can breed young heifers too young, which can really cause problems at calving time. Also, bulls can walk right through your fences, attack people, and cause a general nusiance. Stick with steers (castrated bulls); they are more docile and some people say they grow faster.

Young calves are raised on mother's milk in much the same way as young sheep or goats. If you don't have your own cows, you still might come across a young orphaned calf, or a young calf that was a cull in a breeding herd. You can often buy these bummer calves cheap, but you have to bottle feed them and worry about diarrhea (scours). It's a lot of trouble (six months worth) to play mama to a baby calf.

For beginners, I'd recommend buying a feeder calf. This is a calf that is six to eight months old, and already weaned. You won't slaughter it until it is 18 to 22 months old so you will have it for 10 to 16 months on your homestead. That's long enough.

Your feeder calf will weigh in the vicinity of 400 to 600 pounds, depending on age and breed. You can purchase a steer or heifer, but steers usually grow faster than heifers.

Don't buy a calf that looks at all sick. If it has dull or rough hair, watering eyes, a running nose or a drooping head, pass it up.

You can buy any breed you like—beef, dual purpose, or dairy—pure-bred or cross-bred. Your best buy is probably a cross-bred beef calf. You don't need a pure breed for an animal you intend to eat; in fact, many people think the crosses grow fastest. Dairy breeds tend to be a little boney. For the biggest eye in your T-bone, go for a beef breed. Obviously, you will have to buy what is available in your area. This is a big animal we are talking about. If you can buy your feeder calf from your next door neighbor, that solves the transportation problem.

Some of the well-known British beef breeds are Angus, Hereford, Polled (hornless) Hereford, Red Angus, and Shorthorn. These are medium weight animals with an optimal steer slaughter weight of 1000 to 1150 pounds. The larger European breeds include Charolais, Chianina, Limousin, Maine Anjou, and Simmental. Optimal slaughter weight for these steers is 1200 pounds or more.

Whatever breed you choose, try to select an animal that is above average weight for its age, has large muscles, and looks wide from the front and from the behind, but trim through the middle.

Housing should provide no problem. In most areas, you won't even need to provide any special shelters. If you have excessive heat, you can provide a shaded area. If you have extremely cold winter winds, you can build a simple three-sided lean-to. But essentially, beef cattle are outdoor creatures. Their heavy coats of hair keep them warm in winter.

You will need fencing as mentioned in earlier chapters. You can use wood, barbed wire, electric wire—you have lots of options. It should be very sturdy. Like every other animal, cattle will jump over or crawl under a fence if given the chance (Fig. 3-7).

You will also need water, plenty of it. Your beef cow will drink 12 to 15 gallons per day. Don't skimp. You should also keep salt available.

Now we come to the great controversy: how to feed beef cattle. Believe it or not, you really can feed your steer only grass. But other people will insist that you have to feed it grain as well. So who is right? And what is the difference between grass-fed and grain-fed beef anyway?

A grass-only diet will give you lean meat. This meat will not be particularly marbled. Marbling refers to fat within the body of the meat. When the government grades meat, it grades on the amount of marbling. Prime (the highest grade) and choice (the next highest) beef are highly marbled. A grass-fed beef will not produce a prime or choice carcass.

You need to ask yourself if you want fat in

Fig. 3-7. Cattle fencing.

your meat. Personally, I am thrilled to be able to eat grass-fed meat that isn't so marbled. This seems healthier. And yes, it is still tender. Young beef is tender whether it is marbled or not.

To feed or not to feed grain is actually a question of personal taste (and economy). If you want choice meat, you'll need to feed grain for five months. If you prefer a leaner meat that is less-expensive to raise, a grass diet is just fine.

Of course, this controversy is one of the wonderful advantages of raising your own beef. You get to make these choices. You can grow an ultra-lean beef, a choice beef, or a beef somewhere in-between. At the supermarket, you can't find grass-fed beef. Home-grown is the only way if you want super-lean beef.

Home-grown is also a must if you wish to avoid all antibiotics, chemicals, and growth hormones that are used to stimulate growth in commercial beef. I mentioned this issue in Chapter 1, and I repeat myself here. If you want to eat pure beef, pure pork, pure lamb, or pure poultry, the only 100 percent safe bet is to grow your own.

If you do raise your beef strictly on grass, it will have yellowish fat. This will not effect its flavor at all. Some local ranchers in my area raise their cattle in the mountains on a diet of birch brush. This forage diet produces white fat.

How much your animal will gain depends on its genetic ability to gain weight as well as what you feed it. Feeding a high-energy grain ration will provide larger daily gains. An animal fed only grass will take longer to reach the same weight.

If you want to feed your steer on irrigated pasture, you will need about a half acre to an acre of irrigated pasture. "But how can I know how much feed my pasture is producing? How can I know if my cow is getting enough to eat?" These are important concerns for a beginner.

Bill Helphinstine, the farm advisor with forty years experience giving advice, says: "If your cow is standing up feeding all day on your irrigated pasture, you know that it is still hungry. If it beds down (sits down and rests) in the late morning on irrigated pasture, you know it is getting enough to eat."

My neighbor Arlo Acton thinks it is best to rotate pasture for cattle and sheep. He likes to cut his land into three or four separate pastures and move his animals every five days. "That way I know my grass will come back and give the animals enough food," he explains.

The same question of whether the cow is getting enough to eat can also come up in dry-lot feeding. Here Helphinstine says, "A good rule of thumb is to feed your cattle twice a day, what they can clean up in 20 minutes to a half hour."

There are two types of cattle feed—forages and concentrates. Forages are what an animal gets on pasture: grasses, legumes, hay, corn stalks—high-fibre foods the cow, because it is a ruminant, can convert into meat. Concentrates are feeds containing more energy per pounds, such as corn, wheat, and oats. They produce greater weight gains per pound eaten. There are also supplements available that contain high proteins like soybeans, plus vitamins and minerals.

For cattle, good quality grass pasture or dried grass hay in adequate quantities supplies all of your animal's nutritional needs. The rest is gravy—or I should say, fat. Whether pastured or raised in dry-lot, your cow's basic diet will be forages. If you wish to feed it concentrates or supplements, be sure to make all dietary changes and increases slowly. Like goats, cows can also get the bloat from rapid dietary changes. A beef animal is a large investment. You don't want to take any chances with it.

Chapter 4

Are You
Ready to Slaughter?

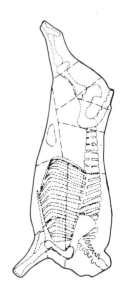

Y OU'VE RAISED YOUR ANIMALS TO PERFECTION.
They are fully grown, yet young—and oh so
healthy. You've enjoyed having them on your
farm, but have not become too attached to them.
You look forward to delicious meals where your
home-raised meat will be the starring entree.

The moment has arrived for you to kill these
animals. You might or might not feel psycholog-
ically ready for the task. Some people seem unable to kill animals, gut them, and cut them up.
If you are among this group who like eating
meat, but can't face the realities of killing, skinning, gutting, and cutting your animals, you will
probably be able to hire someone else to do the
job for you, at least with the larger animals.

Most people who raise meat animals accept
killing their animals as a necessary chore. I don't
love killing—it gives me no sadistic thrill, nor am
I ashamed to kill my animals. It's just part of the
process of turning farm animals into food.

Hopefully you are also a person who
doesn't mind killing animals, who takes pride in
the idea of doing a necessary job efficiently and

cleanly. You might be a little overwhelmed at the
effort involved in processing your animals. Don't
worry—you will become a pro sooner than you
think.

With a bit of practice on your own animals,
you might even turn your knowledge of slaughtering and butchering into a potential home business. Because there will always be folks who
don't want to have anything to do with this aspect of animal production, there is an ongoing
need for home-slaughterers and home-butchers
in any back-to-the-land community. (More about
these lucrative rural business opportunities in
Chapter 10 and Chapter 11.)

I don't think that anyone who slaughters
farm animals should feel guilty about causing
these deaths. Anyone who criticizes you for killing your domestic animals is really out of line.
They have a "supermarket mentality" and can
only face meat under plastic wrap. Don't let
these folks get on your case. The raising and killing of domestic animals has been with us from
prehistory. No one knows if it is right or wrong

to kill these animals. It is simply our heritage. If I thought I could stop the violence in the world by ceasing to kill my farm animals, well I'd never raise a farm animal again.

At the bottom line, I can't tell you how you should feel about slaughtering on the farm. But I do suggest that if you are going to slaughter animals, please try to enjoy it. Make it an offering for your table. See the beauty in the natural cycle.

This year we saved the life of a baby duck whose mother abandoned it. We raised the duck inside the house, played with it, and later killed it for dinner. Everybody was shocked we killed "Huey"; but the reason we saved his life in the first place was to raise him for meat. That's why I keep domestic animals. If I had fun with the animal, that was all the better.

On the other hand, if you raise your own animals, desire to eat their meat, yet can't face killing them, don't feel ashamed of your sentimentality. You have plenty of company. Some folks just can't pull the trigger or wield the hatchet, especially when it comes to their own animals. If you can't do it . . . you just can't do it.

Don't, however, assume that the rest of us adore killing animals. It's just part of the role of a farmer, like picking worms off the broccoli plants. You do these jobs because they are necessary—not because you enjoy the smell of blood or the feel of worms. As my neighbor Hamilton Webb so poetically philosophizes, "No one is enthralled with entrails."

Eugene Lissauer, a retired meat cutter, puts it even better. "I hate the word kill," he says. "You slaughter animals, you don't kill them. Killing is a word reserved for humans. Slaughtering is a knack, an art. Slaughtering is done with a view towards being merciful and inflicting the least amount of pain."

Slaughtering is a task that must be done if you intend to eat home-raised meat. If you have never slaughtered an animal before, you might not be an expert at it the first time you try. But by following the detailed instructions in this book, you will gradually learn how to slaughter and cut

meat, and you will become more and more proficient through practice.

The best way to learn how to slaughter, animals is to get in there and do it. Let the children help. That way, they, too, will learn the techniques required of people who want to eat healthy, chemical-free meat. We need to pass on this knowledge, so that the traditional skills of rural life aren't lost as we move into this high-tech age.

THE KNIVES YOU WILL NEED

Before you begin slaughtering, you should gather together all equipment you will need to get your animal from the live state to the freezer. Although many people get by with only a few tools, and a make-do situation, I want to tell you what equipment is available to you. You decide what you want to beg, buy, or borrow.

An amazing assortment of knives is available that can be used in home-slaughtering and home-butchering. Remember, slaughtering and butchering are serious professions. As a home slaughterer, you can also buy all of the equipment that your counterparts are using in the large-scale commercial slaughterhouses and supermarkets. I've listed several of these supply catalogues in the appendix.

You can buy a separate knife for each type of task you might wish to perform, or you can look for an all-purpose knife that will serve several needs. For example, catalogues list 8-inch and 10-inch breaking knives (thin blade, slight curve) that are used for breaking up (cutting up) the carcass into large sections. There are also 10-inch and 12-inch cimeter knives (wider, more curved) and 10-inch and 12-inch butcher knives (straight blade, wide). Essentially, all of these larger knives serve the same purpose—to cut the carcass up into big chunks. Sometimes these large knives are called steak knives. Ideally, you should have one large knife to use when you cut up your carcass—if you are working with a large animal.

Boning knives are short knives you can use

to remove bones from meat. These come in at least five different shapes, each ranging in size from 5 inches to 7 inches. Some are stiff, some are flexible. If you intend to bone meat, you'll definitely want one.

For slaughtering, there are special sticking knives that are used for cutting an animal's throat. These have a point sharpened in two directions. And of course, there are special skinning knives. The one for beef is slightly more curved than the one available for lamb.

Besides coming with flexible or stiff blades, in so many sizes and shapes, most knives are available with wooden or plastic handles. Some people prefer wooden handles, but you can't put these in the dishwasher. Others prefer the dishwasher-proof plastic. Watch out, the plastic can be slippery.

For your slaughtering operation, at the bottom line you can get by with one knife for everything—cutting throats, skinning, and eviscerating. However, I'd recommend that you acquire at least three types of knives: one specifically for sticking (cutting the throat), one specifically for skinning, and one specifically for eviscerating. Figure 4-1 shows the collection of knives Dennis Atkinson uses when he slaughters animals.

The same holds true of cutting up your meat (butchering). You can get by with one knife—the same knife you used to kill, skin, and eviscerate the animal. But how much nicer it is if you have special knives for special jobs. Having the right tools makes your work so much easier.

Now I realize all too well that some back-to-the-land folks do enjoy struggling away with one knife for the sake of voluntary simplicity. Rushing out and buying everything you need might not be part of your lifestyle. Perhaps you prefer acquiring possessions gradually so that you really appreciate them. In that case, keep your eyes open at flea markets for old German

Fig. 4-1. Basic cutting equipment for slaughtering.

knives, especially Forschner. These are the very best.

Whatever knives you buy, you will want them to have high-quality steel blades. If the blade is too soft (too little carbon), the edge of the knife will bend over. But if the blade is too hard (an ultra-high level of carbon) it is very difficult to sharpen.

One big advantage to having more than one knife is that you can keep each knife sharper for the job at hand. None of these knives are at all useful if they aren't sharp. If you use your skinning knife to stick and eviscerate the animal, it's likely to be dull when it's time to skin, and you could end up popping a hole in skin you really wanted to save. Even if you use many knives, you will probably sharpen them at some point during the slaughtering-butchering operations. Knife sharpening is a definite part of the game plan. Again, this is an art that practice perfects. Whatever knife or knives you use, they must be sharp. There's no getting around sharpness. Dull knives don't work, and they are dangerous.

SHARPENING KNIVES

There are three basic steps in knife sharpening: grinding, honing, and steeling. As an apprentice slaughterer-butcherer, you will have to know all three. Although many people probably think that grinding, honing, and steeling all serve the same purpose—they don't. They are all different techniques, and you use them depending on the condition of your knife.

You grind a knife to give the blade the thinness you want. Grinding definitely removes part of the blade. You'll need to be cautious here, or you could end up with half your knife ground away!

Some knives need to be ground before they can be honed or sharpened. Other knives come with a properly beveled blade. If your knife looks and works like a butter knife, it might need to be ground.

Grinding produces a beveled (angled) edge on your knife. You want this bevel to measure about 1/4 inch on both sides of the knife blade.

To grind down your knife blade so it has a beveled edge, use a round grinding stone that is cranked in a circle while grinding the knife. The knife is held stationary.

Here are step-by-step directions for grinding knives on a grinding wheel:

☐ Wet your wheel with oil.
☐ Hold your knife in one hand with the blade at a 20-degree angle to the wheel. Turn the wheel with your other hand. Draw the knife slowly across the moving wheel.
☐ Try not to grind the blade further back than the 1/4-inch bevel.

Remember, you aren't trying to sharpen the knife at this point. Rather, you are creating the edges that you will sharpen with honing. Go easy.

Honing sharpens this beveled edge. Here you will use a stone that has a finer surface than the grinding stone. In honing, the stone remains stationary.

To keep your honing stone from moving, place it in a wooden base or on a damp cloth. Or buy a high-quality honing stone called a multi-oilstone. This expensive tool has three different surfaces that rotate in their own oil—from fine, to medium, to coarse. Figure 4-2 shows John Taylor, the local custom butcher, sharpening a breaking knife on his three-sided stone. Note how he holds his fingers on the knife. That's the position you want to use. Honing directions are as follows:

☐ Place your stone securely on a flat surface and wet it with oil or water.
☐ Have the length of the stone running from left to right as you look down at it.
☐ Hold your knife handle with your right hand.
☐ Place the back end of the knife blade (the part nearest the handle) on the left side of the stone, near the edge of the stone that is closest to you.
☐ Tilt the blade of the knife so that the

Fig. 4-2. How to sharpen a knife on a multi-oilstone.

bevel lies flat on the stone. This is about a 20-degree angle.

☐ Place the fingertips of your left hand onto the flat side of the blade near the backend of the knife.

☐ Let your fingertips exert pressure on the blade.

☐ With a sweeping motion, draw the knife across the stone from left to right, and inward toward your body.

☐ Turn over the knife, and draw it across the stone toward yourself, from right to left—the opposite motion from the previous step.

☐ Avoid running the knife in little circles in the center of your stone, or you will wear the stone unevenly.

After you have honed your knife, you must steel it. Steeling makes the edge perfectly straight. Think of it this way: Your honing created a sharp 1/4-inch edge on your knife. Steeling keeps that edge from rolling over one way or the other. It's the final touch in sharpening.

For sharpening slaughtering-butchering knives, you will need a polished smooth steel. (If you've never seen a steel, it looks like a dueling sword, but the blade is round and about 10 or 12 inches long.)

You'll have to get used to using a steel. Follow these step by step directions, to get the hang of it:

☐ Hold the steel in your left hand, diagonal to your body, and tipped slightly upward.

☐ Hold the knife in your right hand.

☐ Place the back end of the knife blade against the tip end of the steel, on the right side of the steel.

☐ The blade should rest on the steel at a 20-degree angle.

☐ Bring the blade down across the steel toward your left hand. Your movement should be quick. Use your wrist.

☐ Pass the entire blade of the knife over the steel in this one rapid stroke.

☐ Now repeat this same motion on the left side of the steel.

Once you get good at these downward strokes, from the tip of the steel toward your left hand, you can try to get back up the steel as well. When you finish the first stroke, just run the knife back up the steel to the tip before moving it to the second side. See, you already steel like a pro.

If your knives are honed extra-sharp, steeling can keep that sharp edge for you during the slaughtering process. My local professional slaughterer, Bill Dowling, carries his steel with him into the field, and uses it frequently as he skins a cow.

"Steeling keeps me from pushing with the knife," says Dowling. "By keeping the knife totally sharp, I don't hurt myself and I don't damage the hide. Steeling keeps the edge up." Adds John Taylor: "Lots of people think a steel sharpens, but that's not its real purpose. The steel keeps the edge straight. Honing sharpens."

Now that your knives are ground, honed, and steeled, you'll want to keep them in that ultra-sharp condition until time for slaughter. Keep them clean and dry. Please don't throw them all together in a drawer. After all that work sharpening them, you don't want to let them get dull.

You can make an unbelievably simple knife rack from a cardboard tube that you get inside a roll of wrapping paper. Just saw slits in the cardboard every few inches, one slit for each knife you have. Fasten your cardboard knife holder inside a drawer. It might not be fancy, but it will keep your knives from hitting each other.

In teaching yourself to sharpen knives, consider consulting a professional butcher, or other expert. Most people love to teach their skills to a novice. If you can learn to sharpen the right way from the beginning, it will save a lot of wear and tear on your knives. Sharpening knives is easy—once you know how! (Fig. 4-3).

BASIC EQUIPMENT

Besides your array of sharp knives (plus stones and steels), you will need some other equipment for slaughtering. I will cover equipment again and again in the following chapters. At this point, I simply want to introduce you to basic concepts. If you can come to the slaughtering site properly equipped, you will save yourself a lot of running around. Figures 4-4 and 4-5 illustrate most of the equipment you might need. You can use these drawings as a quick visual reference to help you remember the rather detailed list that follows.

For poultry, you can get by with an ax to chop off heads, or a special sticking knife for killing the birds through the mouth. If you scald the animals before plucking, you'll need a large cooking pot. If you hang the birds upside down for bleeding and dry plucking, you will need a system to shackle the legs. You can hang your birds with bailing wire. (We hold our whole farm together with bailing wire! I couldn't live without that great stuff with its 1000 uses.) Rabbits require even less equipment—just an implement to stun the rabbit, and a hammer and nails to tack the rabbit up on a board.

The larger animals will require more equipment. You must be able to get them up in the air and keep them there! You will need a gambrel for hanging animals upside down from their lower legs (hocks). The gambrel is a metal or wood implement that you insert through the hocks in order to spread the animal's legs apart as it is suspended in the air. Figure 4-5 shows some of the different shaped gambrels you can buy or make. You will also see a number of styles of gambrels in many of the slaughtering photos in the text.

You suspend the animal from the gambrel, and then hang the gambrel from a tree. Thus,

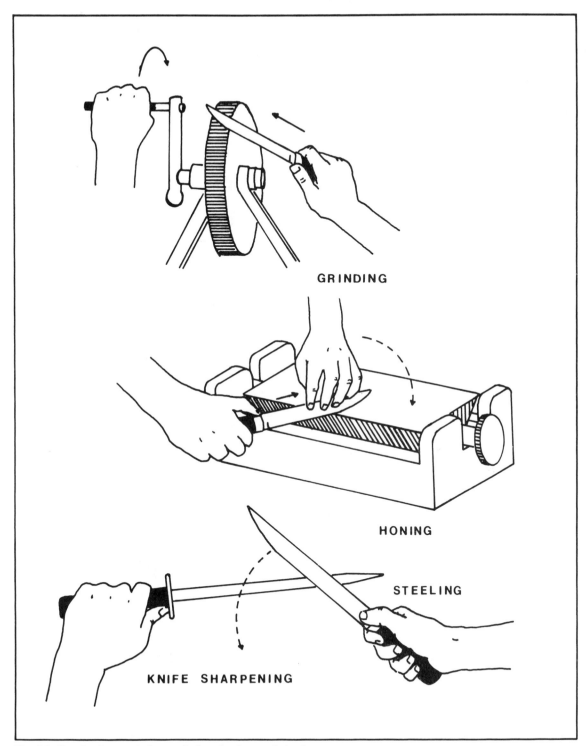

GRINDING

HONING

STEELING

KNIFE SHARPENING

Fig. 4-3. How to sharpen knives: grinding, honing, and steeling.

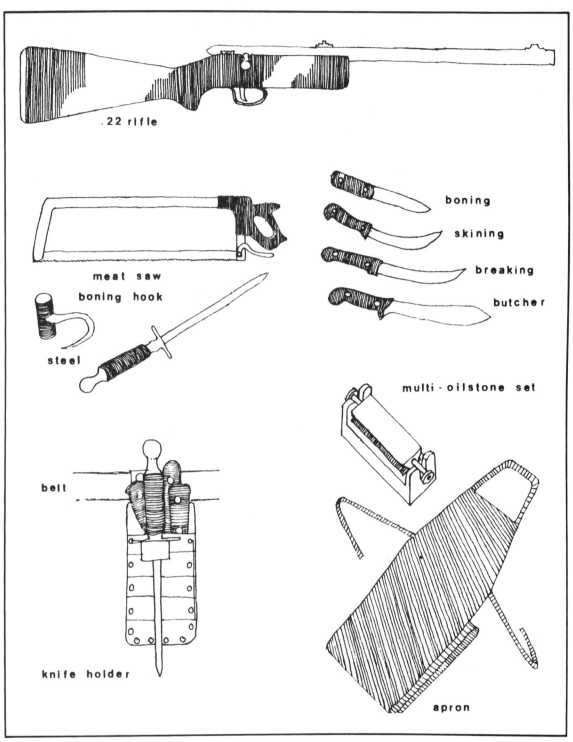

.22 rifle

meat saw

boning hook

steel

boning

skining

breaking

butcher

multi-oilstone set

belt

knife holder

apron

Fig. 4-4. Tools for slaughtering: knives, saws, steels, stones, guns, and more.

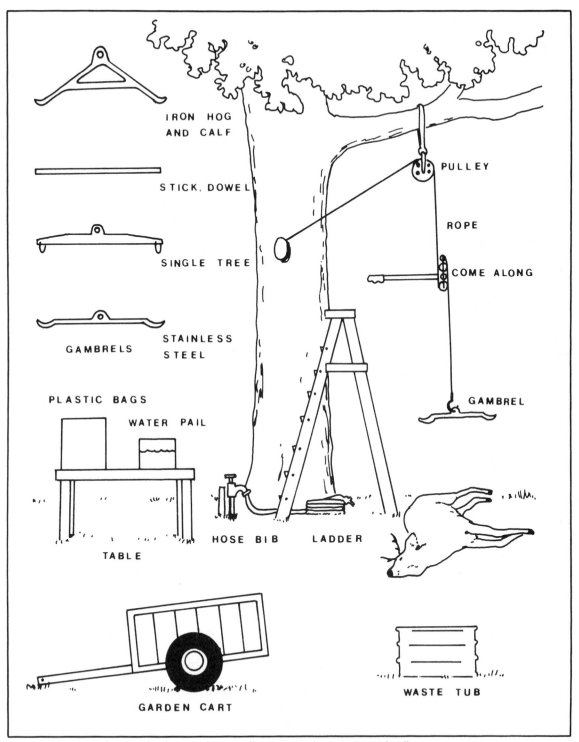

IRON HOG AND CALF

STICK, DOWEL

SINGLE TREE

GAMBRELS

STAINLESS STEEL

PLASTIC BAGS

WATER PAIL

TABLE

HOSE BIB

LADDER

GARDEN CART

PULLEY

ROPE

COME ALONG

GAMBREL

WASTE TUB

Fig. 4-5. More tools for slaughtering: gambrels, pulleys, come-along, carts, and pails.

you will need a tree in your yard that has a strong branch onto which you can hoist the animal on the gambrel. If you don't have a "beef tree" available, you can use a stepladder to hang smaller animals; for larger animals you can make a tripod from timbers or metal tubing. You would suspend the carcass from the middle of the ladder or tripod.

For heavy carcasses, you will need some type of hoist or block and tackle to help you lift the animal up off the ground. Figure 4-5 shows a system using a come-along hoist and a pulley.

Besides the gambrel, hoist, and conveniently-located tree branch, you might need many other types of equipment. Let the following list serve as a broad checklist to help you plan future slaughtering projects:

- ☐ A gun for stunning the animal.
- ☐ A knife for cutting the throat.
- ☐ A bucket to catch blood.
- ☐ A gambrel to spread the back legs.
- ☐ A tree branch or other support to hang the animal.
- ☐ A hoist to get animal up off the ground.
- ☐ Knives and steels for skinning and eviscerating.
- ☐ Buckets or plastic bags for the innards and all disposables.
- ☐ Clean dishes for the organs.
- ☐ A meat saw or cleaver to split the backbone.
- ☐ A garden cart or wheelbarrow to haul all equipment to the killing site.
- ☐ A cold area to chill the carcass before cutting it up.

Don't worry about trying to memorize this list. I will repeat it again under each specific animal you might wish to slaughter. I simply wish to give you a general feel for the dynamics of slaughtering. Moreover, according to the type of preservation techniques you choose, you will need even more equipment—such as a freezer or a smoker, a pressure canner, or a pickle barrel. I will cover all preservation equipment in later chapters, after completing the slaughtering-butchering chapters.

I do have some advice I would like you to take to heart at this point. Please plan to wear overalls while you slaughter. Or at least wear your oldest, toughest clothes. Do not wear light pastels or white. Do not wear your favorite designer jeans.

When Arlo Acton and Robyn Martin taught me how to kill chickens many years ago, they really taught me how to dress for the kill. To this day, I have no idea why they came to my farm to teach chicken killing dressed in white clothes. Maybe they had plans to go to a party afterwards. Two hours and ten chickens later, their crisp white outfits had been sprayed with blood. They looked disgusting. I remember apologizing profusely, as if it was my fault that my headless chickens had dirtied their lovely whites. Really, the secret is out. Slaughtering is a bloody business. Dress appropriately.

IS THE CARCASS HEALTHY?

Before moving on to slaughtering and cutting up animals, you might be wondering how a home-slaughterer decides if a carcass is healthy and if there are any rules that farmers follow in assessing the safety of their home-raised meat?

As a rule of thumb, you don't want to kill animals that seem sick. If your animals have fever, diarrhea, or any other health problems, heal them before you slaughter them. If you use chemical medications, you should definitely follow the directions on the medicine, and not kill the animal until the appropriate amount of withdrawal time has passed.

However, some diseases only show from the inside. You need to examine every carcass, even those you assume to be totally healthy. Your eye will pick up abnormalities very rapidly. You will have to decide how to deal with what you find.

As you become familiar with the look of a healthy carcass and healthy organs, you will know what to expect when you examine an animal you have killed. Obviously, you want any animal you will use for meat to be 100 percent healthy. All of its organs and the general appearance of the carcass should be totally normal.

On rare occasions, you might see bruises, minor injuries, small tumors or abscesses. As long as these are localized conditions, you can cut them out without having to destroy the carcass. Even if you find parasites in organs, you can still use the carcass. Just destroy the organ in question, because this is a localized problem.

However, generalized conditions that have spread throughout the carcass can be dangerous. If you find numerous yellowish or pearl-like growths scattered throughout the organs of the carcass, the lungs, the chest cavity and abdominal wall, this is most likely tuberculosis—and not a healthy condition at all. It is also dangerous if you find that the intestines, kidneys, and abdominal cavity are inflamed, or that all the meat is an odd color.

This might sound terribly frightening, but you must realize that most home-raised animals will be fully healthy. The chance that you will see anything except normal body tissue is quite rare. If you have any questions at all, you must call a veterinarian or other medical expert. You certainly wouldn't want to eat a tainted carcass; nor would you want to throw away wholesome meat out of nervousness. Get expert advice; that is always the safest bet.

Chapter 5

Poultry: Killing, Cleaning, Cooking

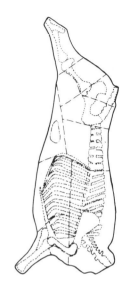

THE MOMENT TO KILL YOUR BIRDS HAS ARRIVED. It isn't easy to kill a lovely bird, but that is the task at hand. Some people like to kill all their birds in one day, and get the whole job over with. Others like the spontaneous approach, killing the bird when they are hungry for a good meal. If you can plan ahead, don't feed the birds for 24 hours before slaughtering. But do keep water in front of them. You don't want them to die of thirst before you can eat them.

In catching your birds, try to avoid bruising them or breaking their limbs. You want your bird to look pretty on the table. After all, you are competing with that perfect supermarket look. A big green bruise on your turkey breast is definitely not what you need.

SLAUGHTERING POULTRY

At our farm, we slaughter poultry by cutting off their heads. Figure 5-1 shows some of the basic equipment you might use for slaughtering birds. With the large meat breeds such as White

Rock chickens—or geese and turkeys—you will want to hold them by the feet and wings. It's hard for a small-handed person like myself to get a good grip on the wings and feet with one hand, but this is quite necessary. If you don't grip the wings, they'll flap like crazy, and blood will go everywhere. Personally, I don't like a mess.

Holding the bird with one hand, place it on your chopping block. Our block is an old stump, nothing fancy. You can hypnotize your bird by stroking its head. You want it to lay its head down on the block, with its neck stretched out. Stroking relaxes the bird so it will lie flat. If you are calm with your poultry, chances are they will be extremely cooperative.

At the right moment, when you are ready and the bird is ready, swing your sharp axe down hard on the neck. You want to get a complete cut. If you don't get the head cut off in your first try, don't despair. Just keep your grip on the bird and wield your axe for one more blow.

Chopping off the head is not the only

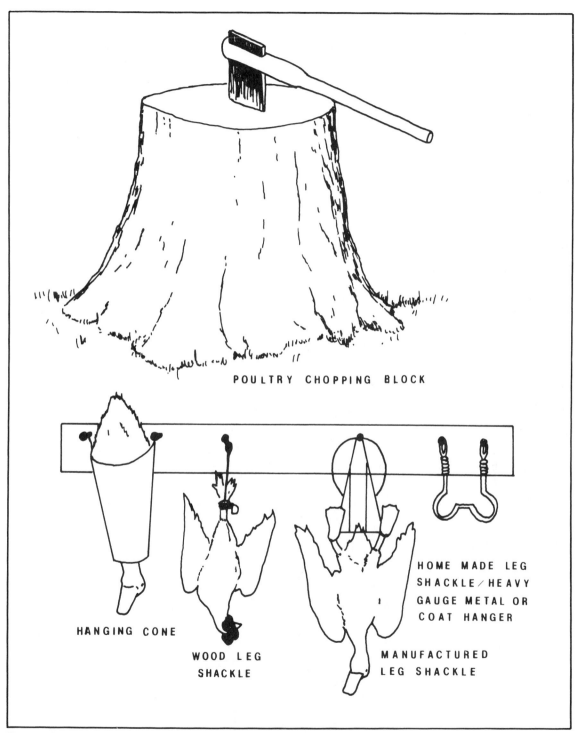

POULTRY CHOPPING BLOCK

HANGING CONE

WOOD LEG
SHACKLE

MANUFACTURED
LEG SHACKLE

HOME MADE LEG
SHACKLE / HEAVY
GAUGE METAL OR
COAT HANGER

Fig. 5-1. Tools for slaughtering poultry.

method available to homesteaders. John Burton, my neighbor, wrings his chickens' necks. He thinks this is the fastest way. "I just pick up the bird by its head," explains John, "and spin it about three times in the air. The head comes off in my hand, and the bird flops around on the ground."

John Burton and many other farmers let their headless chickens run around, bleeding out until they drop. I prefer holding my chickens upside down to let them bleed out, as Sam is do-ing in Fig. 5-2. If you are doing more than one bird, you can devise a rope or bailing wire sys-tem for hanging up your chickens while they bleed. Some farmers also hang the birds upside down for killing, in funnel-shaped containers called killing cones.

By the way, one of the main reasons for withholding food for a day before killing is that birds bleed better this way. Over-excited birds also bleed poorly. Don't chase your birds around the barnyard before killing them. Catch them the

Fig. 5-2. Sam holds a chicken while it bleeds out.

night before, in the dark, if need be.

You can chop off the head of a chicken, duck, goose, or turkey. This method works fine for all your poultry. For the larger birds, head chopping is a two-person job. When we killed "Herkle the Turkle," I held the wings, and my husband held the feet and wielded the axe.

Another method of killing poultry is to cut the two main arteries in the neck by sticking a knife inside your bird's mouth. This is the method used today in most commercial poultry slaughtering.

To stick through the mouth, you can hang your bird upside down in shackles or in a killing cone. Or you can hold the bird on a killing block, the same as the head chop method.

Hold the bird's head firmly in one hand. Press your thumb on one side of the beak and your index finger on the other side, to force open the beak. Now insert your sticking knife, sharp edge downward, and push it in, all the way to the base of the skull. Push the point of the knife into flesh, cutting downward and to the right. You want to sever both of the arteries in the throat. Keep cutting until you get a good bleed. Figure 5-3 illustrates this method of sticking birds through the mouth.

REMOVING FEATHERS

So now your bird is dead. How are you going to get those feathers off? You have several options: wet plucking, dry plucking, and waxing. Or you can skin the bird. Each method has its special applications.

For chickens, I usually scald my birds and do a wet pluck. This is the fastest method. Before chopping the head off, I heat a big pot of water on the stove. I bring the pot outside with me, with the cover on, before killing the bird. After the bird is bled, I hold it by the feet and dunk it into the pot, making sure to immerse the entire body.

If the water is too cold, the scald won't work—that is, you won't be able to pull out all the feathers. If the water is boiling hot, it can burn off the skin. The younger the bird, the more ten-

der the skin. Therefore, scald young birds at about 150 degrees Fahrenheit, and older birds at 160 to 180 degrees Fahrenheit. About 20 to 30 seconds is enough time. Start with a 25-second dunk and then try to pluck the bird. If the feathers don't come out, you can always scald it again. Basically, the higher the water temperature, the shorter the immersion. You'll get the feel for this with practice. I don't use a thermometer, I just know what feels right.

As soon as you've finished scalding your bird, pull it out, lay it down on newspaper, and rapidly pull out all the feathers. They should come out in your hand with no problem. Try to pluck as quickly as possible. If the bird gets too stiff, it's hard to get those feathers out. Moreover, you'll want to develop speed, if you ever plan to do more than a bird or two at one shot. Figures 5-4 and 5-5 show Sam and various helpers plucking birds. It is always helpful to have some extra hands. Act like you are having a great time, and visitors will want to join in. (I call that pulling a Tom Sawyer.)

Another method of plucking is dry picking. As the name implies, dry picking requires pulling out the feathers without scalding. It isn't an easy process, but is useful for birds whose feathers you want to save. It also (theoretically) can give you a better-looking carcass.

A trick that can help you with dry plucking is to debrain your bird, as pictured in the second drawing in Fig. 5-3. As soon as you have severed those arteries from inside the mouth, insert your knife through the groove in the roof of the mouth. Push the knife on through until it reaches the rear lobe of the brain. Then turn the knife a quarter turn. If the bird lets out a squawk, you've successfully debrained it. (If you've cut off the head, debraining is out of the question.)

Debraining actually loosens the feathers, but only for about two or three minutes. Therefore, you will want to start picking immediately, before the bird has finished bleeding.

The technical term for this rapid plucking is roughing. You rough or remove as many feathers as you can in two to three minutes. Pick

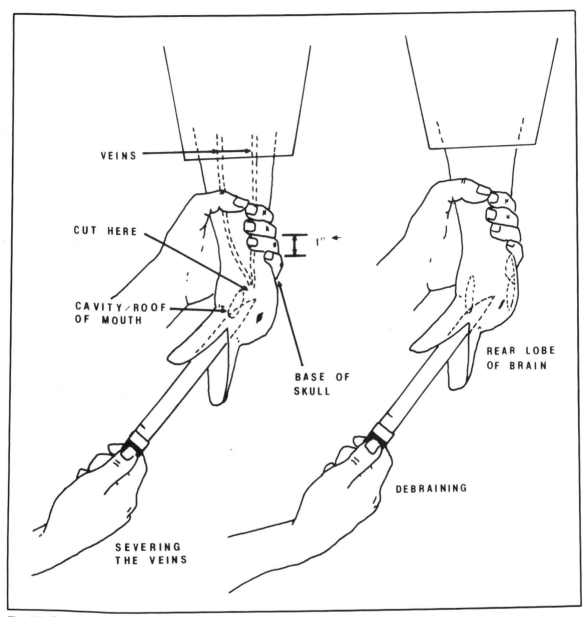

VEINS

CUT HERE

CAVITY/ROOF
OF MOUTH

BASE OF
SKULL

SEVERING
THE VEINS

REAR LOBE
OF BRAIN

DEBRAINING

Fig. 5-3. Slaughtering and debraining poultry through the beak.

from the extremities—tail feathers and wing feathers first—and then pluck the breast, neck, back, thighs, and legs. Try to get as much off as fast as possible. What you don't get off in roughing, you will have to remove with pinning. Pinning refers to getting out the resistant pin feathers. Sometimes you must use a knife blade

and pluck them out between the knife and your thumb. Or you can use a tweezer. This takes time.

If you have too many pin feathers left after an initial plucking (either dry or wet), you might want to try wax picking. This is especially common in picking ducks. You dip your rough picked

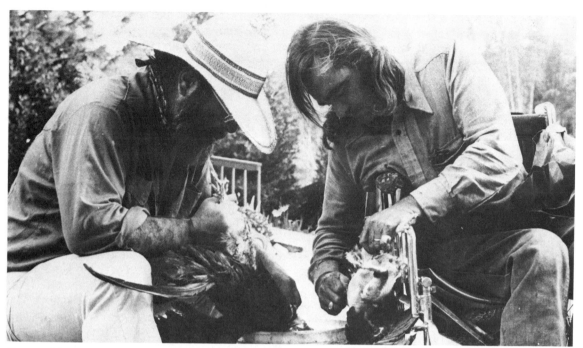

Fig. 5-4. Sam and friend pluck chickens.

Fig. 5-5. Sam works, while young friends watch.

duck in hot wax (or pour hot wax over it). The wax should be at about 150 to 200 degrees Fahrenheit. Before you dip your bird, dry it off as much as possible. This will help the wax adhere to the remaining feathers. Dip the duck a couple of times to get a good wax coating. Then submerge the duck in cold water so that the wax hardens on the remaining pin feathers. Next strip off the wax, which should have the feathers in it. If you don't get perfect results the first time, rewax and try again.

I often solve the duck-pinfeather dilemma by skinning my ducks. Of course, you can't roast a skinned duck, but there are many other duck recipes that don't require the presence of skin. Also, skinning reduces the fat content of the meat. A leaner duck might appeal to some homesteaders.

To skin a duck, remove the head, feet, and bottom joint of each wing. Figure 5-6 shows the foot being cut off of a duck that is about to be skinned. Place the bird on its back and insert a sharp knife under the skin of the neck. Then slit the skin the length of the body, cutting around both sides of the rectum. Now peel off the skin by pulling, as shown in Fig. 5-7. In tough spots, loosen the skin with your knife. It takes a bit of yanking, but it comes off. You can even save this feathered skin. It keeps for several years without any special preservation.

If you have skinned your bird, or done a great job waxing it, you won't have to singe it. But if the skin has been left on, and there are still little hairs visible, the next step after plucking is singeing.

I roll up a few pieces of paper and start a little fire in the gravel driveway. As I hold the bird by the ankles, I rotate it over the flame until all the little hairs have been singed off. This doesn't take long. Don't hold the bird any closer to the flame than you need to. You don't want to cook it.

Fig. 5-6. First step in skinning a duck—cutting off the foot.

Fig. 5-7. Skinning the duck—pulling the skin off the breast.

EVISCERATION

Evisceration is gutting your animal. I like the term. To eviscerate seems to have more class than to gut. People also talk about drawing poultry, or simply cleaning it. You can eviscerate all poultry the same way. This basic technique works for the smallest bantam chicken or the largest goose.

As soon as you have finished killing, plucking, and singeing your bird, cool it down by running it under cold water. This plumps it up, and makes it more attractive as well as easier to clean.

I like to plump my birds in the kitchen sink and eviscerate them indoors. Start by cutting off the head, the feet, and the oil sack. Then cut across the abdomen horizontally from thigh to thigh. Some people prefer making a vertical cut from the breast bone to the rectum. Either way works. Just be sure not to stick your knife in so

far that you gouge the intestines.

You need to open up the bird large enough so that you can get your hand in. Yes, that's what you must now do. Stick your hand into the intestinal cavity, as in Fig. 5-8, and gently pull out everything you feel in there. The entrails will be warm to the touch. You'll have to tug them to get them out.

You'll want to throw away most of these entrails, such as the long, worm-like intestines. But you want to save the heart, gizzard, and liver, which are interconnected with everything else. Carefully disconnect these from the intestines. The liver has a green sack hooked to it, which is the gallbladder. You want to cut this out, without breaking it open. Supposedly the bile inside will ruin the meat it touches. (I've always been careful, so I haven't had to taste bile-drenched chicken!)

The gizzard is really interesting. (If you can

think of this as an ungraded biology class, evisceration is truly educational.) You need to open up the gizzard with your knife, and clean out the accumulated grit, and peel off the yellow lining.

Wash off the gizzard, liver, and heart, and place them in a little dish of water. These are the giblets—the edible viscera of the poultry.

Now return to your carcass, and reach back in the almost empty cavity, and pull out the kidneys and the lungs that are hooked to the back of the bird. If your bird is exceptionally fat, there might be pads of fat to pull out as well. (At a convenient moment, you can melt these down for real chicken fat, a delicacy for cooking. You'll end up with little crisp pieces of fat, a favorite treat in my family.) The cavity should now be empty. If you later roast your bird, you put stuffing into this cavity.

Next, move on to the top of the bird, and cut off the neck. Then cut the skin by the neck and pull out the windpipe by grabbing it and pulling it through. It comes out like a long snake, but you might need to yank a bit. If you can't get it all out from the top, you might have to pull it out through the open cavity. To remove the crop, separate it slightly from the skin. If you mistakenly pop the crop, all the food the bird ate yesterday will be all over your chopping block. That's no big deal, but the objective is to get the crop out without maiming it too badly.

Figure 5-9 shows all the steps required in evisceration. If you get lost along the way, please refer to this drawing.

At the end of the evisceration process, wash your bird by letting cold water run through it. However, this shouldn't be a bird bath. Please don't soak the meat.

At this point, your birds are ready for roasting, just like the skinned, eviscerated duck in

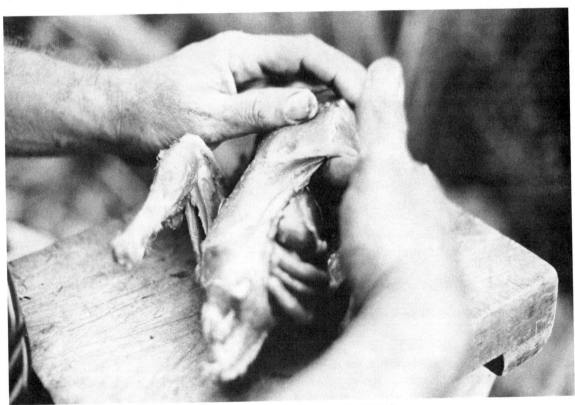

Fig. 5-8. Eviscerating a duck—putting in your fingers, and pulling out the innards.

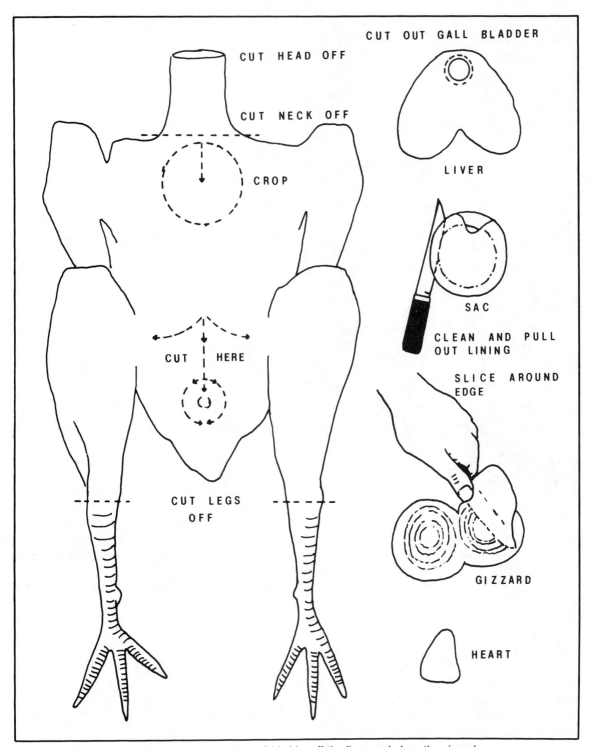

Fig. 5-9. How to eviscerate poultry, plus trim the gall bladder off the liver, and clean the gizzard.

Fig. 5-10. A skinned and eviscerated duck.

ing is three. (More details on freezing in Chapter 12.) If you want to cut up your birds—especially chickens or ducks—proceed as follows, using a sharp knife. Use Fig. 5-11 as a guide to help you:

☐ Cut off the wings by cutting through the joint where the wing connects to the main body of the bird.

☐ In the same manner, cut off the entire leg (thigh and drumstick) by cutting at the point where the leg joins the body.

☐ If you like, you can now separate the drumstick from the thigh by cutting directly through their point of connection. You can also separate the meaty part of the wing from the wing tip in the same fashion. This makes the wing look like a little drumstick, which might make it more popular.

☐ You now have a cylindrical carcass containing two breasts and a back. Cut the back off the breasts by cutting through the ribs on both sides. You can then cut the back in half for inclusion in your recipe. Or you can freeze backs to use for soup making later on. For their size, backs don't have much meat. They are always last choice of the fried chicken pieces.

☐ Your final piece is the whole chicken breast, usually thought of as two breasts. I cut straight through the cartilage connecting the two halves to separate them. If you want four pieces, divide each half breast in half.

☐ To bone a chicken breast, skip the previous step. Place the whole breast skin side down on a cutting board. Cut through the white gristle at the end of the keel bone, which is the dark bone at the center of the breast.

☐ Now pick up the breast in both hands and bend its halves back and forth. You want to pop out the keel bone. You can loosen it by running your fingertip around it. Remove it in one or two pieces.

☐ Cut the rib cages off the breast. You want to leave as much meat on the breast as possible.

Fig. 5-10. You may want to freeze them to eat later. Place the bird in a plastic bag and then lower the bag into warm water, being careful not to let any water into the bag. The bag will adhere to the bird, driving all the air out. At this point, you can wrap your bagged bird in freezer paper. Wrap and freeze giblets separately. You might want to have a bag for necks, another for gizzards and hearts, and a third for livers.

It is recommended that you chill turkeys a minimum of eight to ten hours before freezing them. Or, if you want to eat them fresh, you can keep them ten days in the refrigerator. The maximum number of days to chill turkey before freez-

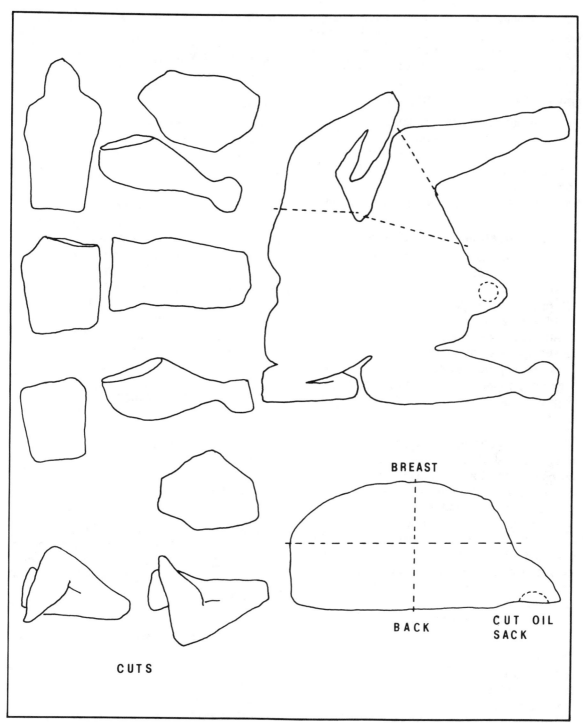

BREAST

BACK

CUT OIL
SACK

CUTS

Fig. 5-11. How to cut up a chicken.

☐ Finally, turn the breast over and cut away the wishbone. You can remove the skin if you wish, or leave it on. Boned chicken or duck is a delicacy used in many gourmet dishes.

GEETA'S POULTRY RECIPES

Everyone has their favorite recipes for the different types of poultry. This recipe section offers a few suggestions for recipes we enjoy at our farm, Sai Lake. Experiment with them if you like, and be sure to add your own special touches. View the recipes as guidelines, not the law.

Sweet and Sour Chicken

1 chicken, cut into small chunks
2 carrots, cut diagonally into thin slices
1/2 cup water
1/2 cup brown sugar
1/3 cup vinegar
2 tablespoons cornstarch
2 tablespoons soy sauce
1 can pineapple chunks
1 green pepper, cut into small strips
vegetable oil
batter

Simmer carrots 10 minutes in boiling water until crisply tender. Mix brown sugar, vinegar, cornstarch and soy sauce in pan. Stir in carrots, carrot water, pineapple with syrup and green pepper. Heat to boiling, stirring constantly, until thick, about 1 minute. Keep warm.

Heat oil in frying pan. Prepare batter (below). Cut chicken into small chunks using a meat cleaver. Dip chicken in batter and fry until done, about 10-15 minutes. Drain on paper towels. Stir chicken into sauce, and reheat until simmering. Serve immediately over rice.

BATTER

3/4 cup water
2/3 cup white flour
1 teaspoon salt
1/2 teaspoon baking powder

Mix all ingredients until smooth.

Crunchy, Nutty, Spiced Party Chicken

1 chicken, cut up
1 cup slivered almonds
1 clove garlic
1 thin sliced ginger root
1 teaspoon salt
1 teaspoon nutmeg
1 teaspoon cinnamon
1/4 teaspoon pepper
1 egg

Put almonds, garlic, and ginger in blender. Blend until finely ground. Mix in spices. Dip chicken in beaten egg; roll in almond mixture. Place chicken pieces, skin side up, on rack in ungreased pan. Cook uncovered at 375 degrees F. until done, about 1 hour. You can make this same recipe using crushed corn flakes or seasoned bread crumbs instead of the almonds. If you use crushed shredded wheat, you can call it porcupine chicken.

Mike's Quick Chicken Soup

1 chicken
1/4 cup sliced fresh ginger
1/2 cup soy sauce
2 1/2 quarts water
2 teaspoons salt

Put chicken in pot with water, soy sauce, ginger and salt, and simmer until cooked, about 1 1/4 hour. This recipe makes a delicious broth. You can use the cooked chicken in the soup, or for chicken tacos.

Friday Night Quick Whole Roast Chicken

1 chicken
1 apple
1 onion
salt and pepper
4 tablespoons margarine
1 cup water

Wash out chicken cavity, and stuff with a peeled onion, and a peeled, quartered apple. Close the cavity with toothpicks.

Salt and pepper chicken and place in a roasting pan with water in the bottom. Roast uncovered at medium temperature, 350 degrees F. Check the chicken every half hour, adding water to the drippings (if it has evaporated), and rub with margarine so that the skin will brown crisp.

Roast 1 1/2 hours, or until done.

To make gravy from the drippings, remove chicken from the pan. Place pan on the top of the stove, over low heat. Add 2 heaping tablespoons flour, and stir in carefully, to avoid lumping. Add additional water, as necessary, to make the gravy.

Roast Duck in a Paper Bag

1 duck
salt and pepper
paper bag

Place seasoned duck inside paper bag. Sit bag on a baking pan. Bake in 350 degrees F. oven for 2 hours, or until done. Remove duck from bag.

A lot of people have trouble cooking duck without drying it out. This paper bag recipe gives a moist duck.

Steamed Pressed Duckling

1 young duck
1/2 cup soy sauce
1 teaspoon honey
2 celery stalks
3 scallions, or 1 small onion
1 beaten egg
1/4 cup cornstarch
1/4 cup sesame seeds
oil
shredded lettuce
dipping sauce

Combine soy sauce and honey. Brush duckling. Fill duck cavity with celery and scallions. Steam duck for 1 1/2 hours until tender, in a covered pan, on a rack over boiling water. Remove duck, quarter it, and cut out the bones. You can save the broth for soup.

Shape each quarter into even rectangular shapes if possible. Press under a weighted flat pan until flat, about 15 minutes.

Dip the flattened duck pieces in egg, and coat with a mixture of cornstarch and sesame seeds. Fry the patties in hot oil until they are light brown. Cut in strips and place on a bed of shredded lettuce.

Serve with a sweet and sour sauce as a dip. You can easily make such a sauce by heating jam and adding a little vinegar.

Debi's Roast Goose

1 goose
oranges
apples
salt and pepper

Stuff goose with oranges and apples. These will absorb fat. You need not eat them.

Salt and pepper the goose and stab it with a fork. Stab it in 10 to 15 spots. As the goose cooks, if the fat isn't really running out, you can stab it again, a few times in each leg and on the sides, where the meat is.

You can baste with wine, but never use any extra grease. Bake the goose for 3 to 3 1/2 hours at 350 degrees F. Drain off fat as it cooks. If it gets too brown, cover with a tent of aluminum foil.

Roast Thanksgiving
Turkey Injected with Butter

Stuff turkey with your favorite stuffing.

If you want, you can inject the turkey breast with melted butter. Use a hypodermic needle, and inject melted butter into the meaty sections of the turkey.

Then place the turkey breast side down in a large roasting pan. Turning the turkey upside down, will let all the juices absorb into the breast meat.

Cover with a lid, or aluminum foil. Baste occasionally with butter.

A turkey that is cooked upside down might not look perfect (the breast skin might stick to the pan), but the flavor is the best. Injecting the turkey creates your own self-baster. Use 1/2 cup butter.

After going to the trouble to raise and kill your own turkey, there's no excuse for cooking it too dry.

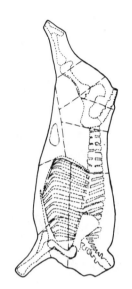

Chapter 6

Can You
Skin a Rabbit?

IF I WERE TEACHING A COURSE IN BUTCHERING, I'd have my students start with rabbits. They are small and easy to handle; yet they are mammals, with four legs and a hide. If you work your way up gradually from rabbits, to a small goat, and then onto pigs and beef cattle, you should gain confidence along the way. Don't let the thought of butchering a cow frighten you. Just think of it as a gigantic rabbit.

Butchering a rabbit gets you rabbit meat, and it also helps you learn many of the basic principles you'll use with the larger animals. Try to develop precision as well as speed. These skills will serve you very well later on.

Before you begin, nail a board to a fence or wall at your eye level. Hammer in two #16 nails (long nails) about 8 inches apart from each other, but don't hammer them in very far. You'll be hanging the rabbit from these nails after you stun it. It works best if your nails slant upward. That way the rabbit can't fall off of them.

You can keep your butchering neat and efficient by having four containers at your side be-

fore you begin. You will need two pans of water—one for washing your hands and knife, and another for washing and cooling your rabbit. A third little dish for the heart and liver would also come in handy. The fourth pan will hold the throwaways, such as the head, intestines, and blood (Fig. 6-1).

KILLING RABBIT

There are two ways to kill a rabbit. Take your pick. You can break its neck, or you can stun it by hitting it in the head.

To break the neck of a rabbit, hold the rabbit by its back legs with one hand and by the head with your other hand. Put your thumb on the back of the rabbit's neck, just below the ears. Put your four fingers under its chin.

Now stretch the animal out. Then press down with your thumb, and at the same time raise the rabbit's head rapidly. This motion will dislocate the neck. If you did it properly, your rabbit is now unconscious.

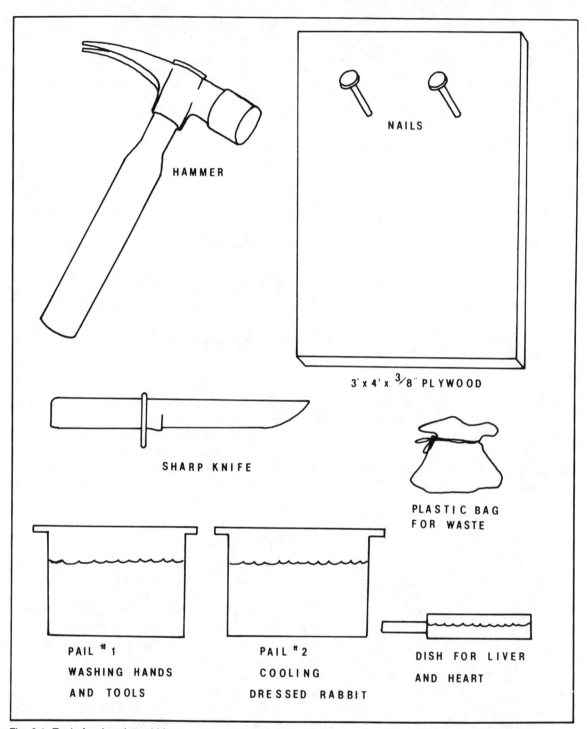

HAMMER

NAILS

3' x 4' x $\frac{3}{8}$" PLYWOOD

SHARP KNIFE

PLASTIC BAG
FOR WASTE

PAIL #1
WASHING HANDS
AND TOOLS

PAIL #2
COOLING
DRESSED RABBIT

DISH FOR LIVER
AND HEART

Fig. 6-1. Tools for dressing rabbits.

Mike Getz, one of my neighbors, had difficulty breaking his rabbit's neck with this technique. "I was taught the method by a fellow who has very strong arms," explains Mike. "But when I tried it, the rabbit started screaming. I don't know if you have ever heard a rabbit scream, but it is a loud, high-pitched scream that just devastates you. Apparently, I didn't have the arm strength to break its neck fast enough, before it knew what was going on."

Mike prefers to kneel with the rabbit between his legs. The rabbit sits up in its normal position, with Mike straddling it snugly. When the rabbit feels calm (and Mike feels calm), he strikes it on top of the head with a large rubber mallet. Then he hangs it up and cuts off its head.

Another method to stun a rabbit is to hold it upside down and strike it with a heavy object at the base of the skull.

Regie McDaniel, who is pictured in Fig. 6-2, stuns them with a hammer. He holds the rabbits by the feet with his left hand. He swings the hammer with his right hand. It takes less than a second. You aren't really killing the animals with either method. You are just knocking them out. Explains Regie, "I can hit them in the head, and have their heart out before it stops beating."

Immediately after stunning the rabbit, cut off its head. You might find that it is easiest if you hang the rabbit up first, and then cut the head off. Or you can cut on a table, and then hang up the headless rabbit. In either case, cut the head off as high up as possible, right behind the ears.

The reason you want to get the head off first, is to let the rabbit bleed thoroughly. A good bleed makes the meat look good. You won't get any of that unattractive redness that you sometimes see around the joints in chicken and rabbits.

Now you skin the rabbit. Figures 6-3 through 6-7 show how Regie does his skinning. You might notice that Regie doesn't cut off the head until he has pulled off the skin; however, he goes so fast that the head is literally off within

Fig. 6-2. Regie McDaniel holding a rabbit that has just been stunned with a mallet.

moments. Follow these steps:

☐ Hang up your rabbit. Make a little slit in the back legs, just above the hock. (The hock

61

☐ Cut the skin around each hind leg. To do this, you will run your knife in a little circle right below your nails.

☐ Cut a slit in the skin between the two hind legs. Run your knife from the inside of one leg to the inside of the other leg.

☐ Cut off the tail.

☐ Cut off the front paws.

☐ Starting at the hind legs, carefully separate the skin from the carcass. You want to leave all fat on the carcass and not on the skin. Work your fingers between the hide and body as you pull the skin off. Basically, you can peel the skin off like a sweater.

☐ If need be, you can run your knife between the skin and body, to help separate one from the other. In an older rabbit, this may be necessary. Remember to be careful if you plan to save the skin. You don't want to slit it. (I'll deal with care of rabbit skins in Chapter 15.)

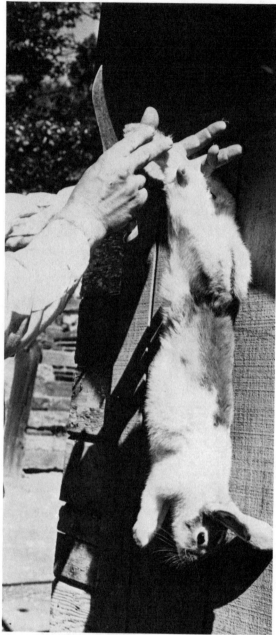

Fig. 6-3. The place in the rabbit's hock where you will hang it on the nail.

is the bend in the leg above the foot, like an ankle in reverse.) Feel for the spot between the tendon and the bone, and pop your knife in there to make a convenient little hole for hanging.

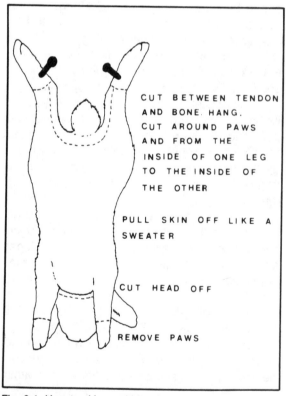

CUT BETWEEN TENDON AND BONE. HANG. CUT AROUND PAWS AND FROM THE INSIDE OF ONE LEG TO THE INSIDE OF THE OTHER

PULL SKIN OFF LIKE A SWEATER

CUT HEAD OFF

REMOVE PAWS

Fig. 6-4. How to skin a rabbit.

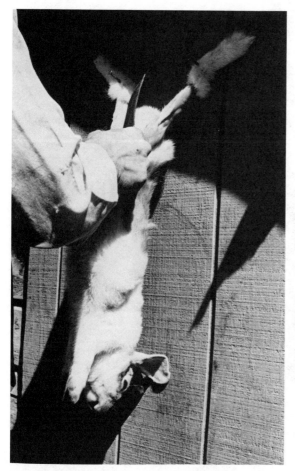

Fig. 6-5. Skinning the legs of the rabbit.

EVISCERATION

The skin is off, and you are ready to clean your rabbit. You will be cutting the rabbit open, from a point between the two back legs, all the way down the belly. Use Figs. 6-8 through 6-10 for guidance.

Insert your knife between the hind legs, and cut the pelvic bone. Now slit down the belly. To make sure you don't cut the intestines by mistake, keep your finger ahead of the knife as you slice downward. If your knife strays, it will hit your finger, and not the rabbit's bladder. Cut all the way down to the chest. This is a much longer incision than you made with chickens.

Now that the intestines are entirely ex-

posed, pull them out by grasping the stomach with one hand. At the same time, hold the liver in place with the thumb of the other hand. You don't want to pull it out just yet. Throw the intestines and stomach away.

Remove the liver, as in Fig. 6-11, being careful to cut off the gall bladder without breaking it. The gall bladder is the little green sack that is hooked to the liver. Throw it out.

Remove the heart, also, and save the liver

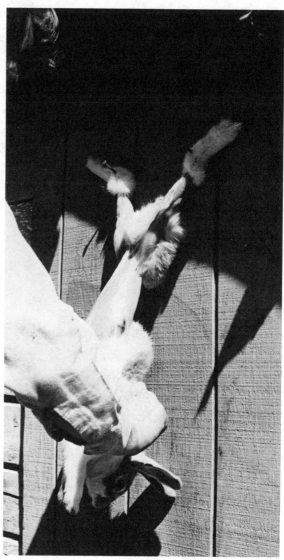

Fig. 6-6. Pulling down the rabbit skin.

Fig. 6-7. The rabbit fully skinned; the head will be cut off with the skin.

and the heart in your little dish. The lungs and kidneys are still inside the carcass. Pull them out, and throw them with the intestines and other refuse. If you can't get the kidneys out, just leave them inside.

You can now rinse off your carcass with cold water. If you want to cool it rapidly, you can leave it in cold water for 10 to 15 minutes for cooling. But don't soak it too long. Water adulterates meat. Chill in your refrigerator.

Figure 6-12 shows the rabbit carcass. You can cut it up, as in Fig. 6-13. The method is basically the same as for chicken. Note that you have already split the breast in two. You did that

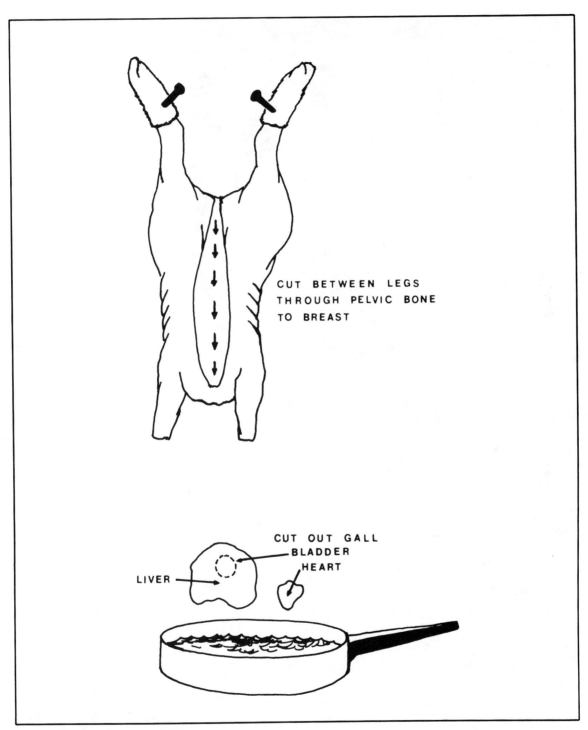

CUT BETWEEN LEGS
THROUGH PELVIC BONE
TO BREAST

CUT OUT GALL
BLADDER
HEART

LIVER

Fig. 6-8. How to eviscerate a rabbit.

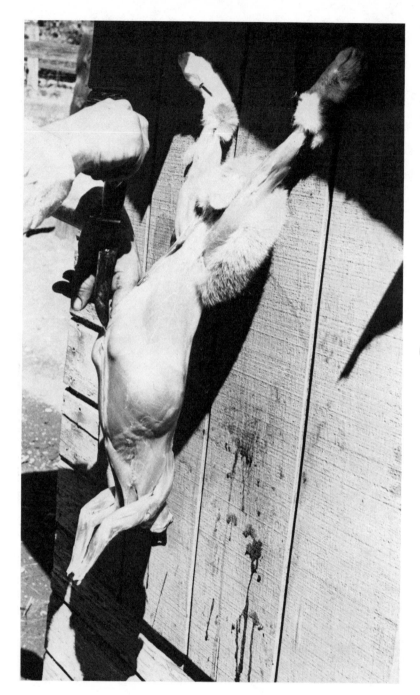

Fig. 6-9. How to cut open a rabbit.

when you made the incision for eviscerating.

You've now butchered a rabbit. That wasn't so hard, was it? Regie McDaniel says, "If you can butcher a rabbit, you can butcher anything."

Of course, he was raised in the country. It's a lot easier to butcher when you've seen it done all your life. But rabbit is simple enough for you to learn it all on your own.

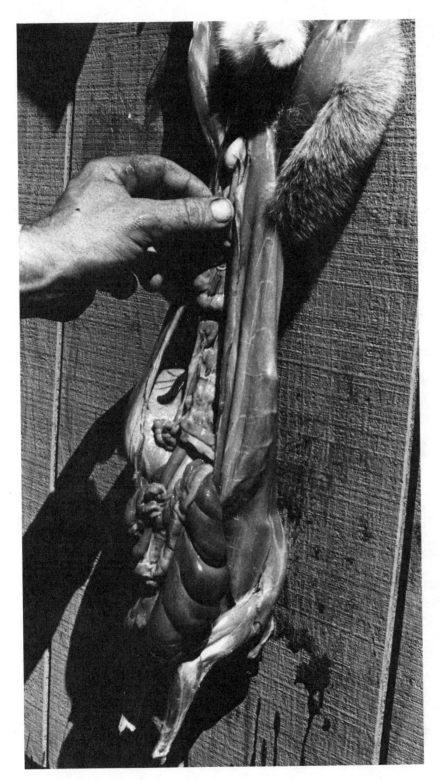

Fig. 6-10. The intestines of the rabbit.

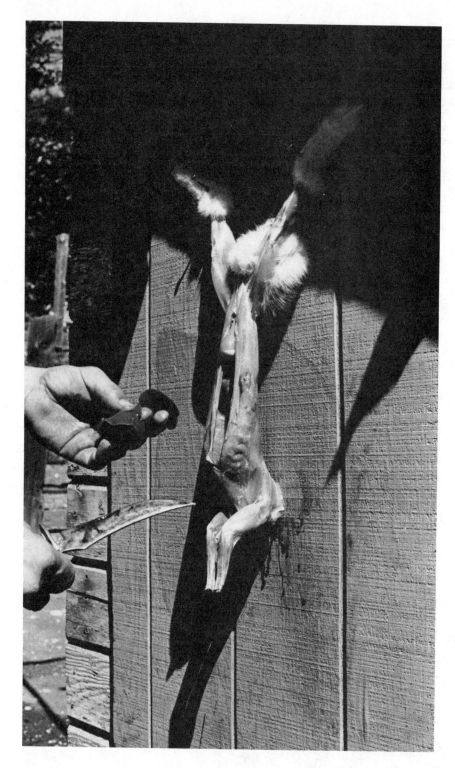

Fig. 6-11. The liver that has been removed from the eviscerated rabbit.

Fig. 6-12. The rabbit carcass cooling off in the bowl of water.

RABBIT RECIPES

Barbara's Hasenpheffer

3/4 cup vinegar
3/4 cup red wine
3/4 cup water
3 medium onions, finely sliced
4 whole cloves
2 bay leaves crumbled
2 teaspoons salt
1/2 teaspoon tarragon
5 teaspoons sugar
3/4 teaspoon black pepper
1 rabbit, cut in pieces

Make a marinade from the vinegar, water, wine, onions, cloves, bay leaves, salt, tarragon, and pepper. Let rabbit sit 24 hours in the marinade at room temperature. Remove rabbit.

Dry off rabbit and dredge pieces in salted flour. Brown in melted butter or bacon drippings.

Pour marinade back over browned rabbit. Cover and cook over low heat, 45 to 60 minutes, until tender. Remove rabbit.

Combine 3 Tb. flour and water to make a paste and blend it into gravy. Heat and stir until thickened. Serve over rice.

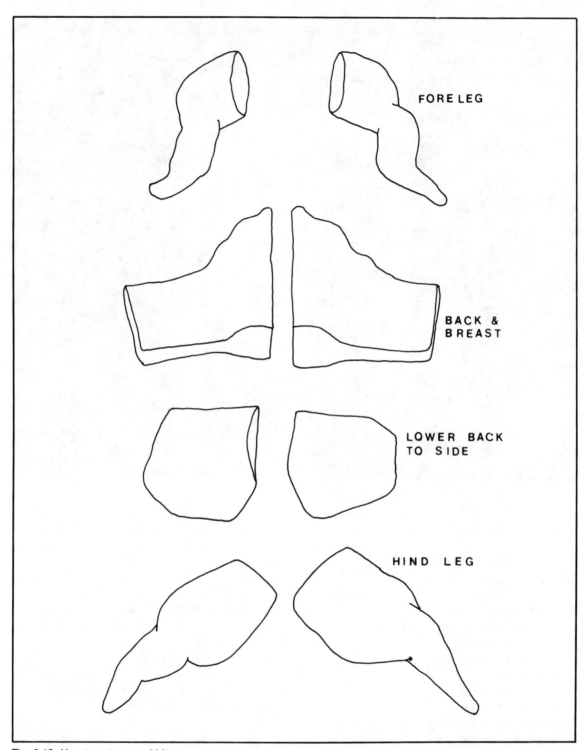

FORE LEG

BACK &
BREAST

LOWER BACK
TO SIDE

HIND LEG

Fig. 6-13. How to cut up a rabbit carcass.

Favorite Lemon Barbequed Rabbit

This recipe is quite similar to the previous one, but has a distinctive flavor.

Marinate cut up rabbit in a lemon sauce made from:

1/2 cup lemon juice
3/4 cup water
1 clove garlic, crushed
2 1/2 teaspoons salt
1/3 cup oil
1/4 cup finely chopped onion
1 teaspoon black pepper
1 teaspoon ground thyme
2 teaspoons sugar

Remove rabbit, pat dry, and roll in seasoned flour. Brown pieces in butter. Pour marinade into pan over rabbit, and cover tightly. Cook about an hour, until tender. Remove rabbit, and thicken gravy.

Sam's Fried Rabbit

Parboil pieces of rabbit for ten minutes. Cool.

Dredge rabbit pieces in seasoned flour, then dip in egg, and dredge again in flour or rolled cracker crumbs.

Fry in oil until golden brown on all sides. Reduce heat and cover, and continue cooking 40 minutes, turning every 10 minutes or so.

Make a gravy from the pan drippings if you wish.

In general, you can use any chicken recipe for rabbit. However, rabbit does tend to be a tougher meat than chicken. You should either parboil the rabbit before you start, or cook the dish longer than you would for chicken, or both.

Chapter 7
Butchering Goats, Sheep, and Venison

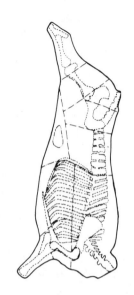

T HIS CHAPTER COMBINES THREE ANIMALS WHO look different and taste different, but have remarkably similar anatomy. Thus, when slaughtering, eviscerating, and cutting up goats, sheep, or venison you go through basically identical procedures. Rather than repeat the same material three times, I will combine all data where applicable. I include venison in a back-to-the-land book, because so many people supplement their family's meat supply with deer meat.

In many ways, slaughtering one of these medium-sized animals is similar to slaughtering a chicken or a rabbit; however, the first time you go out to kill such animals, you might be struck by the differences rather than the similarities.

These animals are big. They can be close to your size or even larger. They have a high level of intelligence. They are strikingly beautiful. Killing these medium-sized animals isn't quite as easy as chopping off the head of a chicken. The size factor can definitely get to you.

You might want to have someone with more experience guide you through slaughtering and butchering these animals the first few times. If you don't feel comfortable going out to make your kill, rifle in one hand, and textbook in the other, ask someone who has done it before to help you. My neighbor Bill Schell helped me the first few times I killed goats. It's normal to want that kind of moral support. On my own, I might never have gotten up the nerve.

The same holds true for hunting deer. Young people learn how to hunt from their elders. It's traditional to be initiated into killing animals by folks who are more experienced. If you think you'll need help, ask for it. We all need skilled teachers.

PREPARATIONS FOR SLAUGHTER

If possible, don't feed your animal for 24 hours before it is slaughtered. On the other hand, do give plenty of water during this period. A 24-hour fast helps the evisceration process.

Select your slaughtering site carefully. Ask yourself where you are going to kill the animal.

You will want to kill it out of sight of your other animals. You also don't want your animal to be able to run away from you. And very important: if you are shooting the animal, you need to choose a safe location where no one could get hurt from a stray bullet.

We lead our goats from their pen to a special spot we use for killing them. Then we stake them there, in the lush clover, and they nibble contentedly for the few moments until they die. You want your animals to be relaxed before their death. Letting your animal become highly agitated and nervous hurts the quality of the meat.

Bring all equipment with you to the slaughtering site. You will need a large bucket for all the entrails and the head. A 5-gallon bucket is barely large enough. Those large black plastic trash bags might work well for you. You can insert them in a galvanized wash tub.

You will also need a gun, a sharp sticking knife for cutting the throat, a knife for evisceration (probably the same one), a skinning knife, a sharpening stone and a steel. You will be surprised how fast your knives will become dull. Also bring along a meat saw for splitting the backbone, and a clean bowl for the heart and liver. If you can't remember everything you might need, make a list.

It is convenient to have a water source nearby. If not, bring a bucket of water with you. You'll want to wash your hands, wash off knives, and rinse the liver and heart. You also might want to wash off the carcass, especially if it gets blood, dirt, or hair stuck to it.

Where are you going to skin your carcass? Obviously, you could do the whole job on the ground. Hunters always field-dress deer on the ground. Another option is to place your animal in a trough-like skinning rack called a lamb rack. You could also work on top of a low table, or skin an animal that is hanging up.

If you plan to hang your goat/lamb from a tree, make sure the chosen branch is high enough. You want your carcass totally off the ground. A limb 8 to 10 feet off the ground should work well for you. But is it strong enough? You

don't want the limb breaking under the weight of your animal. In general, a healthy limb with an 8-inch or larger diameter should do fine.

You will want some type of rope, gambrel, and pulley to get your animal into the tree. (If you need to review equipment needed for hoisting and hanging meat, refer back to Chapter 4).

Please examine your slaughtering site carefully. Is it adequately clean? You don't want dirt or manure to get on your carcass. However, if you wash down a slaughter site—such as a barn—with disinfectants, be sure to rinse, rinse, rinse. You also don't want to taint your meat with strong chemical odors.

And what about the weather? Slaughtering a goat or sheep can take you an hour or two. You will want to start early enough, or late enough, so that you don't slaughter during the hottest part of the day. Meat can spoil very rapidly. You don't want to expose your carcass to any more heat than absolutely necessary. Bacteria love warm temperatures. You also probably don't want to get stuck out in the rain, halfway through your butchering job.

Besides considering the weather, you have to think about how you will handle your carcass when you have finished eviscerating it. You might want to have a clean sheet available to wrap your carcass in. Ask yourself how you are going to move the carcass from the field or barn to the chilling site. If you are transporting your carcass or hanging it in the open, you need to wrap it to keep it clean. And have you decided how you will be cooling the carcass? Will you be hanging it outdoors (is the weather cool enough?), holding the carcass in your refrigerator, or taking it to a cold storage unit away from the farm?

As you gather your equipment, think through all the steps you will take when slaughtering and eviscerating your goats or lambs. If you plan ahead, you'll have a much easier time at your job. Slaughtering can be a smooth or sloppy task. The choice is up to you.

Figure 7-1 shows a typical slaughtering site, very similar to the site we use on our farm. Note

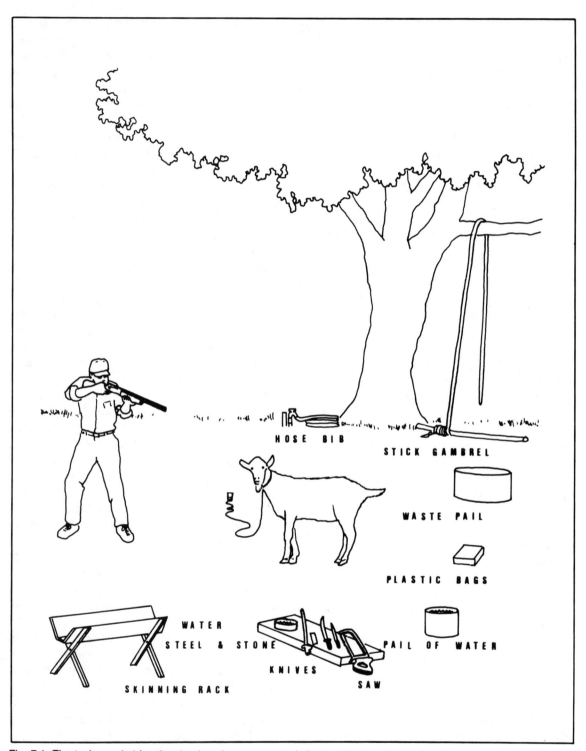

HOSE BIB

STICK GAMBREL

WASTE PAIL

PLASTIC BAGS

WATER
STEEL & STONE

PAIL OF WATER

KNIVES

SKINNING RACK

SAW

Fig. 7-1. The tools needed for slaughtering sheep or goats: knives, rack, gun, gambrel, and more.

the skinning rack, simple stick gambrel, strong tree branch, water outlet and all the other equipment that you must have with you before you ever begin. You definitely do not want to shoot the animal in the head, and then wonder, "Where's the knife?"

SLAUGHTERING GOATS/LAMBS

Many people slit the throats of goats and lambs without shooting them first. I can't do that. I use a gun.

Tie your animal to a tree or stake it. Then shoot it in the head at close range. You are really just trying to stun the animal, not blow it to bits. Aim at the forehead, slightly above the point between the eyes. The animal should drop to the ground without uttering a sound.

Immediately run toward the animal and cut its throat. This is called sticking. You want to bleed it as quickly as possible. Hold the lower jaw with one hand. With the other hand pull the head back and insert the knife in the neck, just under the jaw. Notice that you are inserting the knife (like a stab) into the neck, pushing it back toward the neck bone at the back of the neck. With your knife deep inside the neck, cut at right angles to the neck with a slightly upward thrust.

Cut the windpipe, gullet, and blood vessels. From the outside, your cut will probably measure only a few inches. You can make as big a slash as you need to, but the important cutting is what you do on the inside. Once the blood starts gushing out, you know that your cut is adequate and that you have severed those main arteries. If it doesn't bleed freely, you will have to go back in with your knife and cut some more.

If you are intending to keep the skin, try to avoid getting blood all over it. Here's where a rack can come in handy. You can place your stunned animal on the rack, before cutting the throat. Once cut, keep the head over the edge of the rack or table, letting the animal bleed away from its own body.

If you are working on the ground, you can try to direct the flow away from your pelt. If you can work on a slight hill, this will be helpful. In any case, let the animal bleed out fully before beginning to skin it. If you aren't using a rack, you can block the animal up with a 4 × 4 placed on either side of the carcass. This will keep your animal from rolling around.

If you decide to stick your animal without shooting it first, you can straddle it, and then stick it. Be sure of yourself, and work fast. You want to give your animal as humane a death as possible.

My neighbor Rex Richardson says that he never uses a gun when killing these mid-sized animals. He doesn't believe in it; in fact, he doesn't think a gun is humane at all. "I tie the animal's feet," explains Rex. "Then I lay down on it. If it is a big animal, I may have a couple other people laying down on it with me. Laying on the animal helps you accept that you are taking a life. I pull the neck back slowly. I don't rush into anything. Then I make my slit through the tight skin of the animal's throat. I think knifing the animal is much more humane. It is a human approach. Using a gun is a machine approach."

Everyone you talk to has a slightly different method of slaughtering. That is what makes home-slaughtering so interesting. It is highly personal.

SKINNING THE GOAT/SHEEP

Some people skin their goats/lambs on the ground or on a table. I prefer to suspend my animal as soon as possible. I find it easier to work on an animal that's in a vertical position.

It is helpful, however, to make a few initial cuts while the animal is still on the ground and easy to reach. If you can skin the back legs, as in Fig. 7-2, you won't have to stand up on tip toe to reach them when your goat/lamb is hung up.

Make a circular cut around the skin on the back leg, right above the hock, the same way as with rabbits. Then cut down the inside of each leg to the crotch. You can now peel back the skin on the legs. Use your sharp skinning knife, sliding it between the hide and the flesh, while you pull back on the skin. Once you have your legs skinned, you can hang up your goat/lamb.

Fig. 7-2. The first step in skinning a dead goat is to skin the back legs.

Make an incision in each back leg, right below the hock, between the leg bone and the tendons. These holes make perfect places for hanging your animals.

I insert a strong wooden pole or dowel into the back legs (Fig. 7-3). You also could use a metal gambrel. I hoist up my goat by throwing a strong rope over my conveniently located tree limb. I hold the goat at the proper height, while my helper, Mark, ties the rope to each end of the pole.

My method is simple, but it certainly isn't the only way to hang up a goat or lamb. You can devise your own methods for the entire slaughtering-butchering procedure. The point is to get the job done, humanely, neatly, efficiently. Be creative. You could come up with the best method ever invented.

I find skinning to be a rather logical procedure. I suppose I could give ultra-lengthy (and confusing) skinning instructions. But essentially all you need to do is remove the skin in one piece, working from the back end to the front end of the animal. You do this by sliding your knife between the skin and the meat. You want to separate the skin from the protective membrane (fell) that covers the meat.

Figure 7-4 illustrates the step-by-step procedure in skinning sheep or goats. Note that you cut the skin down the center if you wish to remove the skin in one flat piece. However, we skinned our goat without even making this center cut. It is so easy to take off a goat or sheep skin, we simply pulled it down like a sweater, the

Fig. 7-3. Geeta and Mark Yokum hang the goat, with back legs skinned, on the wooden gambrel.

same way we did with the rabbits.

There's no mystique involved in skinning lambs and goats. It's as easy as skinning rabbits. You start at the back legs, proceed down the belly and back, to the head and front legs. It is a logical procedure. Relax and turn it into a party.

Some Mexican villagers in the Isthmus of Tehuantepec use an unusual (to me) method of skinning goats. I had the opportunity of watching them when I lived a month in their village in 1980.

On the morning before a birthday party, the village slaughterer, Alexandro, slit the throat of

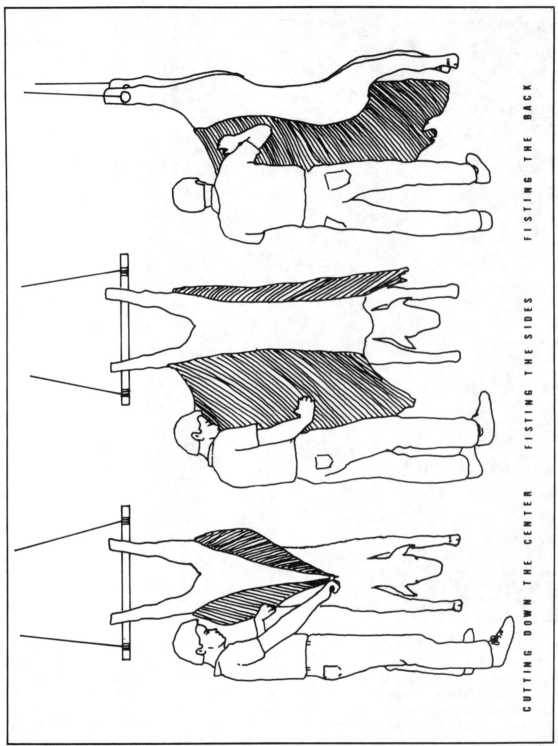

CUTTING DOWN THE CENTER   FISTING THE SIDES   FISTING THE BACK

Fig. 7-4. How to skin a sheep or goat: cutting and fisting.

a small goat making a very small incision. After the goat bled (into a pot—the blood was used in cooking), it was laid on a table. Then Alexandro made a tiny incision above the foot in each leg. Next, he rammed a small diameter stick into each incision and up each leg. The stick created an air cavity running all the way to the top of the leg. After running this stick back and forth a few times in each limb, he discarded it.

At this point, four other men joined the slaughterer. While Alexandro blew air in one of the openings (mouth to the incision), the helpers held the remaining four openings closed. Alexandro blew into one spot for a while, and then gradually moved around the goat, blowing into each opening in turn, while the men held the other openings closed.

The chest cavity of the goat blew up. It looked like a large, brown football with four legs—a goat balloon. Only then did Alexandro skin the goat. The skin seemed to come off with a crackling sound. The men told me that blowing up a goat made it easier to skin.

How everyone enjoyed themselves. After the men finished skinning and eviscerating the goat, they cut it up and marinated it with dozens of limes and garlics. Then the women cooked it with hot peppers, spices, and chocolate. The party lasted all night.

I tell you this story to stress to you that there is more than one way to skin an animal, and more than one way to have a party. So have confidence in your own skinning abilities. Novices can become experts very rapidly.

As you skin the carcass down the legs and onto the belly (Figs. 7-5 and Fig. 7-6), be careful not to poke through the protective membrane that covers the meat. You must also avoid scoring the hide if you want to save it. A sharp skinning knife and plenty of caution are your best friends here.

If you can have a partner work with you the job goes twice as fast and is really more fun. I can't imagine working alone. Half a job is plenty for me. You and your partner can talk while you work, but try to keep up with each other. It works best if you are both at the same point at the same time—one on the right side and one on the left.

Besides using your knife to remove the skin, you can also use your fist, as in Fig. 7-7. Fisting works great with goats and lambs. With fisting, the job goes much more rapidly.

Make a fist, and slide it under the skin. Holding the edge of the already loosened skin with one hand, fist against it with your other (clenched fist) hand. You can use your fist to separate the skin from the carcass, making 6-12-inch advances in just one push. You can also pull the skin down, as Sam is doing in Fig. 7-8.

The tail area can cause you a little problem. You can either cut off the tail along with the skin, or you can cut around it and leave it in.

When you get down towards the front end of the goat, you'll want to skin the forelegs, just like you did the back legs. Start above the hock (you'll be cutting off the feet and throwing them away), and skin back towards the body.

Cut a circle around the neck, and skin down to that point. You won't be skinning any part of the head. In fact, at this point you can cut off the head, right behind the ears.

If you are saving your skin, keep it as clean as possible. Blood and dirt don't enhance it one bit. (I'll describe the next steps with your skin in Chapter 15.)

Rex Richardson and Arlo Acton have a novel method for taking off the skin around the neck area. They tie up the animal real tight, and skin it down past the middle. Then they each put a knee inside the skin, and kneel on the animal skin. "The skin comes right down with your knee," says Rex. "It takes ten seconds, instead of a half hour." I suppose you could call that a variation on fisting. As I said, there are no right or wrong ways to do this work.

EVISCERATING GOATS AND LAMBS

Your skinned, headless carcass is hanging upside down. You now want to open up the chest cavity so you can take out the intestines.

Everyone worries about the rectum and ac-

Fig. 7-5. John Covert and Sam skin the back legs of the goat.

80

Fig. 7-6. Skinning the goat belly.

cumulated feces. You can make sure you don't get any on your meat by using the following technique: Cut around the rectum deep into the pelvic canal. Pull the rectal canal, while pushing all feces downward towards the intestines. Now tie a string around the larger intestines, above all feces. Cut the intestines off above where you tied your string, and let it drop into the pelvic cavity.

Figure 7-9 shows how to cut open sheep or goats. To open up the carcass, first split the carcass upward, from the neck to the breastbone. You can use a meat saw here, to cut through the breastbone. So far, no intestines have fallen out.

Start a cut from the upper end, a few inches below the point between the legs. Cut downward toward the breastbone. You can find your tied-off large intestines and pull them down towards the rest of the intestines.

The intestines and stomach will roll out at you (Fig. 7-10). Have your bucket or bag ready to receive them. Guide them into your refuse containers, rather than let them rip out of the cavity. You want to work them loose, but you don't want to rip them. Disconnect them from the body cavity where necessary. You want to get all the internal organs out of the carcass. Cut through the diaphragm in order to get to the lungs and heart.

Be careful when you remove the liver (Fig. 7-11). You don't want to pop the gall bladder. Cut off the green gall bladder, along with a piece of liver, and discard it. Put the liver in a small bucket. When you find the heart, separate it from the other internal organs and fat, and put it in with the liver. You can wash these off in a few minutes and have them for dinner today. Or you

Fig. 7-7. Fisting off the pelt of the goat.

Fig. 7-8. Pulling off the pelt of the goat.

can give them to your helper. These organs don't keep well. It's fun to eat them after slaughtering, as a payment for your hard work.

If you want to save the tongue and/or brains, return to the head. Cut out the tongue. Then split the head open, and take out the brains. Frankly, I send my head to the dump, intact. That's because we shoot our goats in the head, so the brains are no longer edible anyway. As I said, everyone has their own method of doing things. Wash off the carcass (Fig. 7-12) before you call it quits for the day.

In a small goat you needn't cut upward through the breastbone before opening the pelvic cavity. However, in a large animal, if you don't make this upward cut first, the intestines

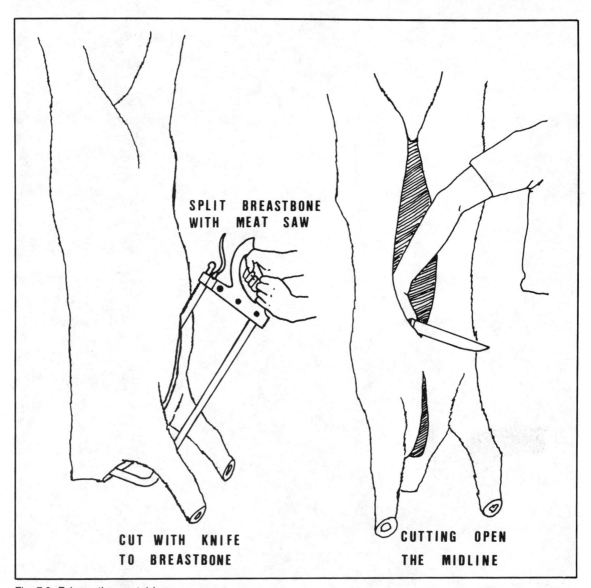

SPLIT BREASTBONE WITH MEAT SAW

CUT WITH KNIFE TO BREASTBONE

CUTTING OPEN THE MIDLINE

Fig. 7-9. Eviscerating goats/sheep.

Fig. 7-10. Pulling out the intestines.

can really get caught up on top of the breastbone. At that point, it is difficult to make a larger
incision because the intestines are in your way.
That's why I advise cutting from the neck to the
breastbone first, to avoid any mishaps.

SLAUGHTERING, SKINNING, AND EVISCERATING VENISON

Report your deer kill to the local game keeper
in accordance with state law. As soon as you can
get the animal home, cut its throat. Put the head
facing downhill if possible, and let it bleed out
fully.

You might want to eviscerate your deer before skinning it, especially if it has been dead
for some time. Leaving the skin on is the traditional method, and it can help to keep your carcass cleaner.

In a male, cut off the genital organs, along
with a large patch of surrounding skin. Discard
them, and wipe off your knife. Now cut open the
carcass, from the anus to the neck. Be careful
not to cut the intestines. You can run your finger under your knife to make sure you don't pop
anything.

Roll out the intestines and stomach (remember, this is all happening on the ground), and disconnect them from the carcass. Cut the
diaphragm to remove the heart and lungs.

To remove the hide, cut circles around the
legs at each hock. Slit up each leg to your cut
down the center. Skin by slipping your knife between the hide and the meat. Be careful to keep
any hair from touching your meat. It can taint the
carcass. After you have completed skinning,
keep your carcass (which you can quarter) as
cool as possible, until you can get it hung up in
a cooler, 10 days at 35 to 40 degrees.

Regie McDaniel says you can skin a deer
with a car. Says Regie, "You take a deer and
you cut around the head. Then you tie the horns
off to a tree. Next you cut around the back of
the head and skin it down the neck. Then you
take a rock and stick it up in there, between the
shoulder blades. You tie the rock off with a rope.
It should look like a knot in the back. Next you
take the end of that same rope and tie it to a car.
As you drive the car forward, you skin the deer
from the neck to the feet." Figure 7-13 illustrates
this unusual skinning technique.

Some people don't care for the wild flavor

Fig. 7-11. Cutting the gall bladder off the liver.

Fig. 7-12. Washing off the carcass.

of deer. You can minimize this flavor (odor) by avoiding handling the musk glands which are located between the feet and the hocks. These really do stink. Don't touch them and then touch the meat. Also, if you can kill a deer who is calm, rather than one who has run all over the place,

your meat should taste even better.

You can save the head and antlers, but you will have to send it to a taxidermist to be fixed. If you just want to mount the antlers, you can do this yourself. You don't need to put any special chemicals on them. Just saw the antlers off

87

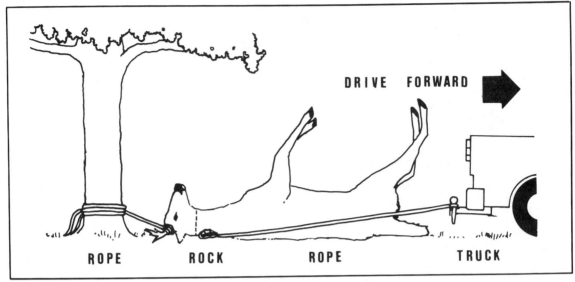

DRIVE FORWARD

ROPE   ROCK   ROPE   TRUCK

Fig. 7-13. Skinning a dear with a rock and a truck.

the head with a meat saw. Save a nice patch of skin to go with them.

CHILLING THE CARCASS

Some people split their lamb/goat carcasses in half, and some don't. One main purpose to splitting your carcass is to create more cooling surfaces. Most mid-size animals are small enough that cooling is no problem. However, I split mine in half because I find it easier to deal with half a carcass at one time.

Promptly chill your carcass below 40 degrees Fahrenheit. This can be done outside if the weather is suitable—about 28 to 35 degrees Fahrenheit—or hang the carcass in a refrigerator. If you don't have a spot for chilling, find someone who does. After your lamb/goat carcass has been chilled for 24 to 48 hours, you can cut it up. You don't need to age lamb or goat, although some people do.

Your deer carcass will be handled a little differently. You might need to quarter it in the field in order to get it home easily. If it is dirty, wipe it off with cloths, but don't wash it with water in the field. You don't want to encourage bacterial growth.

As soon as you get home, hang your deer in a cooler. With deer you will want to age your carcass for a week or two. Aging definitely improves the flavor of deer.

When deciding whether to age your lamb or goat, look at the fat content of the carcass. If your carcass has little fat, then don't age it more than a day or two. A younger carcass also requires less aging. And remember, tastes vary with individuals. Frankly, I never age my goats, I don't care for the resultant flavor.

CUTTING THE LAMB/GOAT
CARCASS INTO PRIMARY PIECES

Gather your equipment together. You will need a good-sized cutting area, boning knife, large steak knife, meat saw, freezer paper, freezer tape and marking pen. A meat grinder would also come in very handy.

There are many different ways to cut lamb/goat, and all the larger animals. People spend several years in school learning the art of cutting up meat. The style of cutting varies between regions of the country, and even between different supermarkets in the same city.

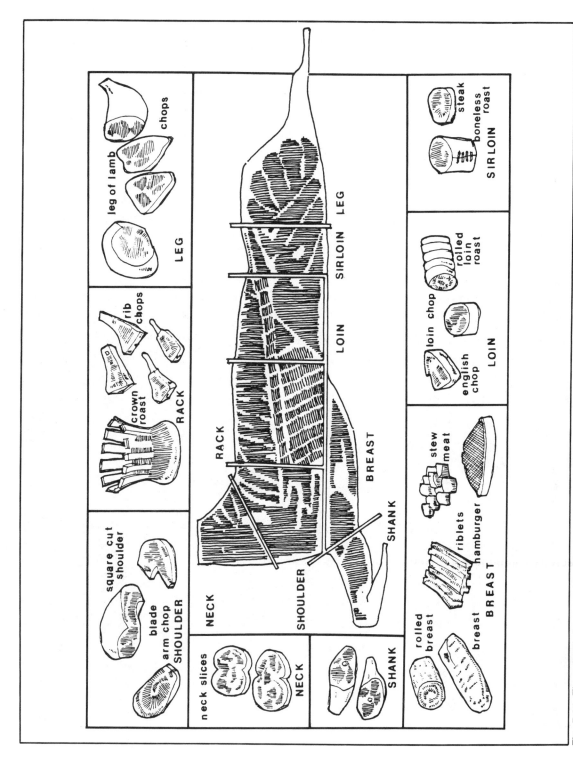

Fig. 7-14. The primal pieces and smaller cuts of a goat or sheep.

89

You should feel free to develop your own individual style. It's your meat.

Figure 7-14 shows how to cut your sheep/goat carcass into eight basic primal cuts: leg, sirloin, loin, rack, breast, shank, shoulder, and neck. The drawing also shows the various smaller cuts that you get from each of the primals. It is really quite a simple procedure. For some of you, looking at the drawing might even be enough instruction.

Nevertheless, I will now explain how to cut up your lamb/goat. I want you to be able to get your carcass into the freezer, in useful, edible pieces. Hopefully, these pieces will even resemble the supermarket cuts with which you are already familiar. And please be assured that your meat will still taste delicious even if you don't make perfect (recognizable) pieces the first time you cut meat.

I will assume that you have already cut the carcass in half to cool it. I'll tell you how to cut up one half. Obviously, you will repeat this procedure for the other half.

I would like you to put your half of lamb or goat on your cutting table (Fig. 7-15) and gaze at it for a few minutes. Without any instructions available, how would you go about cutting it up? Wouldn't you cut off the neck? Wouldn't you separate the front legs and back legs from the body? That leaves the middle or rib section. It looks a little long doesn't it? Wouldn't you split it in two or three pieces? Already, you have cut your carcass into the primal cuts by using your own common sense.

Cutting into the big basic pieces—primals—is the first step in butchering meat. You can learn a lot about butchering by looking carefully at your carcass. Many hints are available

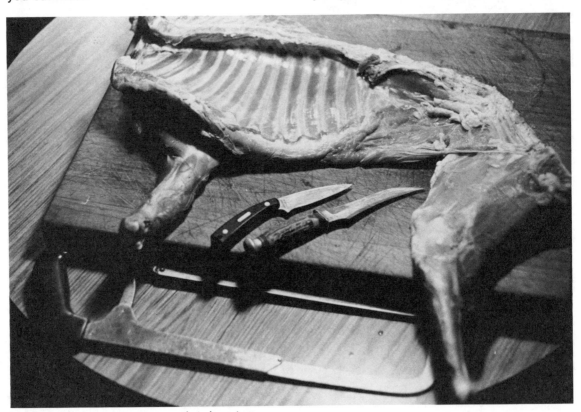

Fig. 7-15. Half the goat carcass, ready to be cut up.

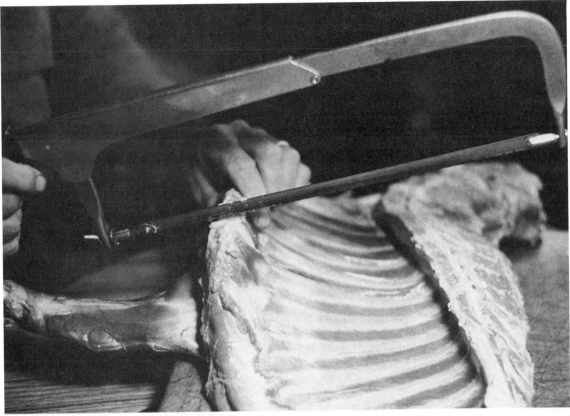

Fig. 7-16. Cut between the 5th and 6th rib of the goat.

within the shape of the carcass itself. The following are my basic lamb/goat cutting instructions:

☐ Cut off the neck. You can keep the neck whole for use in soups, or saw across it to make several circular neck slices. You will wrap one package here: neck.

☐ Separate the shoulder (front leg section) by cutting between the fifth and sixth rib, as in Fig. 7-16. Use your meat saw. Now, cut the front leg (shank) off the shoulder. As you can see, even a hacksaw will do the job. You can cut lamb/goat shoulder chops out of the shoulder by sawing the ribs away from the chops. You can see the rib section and the chop section. Chops are ribs that have a hunk of meat at the top. Use your meat saw to cut down the midline of the shoulder, separating ribs from chops.

☐ You now have one long slab of ribs. You can cut them into smaller slabs of two to three ribs each by slicing between them with your boning knife. Separating the chops is more difficult. You can cut between them (or between two of them, making double chops) with your boning knife, and then saw through the top bone with your meat saw. This is where a power saw could come in handy. Here you have three packages: ribs, shoulder chops, front leg.

☐ Now cut between the 12th and 13th rib, to separate the rack (or rib) section from the loin (back end). You treat this rib section, just the same as above. Cut across the middle, separating the ribs (for barbecue) from the meaty rib chops. Separate ribs and chops as above. Of course, you could bone out the chops, but I think chops taste much better cooked with the bone attached. I am a gnawer. This rib or central section will yield two packages: ribs and chops, formally called rib chops. (You can make a crown roast from the intact rib chops. I'll describe that gourmet treat in the recipe section.)

   ☐ Separate the loin from the leg by sawing just in front of the hip bone. If the leg is large, you can cut a roast-sized chunk called the sirloin off the front end of it. The sirloin makes a nice roast, or you can cut across it to make several chops. You can keep the loin as a roast, or cut it into loin chops with your meat saw. If you bone out the loin with your boning knife, you can roll it into a rolled loin roast. The leg is just what is says—the leg. You will package loin chops, sirloin roast, and leg from this final section. Figure 7-17 shows all the cuts I made from the carcass in Fig. 7-15. The small pieces are

goat chops which are cut without a power saw. They might not look exactly like typical chops, but they taste like them.

CUTTING UP DEER

When you cut up an animal, you will lose some of the hanging weight to the waste pile. What I enjoy about cutting up my own young goats is that I throw very little away. I am not bound by the rules of the supermarket butcher. I can keep every strange-looking piece I want.

   The young goats I kill give about 25 pounds of meat. A lamb will give you about 40 to 55 pounds. A deer can be quite a bit larger. Consequently, you will be able to make more cuts.

   Your first priority after returning home with your deer is to hang it in a cooling room to age for a week or so. Most hunters tell me that the

Fig. 7-17. Half goat carcass cut into small pieces.

92

taste of venison improves greatly with aging. However, nothing improves the taste of the meat where the animal was shot.

When you begin to cut up your carcass, remember that all bloodshot meat should be discarded. It doesn't taste good. If you really want to keep it, soak it in a weak brine (1/2-pound salt to 1 gallon water) overnight, and then grind or stew the meat. You can always use it for dog food. Also remember to trim off and discard as much deer fat as possible. It's the fat that holds the "wild" taste. Don't save it, and don't grind it up in your sausage.

To cut up the deer carcass, split in half and proceed as follows, from head to tail. These instructions are keyed in with Fig. 7-18. Looking at the drawing will definitely make this task much easier for you to follow:

☐ Remove the neck. You can cut it into some neck slices (A) and still leave a sizable chunk for a neck pot roast (B).

☐ Remove the shoulder between the fourth and fifth rib. Separate the front (upper body) portion into a shoulder (or chuck) roast (C). Cut the top of the front leg into an arm roast (D). The remaining section of front leg is called the foreshank (E).

☐ Cut off the mid-section by looking for the seam that separates the rear of the deer from the mid-section. If you can see the seam, cut a thumblength in front of it. Separate the breast (F) from the ribs by slicing it off. This can go in your deerburger pan. Now trim off the ribs. You can keep them for barbecue deer ribs, or trim the meat off of the bones for deerburger.

☐ Cut through the remaining meaty backbone. This is the tenderest meat, because it isn't from an area that is used when running (like the front and back legs). You can cut it into rib chops (G) and loin chops (H) running from front to back. Or if you prefer large standing roasts, you can omit making chops and leave the cuts in one piece. Or you could bone them out for tender rolled roasts or boneless steaks.

☐ The remaining piece in the main body (located between the leg and ribs) is the rump (I). You can trim the flank (J) off of it, and then you have a rump or hip loin. Serve as a roast.

☐ What remains is the whole hind leg (or haunch) of your deer. You can saw the haunch into three sections. The top (wider) section can

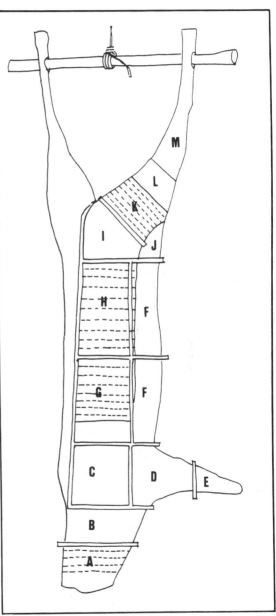

Fig. 7-18. How to cut up a deer carcass. (Letters are keyed into text as a step-by-step procedure.)

be cut into round steaks (K). The next section is called the heel (L). You can make it into a roast, or use it for hamburger or jerky. (More on jerky later.) The remaining leg is called the rear shank (M). This also makes good jerky.

Figures 7-19, 7-20, and 7-21 show a deer carcass being cut into primal sections. As you can see, it is definitely more meaty than the goat I cut up.

GENERAL INSTRUCTIONS FOR JERKY

You can make jerky from lamb, goat, or deer. Jerky is a great way to use up excess meat. It takes about 5 pounds of meat to make 1 pound of jerky—and it won't last long either, unless you keep it hidden away.

Cut your meat into strips measuring less than 1/2-inch thick. The length and width can be to your personal preference. Be sure and remove all connective tissue and fat. And cut with the grain, not against it. You want long, stretchable strips.

You are going to season your meat strips and then dry them. The brine you make (wet or dry), the amount of time in the brine, and the method of drying are all variables that will give your jerky its special, individual taste.

You can make a brine from spices (salt, brown sugar, pepper, soy sauce, garlic, ginger, celery salt, and more) dissolved in water. Or you can pack your meat dry with the spices, and let its own juice become the soaking brine.

You can dry the meat outside in the sun, in a smokehouse, over a campfire, in an electric smoker, or in your oven. You can leave in enough moisture to have a chewable product

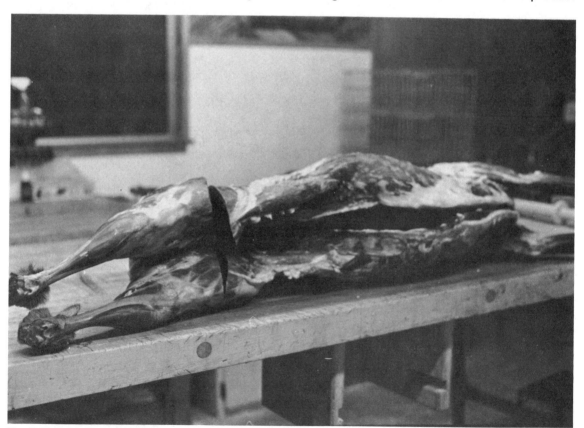

Fig. 7-19. A whole deer carcass.

Fig. 7-20. The rib cage or rack of deer.

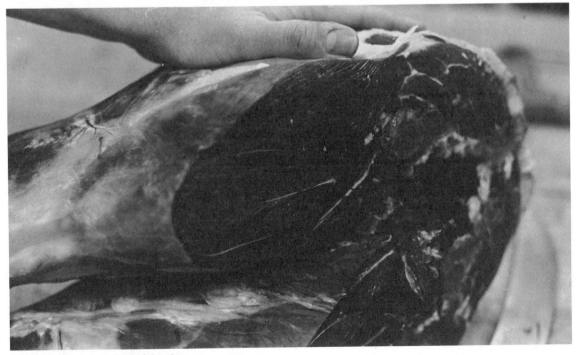

Fig. 7-21. The meaty legs of the deer.

that you keep frozen, or you can dry it totally and keep it in a jar on the shelf. Basically, the dryer the jerky and the more heavily seasoned, the longer it will keep outside the freezer.

RECIPES FOR LAMB, GOAT, VENISON

Ruth Riley's Jerky

Trim off all fat. Cut meat across the grain to make it more tender. Keep all strips about 1/8 inch thick.

Mix 1/2 cup soy sauce with 1/4 teaspoon garlic salt and 1/4 teaspoon lemon pepper. Toss this with meat until well coated, and let it sit for 5 or 6 hours.

Place on racks and dry with the pilot light in a gas oven.

Marlin Ford's Jerky

3 pounds meat
1 tablespoon salt
1 teaspoon onion powder
1 teaspoon garlic powder
2 teaspoons pepper
1/2 cup Worcester sauce
1/4 cup soy sauce

Cut meat into long strips with the grain. Mix marinade ingredients and marinate overnight in ice box. Let excess drain off on paper towels. Bake at 150 to 200 degrees F. about 6 hours, leaving the oven door open 1/2 to 1 inch. Store in plastic jar in your freezer.

California Cheater's Smoked Jerky

6 pounds venison
1 teaspoon liquid smoke in 1/4 cup water
salt and pepper

Using a pastry brush, paint each piece of meat with a brush dipped in the water and liquid smoke. Salt liberally, and sprinkle with fresh ground pepper.

Place strips, layer on layer, in a container. Weight them down with a plate with a rock on top of it. Let stand 6 hours or overnight. Remove meat strips from bowl and dry in the oven at 120 degrees F. for 11 hours. Keep all strips at least 4 inches from the top or bottom of the oven.

Eugene and Irma Lissauer's Stuffed Crown Roast of Lamb

Crown Roast of Lamb is made from the rib chops. Do not separate your spareribs off the rib chops, if you want to make a crown roast.

To make a crown roast, put the 2 slabs of long-boned rib chops on your cutting surface. Cut away meat from between each rib, cutting inward about 1 1/2 to 2 inches. The ribs will now look like staggered spikes. You can save this meat for grinding up for your stuffing that goes in the center.

Bone out the backbone from the meaty section of the rib chops. This is the bone that runs on top of your chop, not the rib section.

Turn your slab upside down, meaty section flat to the table, and ribs sticking up in the air. Shape the two slabs into a circle, and stitch together to make the crown. If you have slaughtered a second lamb, that is even better. You can make a bigger, more circular crown with three or four slabs of rib chops.

1 crown roast of lamb
marinade
lamb/beef meatloaf
bacon rind

Marinate lamb overnight in a marinade made from teriyaki and cooking wine, seasoned with poupon mustard, garlic powder, onion powder, pepper, and paprika.

For the meatloaf stuffing, to your ground lamb and ground sirloinadd one or two eggs, grated raw potato, grated onion, water, teriyaki, poupon mustard, salt and pepper. The meatloaf should be very soft so that it will very tender.

Lay a rind of bacon in your roasting pan and place the crown on top of it. The bacon rind serves as the plate. Then stuff the crown with the meatloaf. Bake at 375 to 400 degrees F., for 40 minutes. Do not overcook.

Geeta's Original Curried Goat (or Venison)

2 pounds tender, young goat, cut into little squares
1 1/4 cups marinade
cooking oil, about 1/3 cup
2 teaspoons tumeric
1 teaspoon cinnamon
1 teaspoon cumin
1 teaspoon curry powder
1 teaspoon paprika
1 teaspoon cayenne pepper
5 cloves garlic, chopped
1 onion, chopped
1 tablespoon chopped fresh ginger
5 fresh tomatoes
3 hot peppers, chopped
(if you don't have fresh hot peppers and tomatoes, you could substitute a pint of hot sauce)
1 cup water
salt
fresh ground black pepper

Marinate goat chunks for several hours in a mix of 1/2 cup soy sauce, 1/2 cup water, 1 tablespoon sugar, 3 mashed garlic cloves, and 4 tablespoons wine. Drain and save marinade.

Heat cooking oil in the bottom of a large cast iron pan. Add spices, chopped garlic, onion, and ginger, and sautee for a few minutes; then add drained goat chunks and cook until browned, stirring so that every surface gets heated.

Add chopped peppers and tomatoes, salt, pepper, marinade, and water. Cover and simmer until done, about 1 to 1 1/2 hours. When done, the curry sauce should have thickened. Stir oc-

casionally, to avoid any sticking on the bottom of the pan.

Taste, and add additional cayenne pepper, salt, and ground black pepper as needed. I like it hot, but I spent a few years in India tuning my taste buds! Serve with rice and/or whole wheat tortillas (called chapatis in India).

Rex Richardson's Venison Backstrap

The backstrap is the filet mignon or tenderloin. It is the tenderest part of the deer.

Rex cuts this backstrap into small pieces, and fries them in oil with garlic and onion. He seasons it to taste with a little molasses, paprika, and soy sauce. He calls it instant stroganoff.

Andy's Venison Mincemeat

2 quarts venison, cooked and ground
3/4 pound beef suet, chopped
3 pounds peeled apples, chopped
3 pounds raisins
1 pound currants
2 quarts apple cider
1 tablespoon cinnamon
1 tablespoon ginger
1 tablespoon cloves
1 tablespoon nutmeg
1 tablespoon allspice
1 tablespoon salt
1 pound brown sugar
brandy/whiskey

Mincemeat is often made from venison. It is any combination of minced meat, chopped suet, chopped fresh fruits, chopped dried fruits, chopped nuts, spices, cider, and liquor. You can make up your own recipe, and simply use this one as a guide. Oranges, lemons, candied fruits, or chopped almonds all work quite well. Use what you have on hand. Simmer all ingredients together, and then add the liquor if you like.

Andy was an old friend of mine who has passed on. He was crazy about mincemeat. He liked to put a cup of black coffee in his as well. He would have loved this book.

Freeze your mincemeat, or can it at 10 lbs. pressure for 60 minutes. If you add enough liquor, you can keep your mincemeat in a crock in a cold room. (More on freezing and canning in Chapters 12 and 13.)

Caleb's Easy Roast Leg of Lamb

Leg of lamb
10 cloves garlic
salt and pepper
water
soy sauce
mint jelly

Salt and pepper lamb. Squeeze garlic onto it. You can stuff a few cloves up under the bone. Place it in a roasting pan, and add a little water. The water helps so you don't loose your drippings.

Bake at 300 degrees F., 35 minutes to the pound. Baste occasionally with soy sauce. Add water to the bottom of the pan as necessary.

To make gravy, remove lamb. Stir in 2 heaping tablespoons of flour to the drippings. Add extra water and soy sauce as needed.

Serve the lamb with mint jelly. It should be pink. If you use a meat thermometer, it should register 170 degrees.

Josh's Easy Venison Stew

2 pounds very lean venison, cut in 1-inch squares with no fat
1 can tiny peas, drained
1 cup sliced carrots
3 white onions, quartered
3 raw red potatoes, quartered
1 can concentrated tomato soup
1/2 can water
1 teaspoon salt
big dash pepper

Put everything in a casserole with the lid on. Cook at 275 degrees F. in an oven for 4 to 5 hours.

Chapter 8

Pigs: Slaughtering and Cutting Up

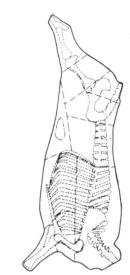

W ITH PIGS, I MOVE INTO THE DOMAIN OF THE larger animals. When you slaughter your 200-pound pig, you will get back about 150 to 160 pounds of meat. Thus, this is a job well worth the effort. It is, however, going to take more time and energy to kill and cut up a pig than a goat or lamb. You will want to plan ahead to have everything ready. And you will want to ask other family members or neighbors to help you. Killing a pig is not a one-person job. Even cutting up the pig would be more enjoyable with more than one pair of hands involved.

In some rural localities pig slaughtering is still a communal project that hasn't changed much in the past 80 years. Neighbors come together to slaughter their pigs in one location—sharing equipment and muscle, and making a festive event out of the annual pig day.

Kim Tabor tells me that she and her relatives have a Thanksgiving tradition associated with their pigs. On the Wednesday before Thanksgiving, the men from Kim's family slaughter the four pigs that are raised each year. They

kill them, gut them, and hang them up to chill overnight.

On Thanksgiving morning, Kim works with five or six other family members to cut up and process the four pigs. They cut up the meat into its usable pieces. They place hams and bacons in curing vats, and grind pork scraps for sausages. While they boil the head for scrapple in one pot, they simmer leaf fat for lard in another. Late in the morning, a distant uncle, who used to be a butcher, comes by the house to season the sausage, which they stuff into casings made from sheep's intestines. And then, after the family has completed all the work with their pig carcasses, they celebrate Thanksgiving by sitting down to eat the traditional turkey.

Perhaps your venture slaughtering and cutting up the family pig will become an equally warm tradition. Of all the farm animals, pigs lend themselves best to a communal work project. There's an old saying that you can use every part of the pig except the squeal. Cutting up pig is especially enjoyable because there are so many different products that you can make from the carcass.

PRE-SLAUGHTER CONSIDERATIONS

You will want to gather all slaughtering equipment together, before you slaughter your pig. You'll need to have a gun to shoot the animal, a knife for cutting the throat, a knife or two for skinning, plus a sharpening stone and steel. If you plan to scald rather than skin the pig, you will need a barrel or vat of water, a fire, plus some heavy ropes, as well as scrapers for taking off the hair. A thermometer would come in handy as well. (More on scalding in a moment.)

You will also need a knife for eviscerating the carcass and a meat saw for splitting it into two halves. Large buckets or plastic trash bags for the entrails are a must. And don't forget to design some sturdy method for lifting your pig in the air. You'll need a gambrel, plus a block and tackle or come-along to hoist the pig, so you can skin it and eviscerate it in a vertical position. You also need a tree with a strong limb, unless you have access to a tractor with a hydraulic lift. Remember, pigs are heavy.

Every spring my neighbors Dennis and Natalie Atkinson buy two piglets. They feed them grain plus all of the whey from their cheesemaking endeavors. In the fall Dennis slaughters both pigs, cuts them up, and cures much of the meat. (More on curing in Chapter 14.)

Dennis always works with a neighbor Steve Belial when he slaughters animals. Since Dennis is a big man, he could probably do much of his work alone. But as a duo, Dennis and Steve get the job done in less than half the time, with more than double the fun. It makes sense to work with a partner.

They shoot the pig in its pen behind the garden, and slit its throat there. Then they lift it into the garden cart (a two-person job for sure), and push it 1000 feet to the tree in the front yard where Dennis keeps his pulley wheel suspended from a limb.

Dennis and Steve partially skin the pig in the garden cart, and then they hoist it up, using the come-along that is attached to the pulley wheel. They finish skinning and then eviscerate the pig in this hanging position. The slaughtering-skinning-eviscerating process takes them about an hour.

I describe this particular pig-killing operation to emphasize that killing and eviscerating a pig is a rather simple, straightforward operation. Dennis Atkinson might look like a pig-killing pro, but he learned how to slaughter pigs only a few years ago.

Come to think of it, no one was born knowing how to kill a pig. Even the "experts" were novices in the beginning. So don't let the size of the pig intimidate you. Remember, it's just a big rabbit. Figure 8-1 shows Dennis Atkinson's big rabbit, looking very much like a pig, ready for slaughter.

KILLING THE PIG

Don't feed your pig for 24 hours before you kill it, but do give it plenty of water. You will shoot your pig in the head at a close distance. You want to shoot it in the forehead midway between and slightly above the eyes.

If you aren't exactly sure how to determine this point, mentally make an **X** from your pig's left ear to right eye, and from its right ear to its left eye. You will shoot your pig at the crossing point of the **X**. You must shoot straight in, not at an angle. You don't want to shoot twice. If you are unsure of your shooting abilities, have a friend who is a better marksperson help you. The animal should drop to the ground.

Immediately slit the pig's throat. Working with your friend, turn the animal on its back. One of you can straddle it to keep it from rolling. That person should also hold on to the front legs to keep it from kicking.

The other person should find the tip of the breastbone, in the middle of the pig, below its jaw. Holding the knife at a 40-degree angle, thrust it under the breastbone with the point aimed toward the tail. Then give the knife an upward (toward the head) thrust to sever the carotid artery, as depicted in Fig. 8-2. The blood should

Fig. 8-1. Live pig.

gush out. If it doesn't, insert the knife deeper and repeat the above. Remember, you want it to start bleeding immediately. It might help to watch someone else stick a pig to get the hang of the thrust. You don't want to cut into the shoulders or the heart. Keep to the center of the throat.

TO SCALD OR TO SKIN
If you plan to skin your pig as Dennis Atkinson does, you won't want to scald it. You either skin pigs or scald and scrape them—you don't do both.

Like poultry, pigs have edible skin. As long

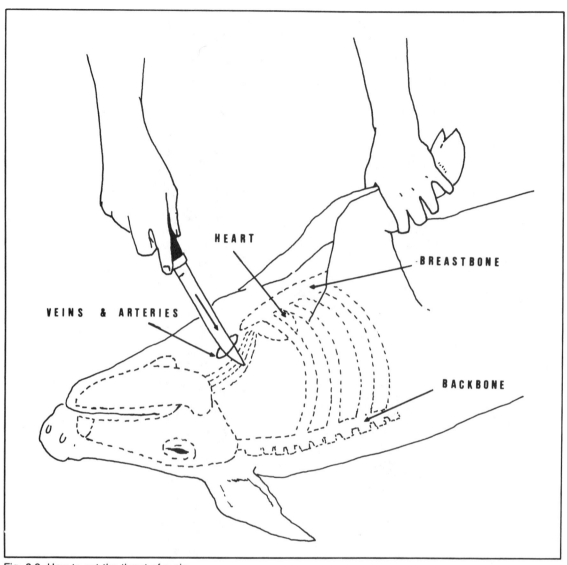

Fig. 8-2. How to cut the throat of a pig.

as you remove their hair, you can leave the skin on. This rind can later be used to flavor soups.

There are pro-scalding people and pro-skinning people. Some experts feel that a fully cured ham keeps better with the skin on. Leaving the skin on the pig also insures that you won't damage any cuts—such as the bacon—by slicing into the fat covering while skinning. And there are people who emphatically say that scalding and scraping is easier than skinning.

On the other hand, proponents of skinning state just as strongly that this is a much easier method than scalding and scraping. Experts on this side of the fence also say that skinned hams take a cure faster and keep just as well as un-skinned cuts.

The bottom line is probably local preference. If you do what your neighbors do, you can't go wrong. If people in your area have a set-up for scalding, see if you can use it. Or if you can get the scalding equipment together, design a pig-scalding center on your own land. Folks will call you an expert in no time.

In my area, most people prefer to skin their pigs. They think of scalding and scraping as historic. In fact, a rapidly growing percentage of the farmers here avoid the issue completely. They simply hire the local professional slaughterer, Bill Dowling, to do their work for them. He also skins pigs. (Much more about being a professional slaughterer in Chapter 11.)

SCALDING AND SCRAPING

To scald a pig, you will need a large vat of hot water in which you can immerse the animal. The hot water loosens the hairs, so that you can pull them out.

Have your water heated before you kill your pig. You want to dip your pig in hot water as soon as possible after it bleeds. The water temperature should be 140 to 165 degrees Fahrenheit. Temperatures that are too low or too high won't work for you.

A 55-gallon drum will work fine for scalding your young pig. You can heat your water and then scald in one drum. Or you use two drums, heating the water in one, and then pouring it into the other.

The advantage to using two drums, as shown in the top drawing in Fig. 8-3, is that you can bury your scalding drum in the ground at a slant. That way it is easier to get your pig in and out. Moreover, you might find it easier to control water temperatures with a second barrel. You can mix hot with cold, and still keep the water in the first barrel boiling.

You could also build a more elaborate scalding set-up using a vat and raised platform. If you were going to scald a lot of hogs at one time, this would be the way to go. The second drawing in Fig. 8-3 shows this scalding system.

Whichever system you choose, get your water heating several hours before you plan to kill the pig. If it gets too hot, you can always add cold water. You don't want to scald your pig in water over 165 degrees because high temperatures (or leaving your pig in the water too long) can set the hair. This complication you don't need! Have a thermometer handy so that can you can measure your water temperature.

Place your pig in the drum, head first. Rotate it around, and pull it out every minute or so. Check the hair to see if it will come out. When the hair will pull out, that is called slipping.

As soon as the hair slips on the front legs, pull the pig out, and immerse the rear end in the hot water. If you plan to save the front feet you can now try to pull off the toenails and dew claws (that back toenail) by inserting a hook behind the nails and pulling. You can also begin a scrape the hair off the face. You don't want to loose time while your carcass is hot.

Don't forget to check the rear end that's scalding in the barrel. As soon as the hair slips on the rear flanks, pull out the pig. Lay the pig in your garden cart or on a flat surface—a table, or a piece of plywood put on the ground.

You can scrape with knives or you can use special hog scrapers called bell scrapers. Always remove the hair in the difficult places—head, feet, jowl—first, and then move on to easier areas—back, sides. The bottom drawing in Fig. 8-3 shows how to scrape a pig with a bell scraper.

You are trying to remove the hair and the scurf, which is the outer layer of skin that has the accumulated oils and dirt in it. Many people add lime, lye, ashes or baking soda to their hot water to aid in scurf removal.

You want to work as fast as possible. If certain areas seem stubborn, cover them with a burlap bag and pour hot water over them. At the end, if you still have a few hairs left, you can singe them off, as you did your chickens and turkeys. Use a propane torch, but don't burn the skin. And of course, you can always give the carcass a little shave, if need be.

SKINNING

Before starting to skin you pig, wash off any dried blood or mud that got on the carcass after

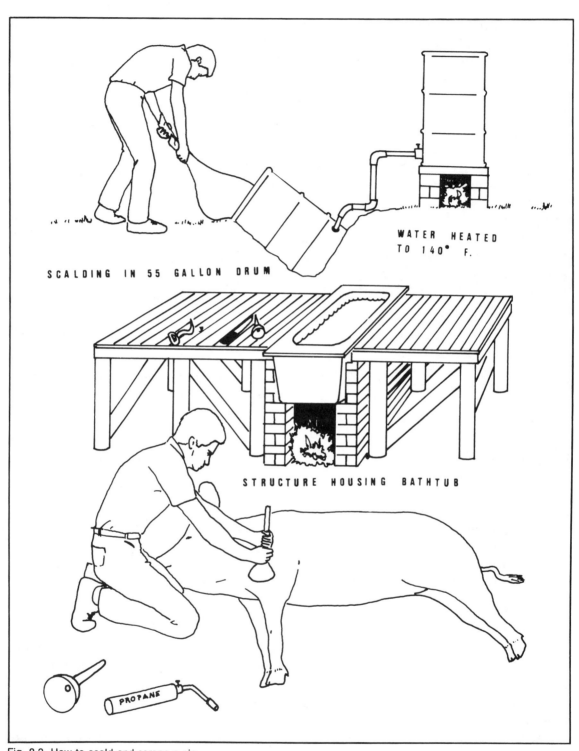

SCALDING IN 55 GALLON DRUM

WATER HEATED
TO 140° F.

STRUCTURE HOUSING BATHTUB

PROPANE

Fig. 8-3. How to scald and scrape a pig.

it was shot and bled. Then block the carcass tummy side up on a sheet of plywood or in your garden cart. A 4 × 4 on either side of the pig carcass will hold it in position. Figure 8-4 shows Dennis Atkinson's dead pig in the garden cart.

Figure 8-5 shows the basic method for skinning a pig. If you study this simple drawing, you shouldn't have any trouble with skinning. You begin, like you did for rabbits and goats, by cutting a little circle around the leg and then making a slit up each leg and across the crotch from one leg to the other. As Fig. 8-6 shows, you peel back the skin of each leg, and then skin out the hams (inner thighs).

Be sure that all your cuts penetrate only through the hide. You do not want to cut into the fat.

In order to proceed further up the carcass toward the head, make a slit down the center of

the carcass, from the anus to the cut in the throat. You can make this cut by inserting your knife under the skin with the point turned upwards. That way you can't cut too deeply.

Continue to remove the hide from the inside of the back legs and all the way up the sides of your carcass. Work slowly but steadily. You won't be able to fist the carcass here, and if you cut too deeply, you can score your fat layer. Hold up the skin in one hand to put tension on it, as you cut up against it with your knife. Figure 8-7 illustrates this technique.

Take the skin off the front legs in the same fashion as the back. And peel back the skin of the jowls (cheeks), as in Fig. 8-8.

At this point, you want to insert your gambrel into the tendons in the back legs (Fig. 8-9) and begin to hoist your pig into the air (Figs. 8-10 and 8-11). If you want, you can hoist the carcass

Fig. 8-4. Dead pig in garden cart.

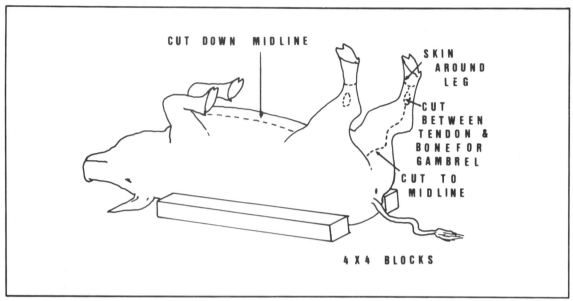

Fig. 8-5. How to block up and skin a pig.

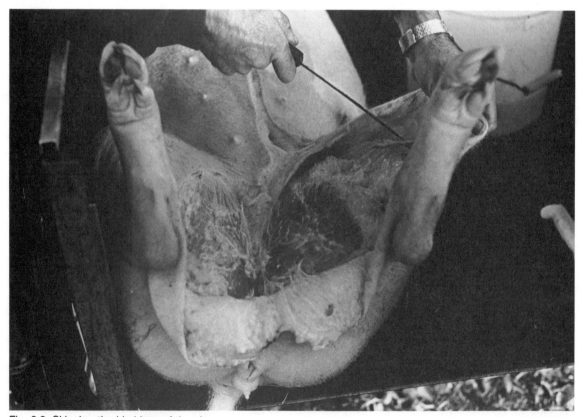

Fig. 8-6. Skinning the hind legs of the pig.

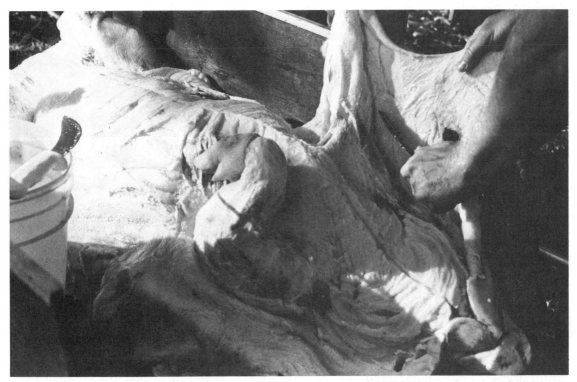

Fig. 8-7. Skinning the underside of the pig.

Fig. 8-8. Skinning the jowls of the pig.

Fig. 8-9. How to insert a gambrel into a pig.

about waist high, so you can take the rest of the skin off the pig's rear end while it is at a convenient height. You can cut through the tail at the joint nearest the body.

Begin to pull the skin off the back of the carcass. You probably won't need your knife. However, if fat starts to come off with the skin, then go back to using your knife in those places.

Hoist the carcass all the way up in the air to complete your skinning job. The only real difference from skinning rabbits or goats is that you remove the skin from the front of the pig first, and then you take it off the back. In Fig. 8-13, Dennis Atkinson and Steve Belial work together to remove the skin from the pig's back.

If you intend to keep the head, you will want to skin the entire face. If you plan to throw the head away, you will still want to skin the jowls (meaty cheek area) as described earlier.

Dennis doesn't plan to keep the head. In Fig. 8-12 he feels for the right spot to begin his

cut to remove the head. He wants to cut off the head right behind the ears, leaving the jowls attached to the carcass.

After cutting off the head, you pull the skin all the way off. You can also cut off the front feet at this point.

EVISCERATION

Eviscerating pigs is just the same as eviscerating rabbits, lambs, or goats. Only now, everything inside is bigger. You'll need bigger containers to catch all the entrails.

If you are worried about feces getting on your meat, you can cut around the anus. After you've freed the rectal canal, you can push any accumulated feces back toward the large intestines. Then tie off the rectal opening with a piece of string.

If you've slaughtered a male pig, you will want to cut off the penis during skinning or now at evisceration. Just cut through the skin and

108

Fig. 8-10. Steve Belial (top) and Dennis Atkinson (below) begin to hoist the pig into the air with the come-along.

fatty tissue at each side of the penis, and underneath the penis along the middle of the belly. Pull the penis and extra flap of skin up between the pigs legs and cut it off. Don't be shy. The pig is dead.

In large animals, if you cut down the midline from top to bottom, the intestines might start coming out right on top of your knife. You might never get your cut neatly completed.

To avoid this potential complication, first cut

109

the pig open from the neck where you stuck it, through the breastbone. You might need to use your meat saw to get through that breastbone. It's tough.

Return to the rear end of your pig, and split the two hams (back legs) apart with your saw or knife, cutting right through the pelvic bone (often called the **H** bone).

Cut down the midline of your pig. Remember, you don't want to puncture the intestines. Therefore, if you wish you can do a cutting trick: Insert the handle of the knife into the pelvic

Fig. 8-11. Partially skinned pig hangs on the gambrel over a galvanized pail, useful for catching innards.

Fig. 8-12. Skinning the backside of the pig.

Fig. 8-13. Feeling for the right spot to cut off the head.

opening. Your blade is pointing outward toward you. Cut downward. This is another way to insure you don't pop those intestines. Figure 8-14 shows this clever knife trick.

The intestines are now falling out, as in Fig. 8-15. Catch them in your tub. Don't let them rip. You'll recognize the bladder—a little bag of urine. If you can get it out without bursting it, more power to you. You should be able to lift it out between the legs.

Remove the liver, and trim off the gall bladder. Cut through the diaphragm (which is a muscle area separating the intestines-liver area from the heart-lungs area). Then cut down each side of the windpipe. Remove the heart.

Wash both the liver and the heart, and run them to the refrigerator. Hopefully, you will enjoy them for tonight's dinner. They also make a nice present for your helper.

You will see the leaf fat inside the chest cavity, next to the ribs and running toward the rear of the pig (Fig. 8-16). This is the pure lard used for making pastry. At this point, leave it in place inside the carcass. It can cool overnight along with the carcass.

You can now saw your carcass into two halves, as in Fig. 8-17. Start sawing between the hams. You want to saw as close to the center of the backbone as possible. As you saw from the inside, have your helper watch from the outside to make sure you are on line.

If you plan to use the small intestines as sausage casing, you might want to clean them now. The small intestines run from the stomach to the large intestines. Cut them out, and run them through your fingers to flush out their contents. Now turn a 3-inch cuff on one end, and fill with running water. The water will turn the entire intestines inside out. Scrape off the exposed intestinal lining with a blunt knife. Keep the pork casing with your other useful entrails in the refrigerator.

You should now hang up your pig halves to cool. You don't age pork, so you must cut it up within the next day or two.

You can hang the carcass outdoors, wrapped loosely in a sheet, if the weather is 28 to 35 degrees Fahrenheit. Do not let the meat freeze while it is cooling. You can also hang it in a cooling room, at a temperature below 40 degrees.

CUTTING UP THE PIG

Figure 8-18 shows the primal cuts of the pig, as well as the special cuts you make from each primal. You should look at the drawing often while following my cutting instructions. Cutting up a pig is easy. Just wait until we get to a beef cow, if you want to have something to complain about.

Imagine you are creating a very simple jigsaw puzzle. Instead of putting the puzzle together, you are cutting it apart. You are going to cut each side of the pig into five primal cuts—the jowl, the shoulder, the loin (upper midsection), the bacon (lower mid-section), and the ham. Now isn't that really simple?!

Remember, you have already cut the pig into its left and right sides, and cut the head off. And now, place your first half of pig (skin or fat side down) on your cutting surface, and go for it.

The Jowl. Starting from the top, cut off the jowl. (This may seem like a neck cut, but it is really the cheeks, if you remember.) Cut straight across the carcass, above the front leg. You want your shoulder (the next cut) to have a square edge. If you intend to use the jowl for sausage, just toss it into your sausage pot. If you want to cure it for bacon (it is then called the bacon square), you should square it off.

Decide now, will the jowl be sausage or bacon? Then place the jowl in the proper container—the bowl of scraps for sausage, or the pan for cuts that you will cure. You need to be organized here. You'll have cuts for curing, trimmings for sausage, fat trimmings for lard, and fresh cuts for freezing. Try to organize a spot for each type of cut before you begin.

The Shoulder. Moving right along, or down your pig carcass, your next cut is the shoulder. To sever the shoulder, cut between the third and fourth rib. Saw off the foreleg just above the knee

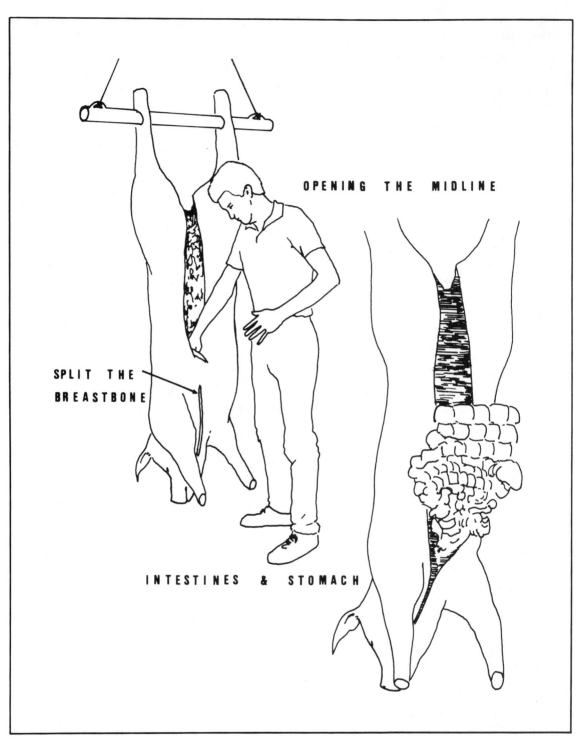

OPENING THE MIDLINE

SPLIT THE
BREASTBONE

INTESTINES & STOMACH

Fig. 8-14. Eviscerating the pig.

114

Fig. 8-15. Pulling out
the pig's intestines.

Fig. 8-16. Steve Belial has his left hand on the leaf lard which remains inside the eviscerated pig carcass.

joint. The longer you make the foreleg, the larger picnic ham you will have.

After trimming the shoulder up square (you want to trim off the neckbones and excess fat), you could save it as one large ham. Or, as most

folks do, you can divide it into two pieces, a picnic shoulder and a Boston shoulder. Figure 8-19 shows Dennis Atkinson separating the picnic shoulder from the Boston shoulder.

To make the picnic shoulder, cut just below

Fig. 8-17. Splitting the carcass in half with a meat saw.

the shoulder blade, a straight cut across the shoulder. You'll probably want to cure the picnic shoulder, or you could freeze it for a fresh roast. It can also be boned, and rolled.

The boston shoulder can also be cured for ham, or served as a roast (Boston butt), or it can be boned and rolled as well. If you have a power saw, you also might want to cut it crosswise into steaks, called blade pork steaks.

When trimming both the picnic and Boston shoulders, try to trim surface fat to about 1/4 inch. Throw excess fat in your fat pot for rendering into lard.

The Ham. Before beginning your cuts on the mid-section, you should cut off the back leg or ham. Where you cut depends on whether you want a long ham or a short ham. To cut a long ham, cut at the bend in the backbone, in front of the pig's hip bone, perpendicular to the side.

When Dennis Atkinson started cutting up his pig for our photo session, he suddenly had a memory lapse and couldn't remember where to make the cut for the ham. This loss of memory can happen to any of us. After all, most folks only cut up a pig once a year, if that.

I told Dennis, "Eyeball the leg." When he still looked confused, I said, "Look for the bend between the leg and body, and cut." I told him to wiggle the leg to find the bend. My point here is: you don't need to memorize every step in cutting your pig. Most likely, you will be able to think it through logically.

To cut a short ham, just leave more meat on the mid-section. In either case, remove the foot at the hock joint with your meat saw. You can use the feet for pickled pigs feet, trim it for sausage and use the rest for gelatin, or throw it out. Take your pick.

117

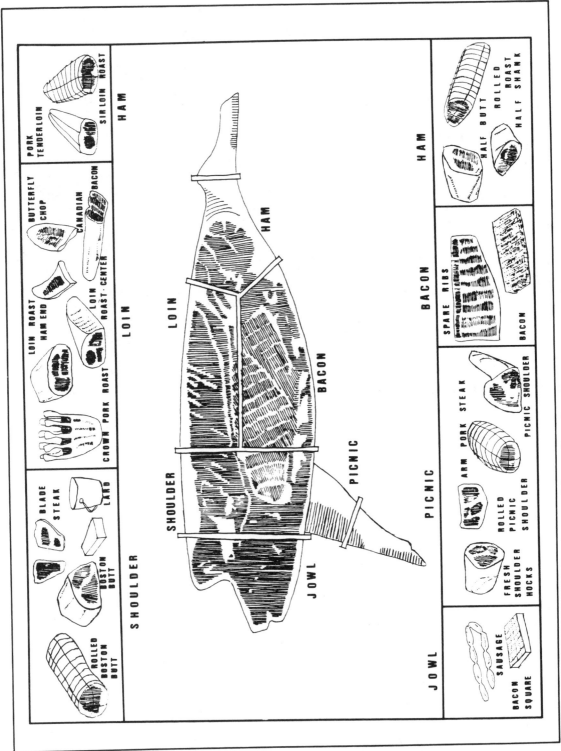

Fig. 8-18. How to cut up a pig: the primal cuts and the smaller cuts.

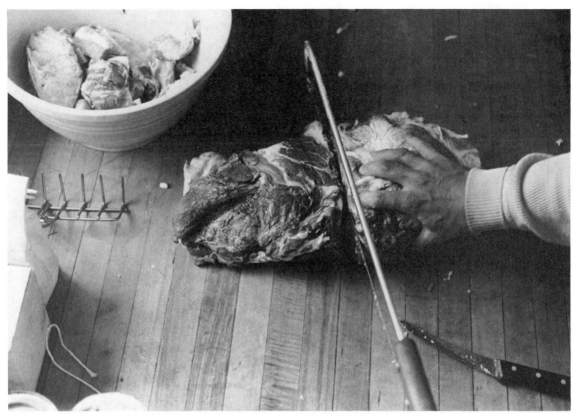

Fig. 8-19. Cutting up the pig: separating the picnic shoulder from the Boston shoulder.

You'll want to trim your ham to make it look neat and smooth. This is not just an aesthetic exercise. Your ham will also cure better this way.

Put your trimmings in your sausage or fat containers. As you are trimming up your ham, you will be cutting out the tail and a piece of backbone.

If you don't want to cure your ham, you could cut it into smaller pieces for roasts, or even bone it out for rolled roasts. You're the boss. In Fig. 8-20, Dennis Atkinson cuts a roast off the ham.

The Loin. You are now left with the mid-section. Your first step is to cut the loin from the bacon. Saw across the ribs at their greatest curvature, about 1/3 the way down from the back-bone, as in Fig. 8-21. Your loin will become your pork chops. (Remember your lamb and the lamb chops. This is quite similar.)

First you want to cut the tenderloin out from underneath the backbone. This is your tenderest cut to eat fresh. It is a round strip of muscle that you can see hiding right under the backbone at the rear end of the loin. You can cut it up for delicious stir-fry pork.

Trim the fatback from the loin. This is literally the fat that covered the back of your pig. Put it in your container for lard. Leave only the amount of fat you might want on your pork chops.

If you boned out the remaining loin, you could cure it and it would be called Canadian Bacon. This was a Sunday night delicacy when I was growing up. You could also bone it out, and still cut it crosswise for boneless pork chops, which Dennis is cutting in Fig. 8-22.

If you don't mind doing a little sawing, cut pork chops from the loin, with the bone intact.

119

Fig. 8-20. Cutting a roast off the ham.

Fig. 8-21. Cutting the loin from the bacon/spare rib section.

Fig. 8-22. Cutting boneless pork chops.

Fig. 8-23. Trimming the bacon off the ribs.

You can make double size pork chops for stuffing, which are absolutely delicious. (See recipe section at the end of this chapter.)

To cut pork chops, use your knife to cut between the ribs (or every two ribs for double chops), then saw through the backbone with your meat saw. For your double chops, cut a little pocket into the meaty section for the stuffing. Or make a crown roast of pork out of several loin sections. You can look this up in the recipe section for lamb and goat.

The Bacon. We are left with the raison d'etre of the pig—the bacon. You separate your bacon from the spareribs (another exciting cut off your pig) by sliding your knife between the ribs and bacon. What is really comforting about this task is that the ribs actually look just like ribs, and the bacon looks like a bacon. See Fig. 8-23.

You can see the ribs, right? The bacon is

the boneless section of fat and meat behind the ribs. You cut the spareribs off the bacon. Try not to gouge the bacon. Square up the bacon by trimming all four sides so that it will cure evenly. Dennis Atkinson trimmed his bacons to be the width of the hanger that he uses for smoking bacons, Fig. 8-24. That was ultra-logical, wasn't it?

It took Dennis about 1 1/2 hours to cut up one side of his pig. Figure 8-25 shows the results of his labor. Of course, he was conscious of being photographed, which may have delayed things a bit. Dennis told me that the first time he cut up a pig it took him three days. "I didn't know what I was doing," he laughed.

You should know what you are doing. It makes the job much easier. But even if you don't, you can still eat your pig. That's one of the delights of cutting meat. You really can't fail.

Last but not least, if you have kept the head,

Fig. 8-24. The bacon was cut to fit on a bacon hanger, which is used for smoking.

Fig. 8-25. The cuts from a half hog carcass.

you need to deal with it. Split the head, remove the eyes, clean the ears and nostrils. You discard the nasal passages and ear drums. I'll include some recipes that can be made from the head in Chapter 14.

RECIPES FOR FRESH PORK

The following recipes can be made from fresh pork, or fresh pork that has been frozen and then thawed. Methods for curing pork, smoking pork, and making various types of sausages are contained in Chapter 14.

By far the most exciting recipe you can make is a whole roast pig. There are two basic methods for roasting a pig whole—the pit method and the split method.

To roast the pig underground, you dig a pit the size of the pig. You put a lot of oak wood in the pit with rocks on top of the wood. You let the wood burn for an hour, until the rocks are hot.

Meanwhile you stuff the pig with whole carrots, cabbage, and potatoes and lay the pig on a large piece of 1-inch mesh chicken wire. You slit the pig under the arm and by the thigh, and pour some of the hot rocks inside these slits. Then you take the wire and bring it together around the pig.

The pig is now ready to go into the pit. First pour lettuce leaves into the pit, or anything else to keep the moisture in, such as banana leaves (my source Lorraine Yokum comes from Hawaii). The leaves go on the hot rocks. Place the wire-wrapped pig on the leaves. Take a wet gunny sack and put it over the pig, followed by a layer of leaves. Put an old canvas over that, and add dirt on top of the canvas. There should be no steam coming from the ground. Let the pig cook eight hours. Figure 8-26 illustrates how to roast a pig in a pit.

The fire must be hot enough before you start. You actually cannot have it too hot. The rocks should be beet red. Lorraine says that in Hawaii they use lava rocks; in fact, her mother brought these rocks to California from Hawaii for roasting pigs. The family is famous in the area for their roast pigs. To roast a pig over an open fire, Lorraine cuts lines down the back of the hog and rubs in rock salt. She also rubs rock salt under the arms and thighs. (Needless to say, the skin is left on for these roast pigs.)

Stick a spit from one end to the other, and keep it constantly turning. The pig should be 4 or 5 feet off the flame. Baste with water. Lorraine says this method is time consuming because you must keep turning it and basting it, plus keep the fire going. She prefers the pit method, because it is easier and comes out moister. She says you could get a similar taste by putting a

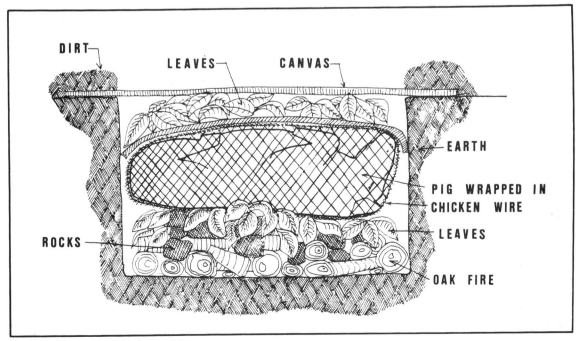

Fig. 8-26. How to roast a pig in a pit.

salted pork roast in a pan in the oven, adding a bottle of liquid smoke and 1/2 cup water, covering it tightly with tinfoil, and baking 4 hours.

And now, here are more fresh pork recipes for you to try:

Mom's Stuffed Pork Chops

6 thick pork chops, with slits for pockets
2 cups stale bread cubes, cut small
1 1/4 stick butter
2 tablespoons finely chopped onion
1/2 cup finely diced apples
1/4 cup finely chopped celery
2 tablespoons brown sugar
salt and pepper to taste

Melt butter, Saute onions, fold in bread crumbs so that they are thoroughly blended with melted fat. Then add remaining ingredients. Place lid on pan, turn heat very low and steam for 4 to 5 minutes. Season to taste.

Stuff the chops with this mix, and season them with salt and pepper. Arrange on rack in shallow baking pan. Bake at 350 degrees F. for 1 hour and 35 minutes. Make gravy with pan drippings.

Roast Suckling Pig with Liver Stuffing

1 suckling pig, about 10 pounds
2 large onions, chopped fine
1 pound butter
1 pig's liver
1 cup chopped mushrooms
1 cup chopped apples
3 cups soft bread crumbs
salt and pepper
thyme
2 tablespoons chopped parsley
2 eggs
1 pig heart
celery and onions
salt and pepper

Make a stuffing for the pig by cooking the onion and liver in 1/4 cup butter. Chop the liver

and mix with the sauteed onion, raw mushrooms, apples, bread crumbs, 1 C. melted butter, salt, pepper, thyme, parsley, and eggs. Stuff the pig and skewer it together.

Put the pig's front feet forward and back feet backward and skewer them in place. Put a piece of wood (the size of an apple) in the mouth, to hold it open for the apple after it is cooked. Cover the ears with foil, so they won't get burned.

Season the pig with salt and pepper, and rub with soft butter. Place in a roasting pan and pour in 1 C. boiling water. Roast at 350 degrees, for 3 1/2 hours, basting every 15 minutes with pan juices.

As the pig cooks, simmer its heart on top of the stove in 4 C. water, plus celery, onion, salt and pepper. When cooked, save the broth and chop up the heart for the gravy.

To serve, place pig on a fancy platter of green leaves, garnished with rings of cut oranges topped with rings of cranberry jelly. Rub the pig skin with butter to make it shine. Take the wood from its mouth, and put in a red apple. You can make the pig a necklace of cranberries, if you like. Make a gravy from the pan drippings, heart stock, and chopped heart.

Geeta's Stir Fry
Pork with Fresh Crisp Vegetables

2 pounds pork, cut in 1 inch cubes
1/2 cup soy sauce
1/2 cup water
2 tablespoons sugar
cornstarch
1/4 cup cooking oil
1 piece ginger
1 onion
4 cloves garlic
1/2 cup bean sprouts
1 cup chinese cabbage
1/2 cup snow peas

Marinate pork several hours in soy sauce and water, with sugar added. Drain. Toss pork in cornstarch until coated. Fry in 2 Tb. oil in wok, until cooked. Remove.

Chop vegetables. Heat oil in wok until very hot. Add vegetables and stir fry for only a few minutes, until hot crisp. Add in pork. Pour on marinade and cook for only a minute, just to heat everything through. Serve over rice.

Sam's Barbeque Spareribs

1 slab pork ribs
salt and pepper
1 bottle good barbeque sauce
1 squirt bottle of water

Start your fire and let it burn down for about 45 minutes, until it has good coals. Put ribs on the grate, and let them brown slowly. Keep the fire low, and keep squirting it with water constantly. You don't want to let the ribs burn or dry out. You can salt and pepper the ribs while they cook, but don't add barbeque sauce right away. After about 30 minutes, you brush on sauce and let it cook on slowly. These ribs should be fully cooked in 45 minutes to an hour, yet still very moist and chewy and well-flavored with sauce.

Chapter 9

Veal and Beef: Slaughtering and Cutting Up

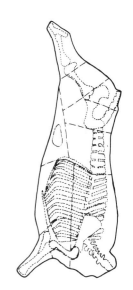

T O MANY HOMESTEADERS, SLAUGHTERING AND cutting up a beef seems a bit out of their range. They don't mind raising a steer, and they don't mind eating the meat. But those in-between steps of killing and cutting up seem overwhelming. After all, the live weight of a beef steer ranges from 1000 to 1800 pounds. It is logical that a back-to-the-land person (especially one who was urban-bred) might panic over dealing with such an immense animal. Many questions come to mind immediately: How would you hoist the animal? Where would you chill (age) so much meat? How and where would you cut it up? Where would you freeze it?

Because so many folks feel that they are unable to handle the slaughtering and cutting up of their beef, they pay local slaughterers and butchers to do their work for them. This fact of modern farm life has made professional butchering and professional slaughtering into viable rural home business opportunities. (Much more on these topics in Chapters 10 and 11.) In fact, many rural people let the "professionals" take

care of their pigs, sheep, goats, lambs, and deer as well.

However, as you have already learned, it is definitely possible to kill and cut up your own mid-sized animals. It is equally possible to handle your own beef. Size needn't be a deterrent.

If you are thinking of killing your first steer, and wondering if you are up to the job, I'd advise that you practice positive thinking. Instead of saying, "This animal is so large, I'll surely blow it," tell yourself, "I'll be able to see exactly what I am doing and where everything is. Therefore, I'll be able to do the best work possible."

This is the exact opinion of Bill Dowling, the professional slaughterer in my area. Bill Dowling says, "I didn't learn to slaughter from killing small animals. I started with beef. A big animal is easier because it is larger. Of course, you need to have the equipment. But once you've gotten that together, the actual work is no problem at all."

My neighbor, Regie McDaniel, says the same thing. "People are scared of doing their own cows, but I don't know why. It's simple. They could learn from rabbits."

One way to help you ease into killing a steer, is to kill a veal calf. It's the same animal—only much smaller—and it could help build your confidence. A veal calf is from 1 to 3 months old, still drinking mother's milk, and weighing from 75 to 150 pounds. And the meat is a gourmet's delight.

Figure 9-1 shows Natalie Atkinson and her baby offering farewells to their veal calf called "Little Guy." Such goodbyes are never easy; however, they are a reality when you raise animals for meat.

GATHERING YOUR EQUIPMENT

You need to be thorough when gathering equipment for slaughtering veal or beef. You don't want to be running back to the farmhouse in the middle of the procedure.

You will need a gun to stun your animal before you cut its throat. Of course, you could avoid the use of the gun with the veal calf. Dennis Atkinson simply hit his calf in the head with a mallet before slitting its throat, as depicted in Fig. 9-2. But I think "Little Guy" took much longer to die by this method. He never made a sound, but he actually stood up while he slowly bled to death. Now, this was hard on me, if not hard on the animal. I prefer to have an animal drop down fast, with a bullet in the head. This is definitely a personal choice. You'll find differing opinions on stunning methodology, and most folks will defend their chosen technique by claiming it is most humane.

I believe that you will want to shoot your steer before cutting its throat. Bill Dowling uses a .22-magnum long barrel rifle with hollow shells.

Fig. 9-1. Natalie Atkinson and her baby tell their veal calf farewell.

Fig. 9-2. Dennis Atkinson slits the throat of the veal calf.

He says that the magnum gives it more force (or velocity), and the hollow gives it more spread. Bill gets the steer to look at him, by approaching it with some grain. He shoots it straight on, in the center of the brain. Says Dowling, "If I miss, then I can really have problems."

That is the next pre-slaughter consideration I want you to think about. If you miss your shot—and even the pros miss the target on occasion—where will that steer run? Will you be able to catch up with him, to fire that necessary second bullet? Bill Dowling told me that he once had to chase a frenzied steer for an hour. Needless to say, he didn't enjoy that one bit.

When I photographed Bill Dowling killing Arlo Acton's steer, Bill knew that if he missed his shot, the steer had 120 acres to run in. Bill shot the animal in the head, and followed that shot with a rapid second shot. He didn't want

to take any chances that the steer could get up after the first shot and lead him on a rampage over Arlo's spread.

Therefore, if you can tie your steer to a tree, that would be ideal. Or if you can enclose it in a strong, small area, that is also excellent. Killing it out in the open is a last choice.

Besides your gun, you will need sharp skinning knives and butcher knives. Be sure to bring along a steel and honing stone to keep everything super-sharp.

To hoist your steer, you must have a block and tackle or other hoisting method, plus a gambrel strong enough to hold your animal. You also need to have a strong tree limb available or a tall, strong tripod, so you have a place to hang up the animal. Before you hoist the steer, you can use chocks to block up the animal while it lays on the ground. These can be concrete blocks or 4 × 4 pieces of wood.

In Fig. 9-3 Dennis Atkinson has his calf blocked up with 4 × 4s as he makes the incision for inserting the metal gambrel. In Fig. 9-4 and 9-5 Dennis and his friend, Steve Belial, work together to raise the calf off the ground using a come-along and pulley system. When relying on muscle-power, this is a two-person job. However, if you use electric hoists, as Bill Dowling does, you can handle the job alone, even on a much heavier animal.

Besides the gambrel and hoisting equipment, don't forget a meat saw to saw through the heavy-boned areas. For splitting the backbone, Bill Dowling uses a special type of power saw that has back-and-forth or reciprocal motion. I will describe all of his equipment in detail in Chapter 11. Having power equipment makes the job easier, but it certainly isn't essential.

Finally, bring along your buckets (gal-vanized wash tubs lined with black plastic bags) for the innards. Include a clean bucket for the tongue, liver, and heart. You'll also need water so that you can wash the carcass as well as keep your hands and knives clean. If you want to tie off the anus or esophagus, have some string handy. And you will need clean cloths to wrap around the carcass as you transport it to the place (have you thought where?) it will be aged.

Whether you kill a small veal calf or a large steer, you should come to the slaughter site with all necessary equipment. You will definitely want to carry these instructions with you. The written words, the photos, and the drawings are all intended to serve as a thorough guide for you. However, the best guide is experience.

I suggest that you watch (and help) someone else slaughter several large animals before you attempt killing your first steer. Or ask a knowledgeable friend to help you your first few

Fig. 9-3. How to insert a gambrel.

Fig. 9-4. Dennis Atkinson (left) and Steve Belial (right) hoist the calf.

times. You'll need helpers at any rate, and they might as well be folks who know what to do.

Eventually, slaughtering beef will become a natural routine. You won't need to read instruc-

tions. You will charge ahead, now familiar with slaughtering and eviscerating as a logical step-by-step process.

Nevertheless, the professional slaughterer, like Bill Dowling, always has the advantage. He slaughters dozens of steers every year, where you might do one or two at the most. It's that practice that makes him able to work so rapidly and with such self-assurance. Moreover, his power-winch and power-saw definitely increase his speed. He also steels his knife before every cut.

Bill Dowling can slaughter and eviscerate a beef steer in 45 minutes to an hour. It may take you three hours, but you will still get the job done.

One of the primary joys of the back-to-the-land lifestyle is the pride that comes from doing a hard job all by yourself. It is very likely that you have enough money to hire other people to work for you, but you still might prefer to cultivate your own soil, build your own house, and slaughter your own animals. It puts you closer in touch with reality to do these things. It's hard work to do these jobs yourself, and it takes longer, but in the end it gives you a satisfied feeling that many people never experience today.

I am sure it would be easier for you to buy cut and wrapped beef at the supermarket. But it wouldn't be quite the same, would it? When you finish slaughtering, eviscerating, and cutting up your own steer, please give yourself a strong pat on the back. You deserve it.

STUNNING AND BLEEDING THE BEEF ANIMAL

Mentally draw an **X** on the forehead of your animal, one line running from the left ear to the right eye, and the other line running from the right ear to the left eye. If possible, secure your animal to a tree. Shoot the animal in the head, at the cross of the **X**. Figure 9-6 shows you where to put your bullet.

For Bill Dowling, a proper kill is the most important feature of the slaughtering operation. He feels that excellent marksmanship is important

Fig. 9-5. Hoisting the calf with the come-along.

133

here. But he says that understanding animal behavior is even more important. "Anyone can hit a still tin can," explains Dowling, "but there's more than that to stunning a steer. You have to get the animal to look at you just right. To do this you have to know your animal."

Continues Dowling, "To get the steer's attention and keep it, you have to talk to the animal, so it can hear you. I cluck, or stomp my feet, or go shoosh, shoosh. That makes the animal look at me. "The moment you have the animal's attention, fire the gun. Don't wait an extra moment."

As soon as the animal drops, you want to slit its throat. But you don't want the animal to kick you. It's legs may move reflexively, and such a kick could be quite painful. There are two ways to slit the throat. You can simply cut deep from ear to ear, cutting the head about half off, as shown in Fig. 9-6. Or you can do as Bill Dowling does, making an incision from the breastbone toward the jaw, and severing the carotid arteries and jugular vein on the inside, right above the heart.

Either way, the animal should begin to bleed profusely. You can increase this bleeding by pumping the animal. To pump an animal, you work the free set of front and back legs back and forth a bit to simulate walking. This helps to get a rapid, full bleed. See Fig. 9-6 for an illustration of pumping.

You now want to move your animal over to your hoist, if it didn't die right there. You want to drag it over now while it still has its skin on, rather than risk contaminating your carcass later.

Once your animal is in place, next to your hoist, you will still need to do some initial skinning on the ground before hoisting it in the air. Of course, you could do the whole job on the ground—people field-dress deer all the time, so why not a beef?—but it is much easier to do a lot of your work off the ground. Hopefully, you have already planned an efficient hoisting method.

SKINNING THE CALF/STEER

Roll the animal onto its back, and block it there with your chocks. Begin skinning the hind legs, as Bill Dowling does in Fig. 9-7.

The big difference with skinning a beef, is that you might want to save the skin, as you can sell the salted hide for cash. Therefore, you want to save as much of the skin as possible (it sells by the pound), and you also want it free from nicks. (In Chapter 15 I explain more about saving steer hides.)

When Dennis Atkinson skinned his veal calf, he knew he didn't want to save the skin. Therefore, he worked fast, and if he made cuts in the hide, it didn't matter. After all, he was going to throw it out anyway.

When Bill Dowling skinned Arlo's steer, however, he knew each nick would cost him money. (A professional slaughterer is paid a fee plus the skin.) That's why Dowling constantly steeled his skinning knife. A dull knife would have made the skinning much more problematic.

After you have skinned the hindlegs, you can cut the feet off at the first joint, using your meat saw. Do not cut through the large tendons that you will use for hanging up your animal. As you know, these are located just below the hock. You can also skin, and then cut off the front feet at this time.

Now you can cut a large I on the belly of the calf/steer. Carefully slit the skin from rear leg to rear leg, from front leg to front leg, and from the anus to the throat. The dotted lines in the first sketch in Fig. 9-8 illustrate exactly where you should cut.

You can make this slit in the skin by inserting the knife under the hide with the blade turned up (or outward). You want to use all precautions to avoid cutting into the meat and contaminating it. (If you have butchered a cow, do not cut through the middle of the udder. Cut around the udder first, and remove it.)

You are now ready to side the carcass. In siding, you remove all the skin that you can in

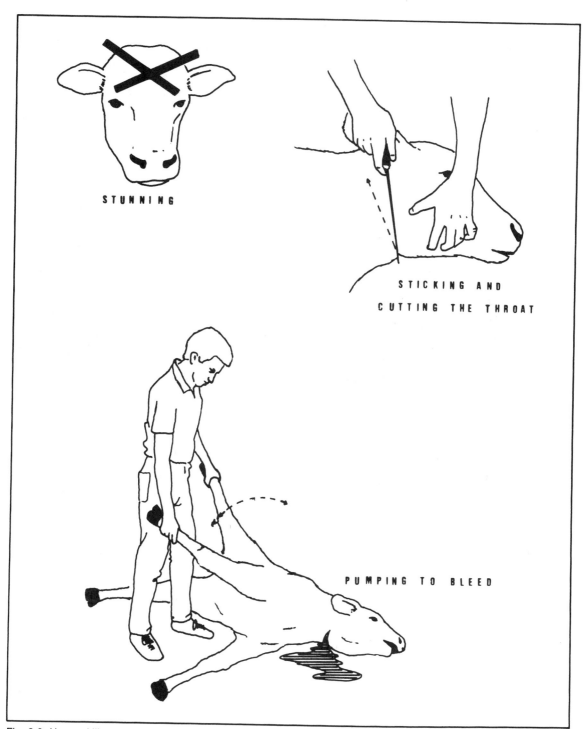

STUNNING

STICKING AND
CUTTING THE THROAT

PUMPING TO BLEED

Fig. 9-6. How to kill a steer: stunning, sticking, and pumping.

Fig. 9-7. Bill Dowling begins to skin the legs of the steer.

this prone position. In other words, you take the skin off the sides of the animal. Please move slowly, and do not cut through the fat into the meat. Leave all fat on the carcass, not on the hide.

You will remove the hide from the inner thighs (rounds), and then from the belly. You won't be able to fist the hide. And you might find the work a little slow moving. Be patient. Figure 9-9 shows Bill Dowling beginning to remove the steer's hide. Note the pre-cut he has made down the midline of the carcass.

Keep your knife as sharp as you possibly can. Hold the loosened skin tightly in one hand, stretching it upward, and away from the animal. This will expose the line to be skinned. Can you see how Bill Dowling holds the hide in Fig. 9-10?

Realizing that you don't want to cut into the

skin and you don't want to cut into the meat, let your knife glide down this line—from the rear end to the front end of the steer. If you can't seem to separate the skin from the meat, it is better to leave a little meat on the skin, than cut into a skin you want to save. If you hold your knife firmly, with the blade flat against the surface of the hide, and keep the loose skin tightly stretched, you should have little problems with siding. It is actually easiest to side beef in this position on the ground, rather than do it later, after hoisting the animal.

When you've completed siding, you can skin the head. (If you aren't saving the skin, you wouldn't need to go to this trouble.) Continue to split the hide down the middle of your steer, from the gash in the throat up the neck and over the front of the head.

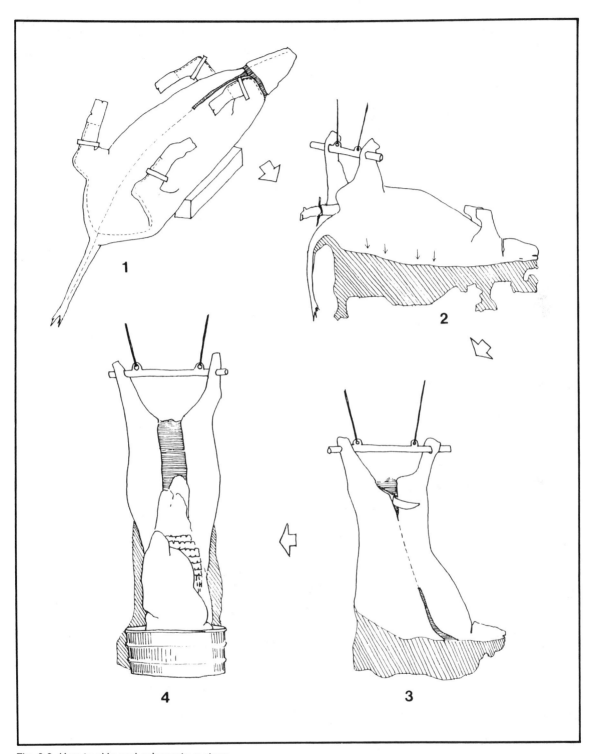

Fig. 9-8. How to skin and eviscerate a steer.

Fig. 9-9. Siding the
steer.

138

Fig. 9-10. Continuing to side the steer.

Remove the tongue. Wash it and put it in cold water. Then remove the cheek meat. The cheeks constitute two sizable chunks of meat on a steer, which can be used as a stew meat.

When I photographed Bill Dowling slaughtering Arlo Acton's steer, Arlo gave me the cheek meat as a present. I thought that was a really nice gesture. I immediately took it home for that night's dinner. Who would have thought that eating cheek would be a taste delight?

You are now almost ready to hoist your calf/steer. But first, you need to cut open the breastbone or brisket with your meat saw. If you make this pre-cut now, you won't run into the problem of having the entrails getting caught on top of the breastbone.

Cut lengthwise through the brisket (chest) from the neck to the end of the breastbone. You can loosen the esophagus and tie it off with string, so that nothing can spill out of it when you turn your steer upside down. Figure 9-11 shows Bill Dowling cutting from the chest down the neck of the steer. In Fig. 9-12 he splits open the brisket with his meat saw.

HOISTING, EVISCERATING, AND SPLITTING THE CALF/STEER

You are now ready to insert your gambrel (also called a leg spreader or a single-tree) between the large tendons on the back legs. Refer to the second illustration in Fig. 9-8 to review how much of the skin has been removed before you need to hoist the animal.

As you insert the gambrel, you might want to tie the legs onto the spreader hooks. You don't want to take any chances that your carcass will fall on you (or fall in the mud). Remem-

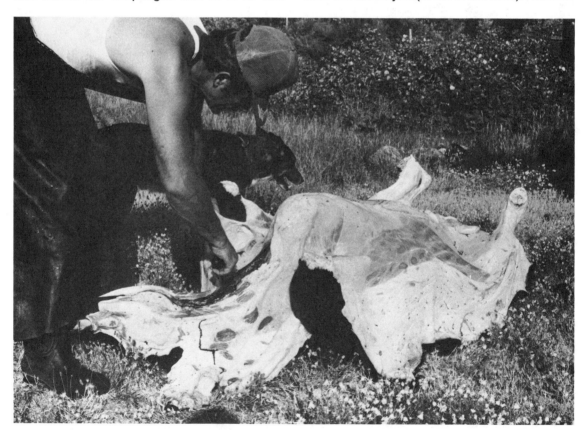

Fig. 9-11. Cutting down the chest from the neck of the steer.

Fig. 9-12. Splitting the brisket.

ber, it weighs a lot more than you do.

In Fig. 9-13, Bill Dowling inserts his gambrel between the steer's legs. He hoists the animal using an electric hoisting system attached to his truck. (I will discuss his equipment in detail in Chapter 11.)

After hoisting, you continue to skin the animal, from wherever you left off working on the ground. Figure 9-14 shows Dennis and Steve continuing to skin the calf, and Fig. 9-15 shows Bill Dowling moving ahead with his skinning project. As you can see, Bill chose to skin more of his carcass on the ground than Dennis did. With a large carcass, such as a steer, it is definitely easier to skin on the ground, but the choice is up to you.

As you skin the back of the thighs, you can cut around the anus, deep into the pelvic canal.

Pull out the large intestines and tie it with a string, so that no feces can spill out on your meat. Remove the penis by cutting under it and cutting it off it off at the anus. Remove the hide from around the anus. You can also cut the hide off the underside of the tail. Then continue skinning down the steer.

You can now split the pelvic bone with your meat saw. The pelvic bone is also called the **H** bone, and it is located between the animal's back legs. You can see the seam between the inner hind legs. Saw straight down the seam.

As you recall, Bill Dowling pre-cut the brisket while the steer was on the ground. However, because the calf is a small animal, Dennis cuts the brisket with a knife while the animal is hanging up. Figure 9-16 illustrates cutting the brisket on the calf.

Next cut the calf belly open with your hand on the inside, knife blade pointing outward. That way you can't slit the intestines. Figure 9-17 shows Dennis cutting open the calf's belly, knife blade pointed out. The third illustration in Fig. 9-8 also shows this cut.

In the case of the steer, the intestines that will now come rolling out weigh several hundred pounds. Figures 9-18 and 9-19 should give you some impression of what to expect. Bill Dowling cuts open the stomach, and empties it out onto the ground. This is just undigested food, and could be used to feed hogs or chickens.

Remove the liver, and cut off the gall bladder (along with a bit of liver). Wash off the liver, and put it in with the tongue, in cold water.

Cut through the diaphragm, as in Fig. 9-20, and remove the heart, lungs, and esophagus. Disconnect the heart, wash it off, and put it in

your bucket with the liver and tongue.

You can now finish removing the skin, if you haven't already. Remove the hide from the tail. Skin down the back. Skin over the head and down the face. Drop the hide. In Fig. 9-21 Bill Dowling completes the last touches of skinning. Note that he has already completely eviscerated the steer.

You can cut off the tail, wash it, and save it if you wish. This will make oxtail soup. Saw off the head, and discard it. If you shot the animal, you won't want to save the brains because they could contain slivers of metal from your bullet.

To help you in splitting the carcass in half, you can mark your cutting line with the point of your knife. You want to saw through the center of the backbone, which isn't easy. If you get off of center, try to come back to center with the

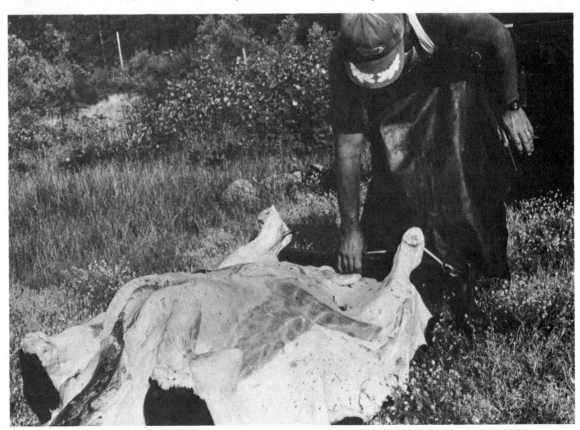

Fig. 9-13. Inserting the gambrel.

Fig. 9-14. Skinning the calf.

Fig. 9-15. Skinning the back side of the steer.

Fig. 9-16. Splitting the brisket of the calf.

Fig. 9-17. Cutting down the midline of the calf.

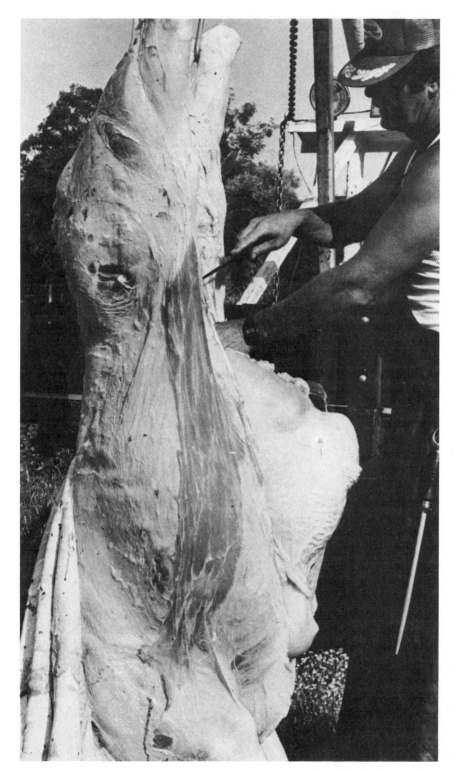

Fig. 9-18. Eviscerating the
steer.

147

Fig. 9-19. The intestines of the steer.

Fig. 9-20. Cutting through the diaphragm of the steer.

149

Fig. 9-21. Finishing skinning the steer.

next vertebrae. You always want to be careful cutting through the backbone. If you swerve too far to the right or left, you could damage the filet mignon. In Fig. 9-22, Bill Dowling splits the carcass in two halves with his reciprocal saw.

Wash the carcass off with clean water, as in Fig. 9-23. You can also pump the front legs up and down to help drain out any remaining blood.

At this point, Bill Dowling hoists his halves into his truck bed. He takes them over to John Taylor's meat cutting shop. John has a walk-in cooler, where the half carcasses can hang for a week or two. (Much more about John Taylor's home business in Chapter 10.)

If you are cooling and aging your meat at home, you will probably want to cut it into quarters. You need to be able to carry it without hurting your back. To separate a half into quarters, look at the rib cage. Counting down from the rear end, cut between the third and fourth ribs. Before you cut fully through, make a slit between the fourth and fifth ribs and tie a rope there. That is how you will hang up the forequarter. Someone should hold this up, while you continue cutting through the hind quarter.

Chill the carcass. You can use a walk-in cooler, or you can hang it outdoors if the weather is cool enough—28 to 35 degrees. Do not let it freeze.

You won't age veal because it has no fat covering. However, aging will definitely improve the flavor of your beef. This is also called ripening.

What happens in ripening is that the enzymes in the meat break down the connective tissue (tenderizing it) and releasing juices (flavoring it). You can ripen your fat-coated meat for 7 to 10 days. If it is highly finished (if it is choice meat with a lot of fat), you can ripen it even longer.

John Taylor recently had customers who insisted that their 1800-pound beef be hung for three weeks. When I watched John cut up this beef, he had to cut off surface fat covered with green slime and fuzzy, gray mold. John didn't especially like doing this work, but that is how the customer wanted the meat aged. That's the joy of growing your own beef. You can eat it just the way you want it.

FIRST LESSONS IN CUTTING UP BEEF

Many people who raise beef prefer to have it cut up by a professional butcher. The term "professional" refers to someone who has had a lot of experience cutting up meat. If you want your beef to look exactly like beef in the supermarket, you might want to find a custom butcher. Even if you know your way around a side of beef, you still might prefer paying someone else to do the job for you rather than spending the time that 600 pounds of meat requires.

On the other hand, if you have already practiced cutting up rabbit, lamb, and pig, and have familiarized yourself with the basic cuts that you make on any animal, you might want to take a stab at beef. If you are a committed do-it-yourselfer, you will take great pride in your home-cut steaks and roasts.

You can learn how to cut beef by watching a custom butcher like my neighbor, John Taylor. Right now, John has several apprentices to help him. In return for their help, he teaches them the secrets of butchering. I say secrets, because when you look at a forequarter of beef that weighs 150 pounds or more, it is not immediately apparent to the uninitiated individual what to do with that piece of meat. In other words, there is so much meat, that the cuts aren't always obvious to the naked eye.

Most people who buy their meat at supermarkets every week do not know what they are buying. Imagine interviewing average folks as they fill their carts by the meat counter. They are buying lovely red packages of meat, wrapped snugly in plastic wrap. If you asked them to tell you where their chosen cut came from on the beef carcass, I am sure a large percentage would go totally blank. They would take a wild guess at best.

I feel that before you start cutting meat— and actually before you start raising meat—you

Fig. 9-22. Splitting the steer carcass with his reciprocal saw.

Fig. 9-23. Washing the steer carcass.

really should know the primal cuts of beef by heart. Agricultural students are often tested in this manner. They are shown unmarked cuts of beef, and they must be able to name them accurately. You have to know your beef to pass this sort of test.

In this chapter I will teach you home beef cutting techniques. However, before we begin, I want you to learn the primal cuts. It will definitely help you to know the names and shapes of the cuts of beef before you pick up a knife. If you know what you are looking for, you will have a much easier time finding it. You won't be so overwhelmed. Once you know their whereabouts, the mystery really goes out of cutting beef.

I will begin with the forequarter (or front end) of the beef. The *forequarter* contains four basic sections: chuck, brisket, rib, and plate. Please refer to Fig. 9-24 as you read this section. It should help you understand the forequarter.

The *chuck* is the front shoulder of the beef. This is not a highly tender cut. Can you guess why? Your steer used his legs (and that includes the shoulder and the rear end) for walking about. Moving parts are never the most tender. (A piece of meat can be called a steak, but if it is from the front or back legs, it is not nearly as tender as a steak cut from the back which doesn't really get exercised in the same way.)

The chuck represents approximately 9 percent of your carcass. On a typical half steer (I'll use 300 pounds per half as a ball-park figure), this would be a 27-pound piece of meat. Obviously, you will need to cut it down into smaller sections.

The chuck can be cut up into roasts (larger cuts) or steaks (narrower cuts). Or it can be boned out into boneless rolled roasts or boneless steaks. From your chuck you could cut blade bone roasts and arm bone roasts. Or you could cut blade bone steaks and arm bone steaks. Or you could make a rolled boneless roast called a cross rib roast.

These names can really change from market to market and region to region. For exam-

ple, a boneless steak from the chuck portion of a beef can be called a cross rib steak, a shoulder clod steak, a family steak, a barbeque steak, a patio steak, or a fluff steak. All six of these steaks are just the same boneless chuck steak—not an especially fancy cut of meat. Taking out a bone from the chuck, and calling the meat patio steaks does not change the cut of meat, but it can confuse the beginning meat cutter, as well as the consumer.

The next cut on the forequarter is the *brisket* (with the shank attached). This cut runs below the chuck on the thigh and upper leg of the steer. The brisket is boned out, with the fat removed. It looks very familiar to anyone who has ever eaten corned beef! The shank section is boned and cut up for stew meat or hamburger. This section, representing 10 percent of the carcass weight is luckily quite easy to find. In other words—a brisket is a brisket. It doesn't become another cut at the whim of the butcher.

Moving down the forequarter, the *rib* section contains a cut I am sure you know—the rib roast. Because it is not in the part of the steer that walks, it is one of the most tender cuts. This can be called prime rib roast, standing rib roast, small end rib roast, and numerous other names. It will always be roast beef to me.

Because the rib section represents 10 percent of the carcass and can weigh 30 pounds, butchers often cut the rib roast into several roasts. If the roasts are boned out, then they are called rib eye roasts. If the roasts are cut into steaks, they are rib steaks (with bones), which are also called club steaks in some markets. Boneless rib steaks are called rib eye steaks, or market steaks and spencer steaks.

Remember how you cut the spareribs from your pork chops and lamb chops? Here the same cut is made below the meaty portion of the rib. You can cut back ribs, barbeque ribs, short ribs, rib lifters (boneless strips off the ribs). These actual ribs will be easy to find. They look like their name—ribs.

To complete the forequarter, we have the *plate*. (In some schools of cutting, the plate in-

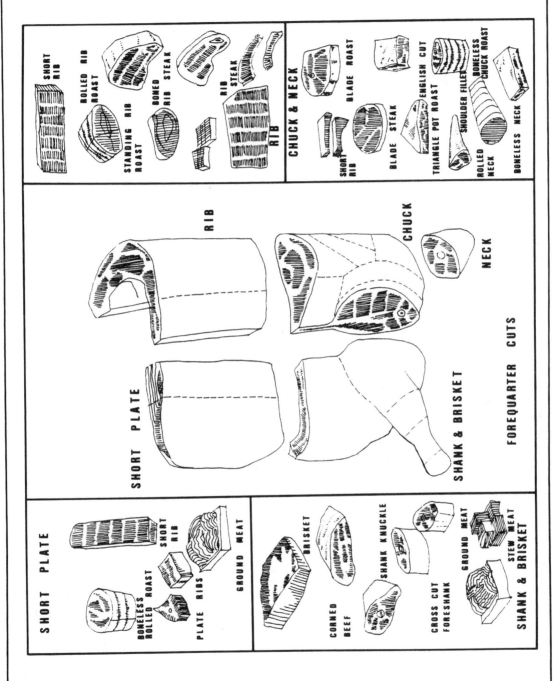

Fig. 9-24. The forequarter of beef: primal cuts and smaller cuts.

155

cludes the brisket, but I am treating them separately.) The plate needn't worry you much. It contains no well-known cuts, and can be boned out for soup or stew meat. If kept in one piece after boning (and rolled and tied), it is called a rolled plate.

Now look at Fig. 9-25, a detailed drawing of the hindquarter. The *hindquarter* contains the following four primal cuts: the round, rump, loin, and flank.

Starting at the rear end of your steer, you have the *rump*. The name is self-explanatory. The rump is the rear or the fanny of your steer. It measures about 4 percent carcass weight, or 12 pounds. You will probably bone it out for a rolled rump roast, or leave the bone in for a rump roast. That's straightforward, isn't it?

The *round* is a larger primal cut—your steer's entire back leg, from thigh to knee. The round represents 20 percent of your carcass weight, or about 60 pounds of beef. Obviously, it will need to be made into several smaller cuts.

The hind shank is cut off the round. This is the lower leg and it is used for soup or hamburger. Then the round is often divided into three sections: top round, bottom round, and eye of round. If the round has been cut to include a section from the sirloin (next primal over), then it can also include a sirloin tip.

These roasts from the round can also be cut into steaks. Top round steaks are called many different names, including London broil, butterball steak, chicken fry steak, and barbeque steak. Bottom round steaks are called sandwich steak, swiss steak, and breakfast steak.

The eye of round is sometimes mistaken for the filet mignon. It looks similar. If it is cut into steaks, they are called minute steaks or cube steaks.

The primal cut at the center of the hindquarter is the *loin*. The loin contains the most tender cut, the ones that make raising meat on the farm really worthwhile. These are the fancy steaks, the ones we mean when we use the term steak. The loin is often divided into two primal sub-sections—the loin end and the short loin.

Starting from the rear, or loin end, you have your sirloin steaks. Moving into the short loin, these are followed by porterhouse steaks, T-bone steaks, and club steaks. If this tender meat from the loin is boned, you get my favorite cut of meat, the filet mignon—also called chateaubriand. This delectable boned tenderloin can be served as a roast or cut into steaks.

Returning to the loin end, if you don't cut sirloin steaks, you could bone them out for a rolled sirloin tip roast. The range of possibilities open to you as a meat cutter are quite large. As you can see, you are going to have many decisions to make on your steer.

The final primal section from the hindquarter is the *flank*. This is the home of the flank steak, which is hidden midst much fat. Flank steaks can also be called London broils. The flank also contains meat for stew and hamburger.

As a general note, when you cut your steer, you will end up with a 25 percent cutting loss. In other words, you will throw out 25 percent of the weight of the animal as fat and bones. Thus, a 600-pound carcass (1000 pound live weight) will give you 450 pounds of meat. Of this, 150 pounds will become ground beef and stew meat, 150 pounds will be steaks, and 150 pounds will be roasts. Of course, you can vary these amounts by your personal cutting techniques.

I want to reiterate here that the pleasure in cutting up your own meat is that you can cut it exactly how you want it. Supermarket butchers have numerous rules they must follow so that meat cuts are standardized. They also cut meat with the profit margin for the supermarket as a top priority. You won't be bound by any such rules and regulations. You can bone out the entire carcass if you wish. You can grind tender cuts into hamburger. You can trim all the tails off your steaks. You can save every bone. It's your beef.

Before you begin cutting, you should definitely confer with the other family members (and the cook, in particular) about how they all want the meat cut and packaged. Family prefer-

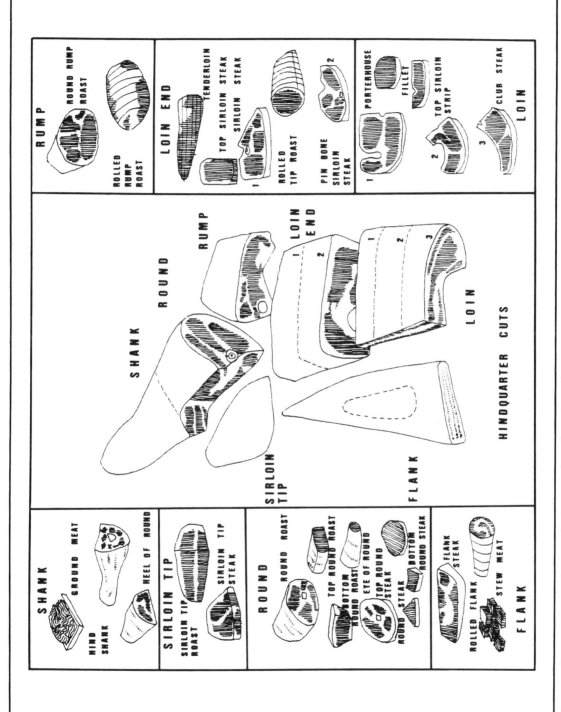

Fig. 9-25. The hindquarter of beef: primal cuts and smaller cuts.

157

ences differ widely. Some folks are great hamburger fans (I am not), and others prefer roasts over steaks, or vice versa. You don't want the cook to be hysterical because you cut the standing rib roast into rib steaks. Communicate first, cut second.

A word about the quality of your beef. People who raise steers at home expect to grow a top-quality product. It is a large investment in time and effort, and it is natural to want excellent results. However, you should not assume that your beef will taste like prime and choice store-bought meat, just because it is homegrown. This is a rather naive way of thinking. Unless you have fed your steer exactly what commercial growers feed their steers, it will not come out tasting the same. Choice meat requires 150 days on grain. You can feed your steer all the unsprayed grass you wish, and it still won't come out choice. Even if you add in some homegrown corn stalks, it won't come out with much marbling. It will be organic meat—but it won't taste exactly like choice meat.

Why should you expect your meat to taste like store-bought meat? You probably are not feeding the amount of grain used commercially. And you aren't using antibiotics and growth hormones either.

"You can't beat a professional at his own game," says Bill Dowling, the local slaughterer in my area. "It's hard to compete with a feed-lot product." Bill says that home beef growers are often disappointed when they can't cut their steaks with a fork. He thinks they should know better.

Distraught small farmers who grow one or two steers a year sometimes accuse custom butchers of switching meat on them. "When their meat doesn't come out as tender as they wish, they can't accept that this meat is from their own precious steer," explains John Taylor, my local custom butcher. "They assume it must belong to someone else. They don't realize that growing choice meat is a science that requires following a regimented and expensive technique."

I would advise that you expect your meat to be a little tough—even the fancy steaks. Then, when it is more tender than you expected, you can be pleasantly surprised! Don't set yourself up for disappointment by expecting the miraculous. And remember, even if your meat is a little more chewy, it isn't full of dangerous chemicals that constitute a health hazard. That's the bottom line—you are growing meat that is safe to eat. You should be very proud of yourself.

CUTTING UP BEEF

It takes an experienced butcher four to six hours to cut up a beef. It will probably take you even longer. However, because you need to age your beef, you have a lot of time available for cutting it up. As long as it is hanging in a cool location, you won't have to worry about it spoiling. You can hang all of it for about five days, and then slowly begin to cut it up. If you get the job done in ten days, you are still in good shape, and your meat will have become more tender while waiting. In fact, if it begins to grow mold on the surface, this should not be viewed as a problem. Just trim off any moldy sections, and cut as usual. You may not like the look of mold (I don't), but it won't hurt the taste of your meat at all.

Most people who cut up their own beef, work on only a quarter section at a time. A quarter, which will weigh about 150 pounds, will keep you busy for an evening, but shouldn't be too overwhelming.

I can't tell you that cutting beef is easy for the beginner. It isn't. The problem comes in knowing where to cut. With smaller animals like your veal calves, you can sense where to cut by looking at the carcass. With all that practice you have had cutting rabbits, goats, lamb, pigs and deer, a veal carcass will look like more of the same.

When you look at your first 150-pound quarter of beef, it might seem like a huge, intimidating, fat-covered chunk. If it doesn't immediately convey to you where to make the specific cuts,

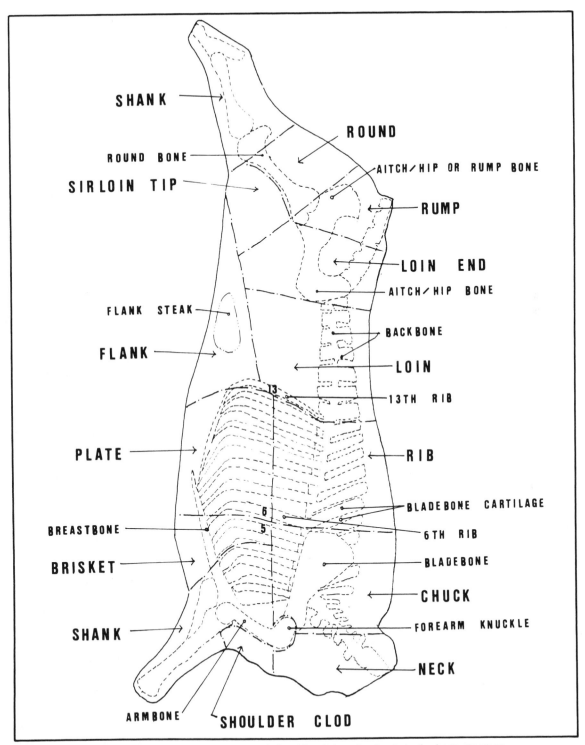

Fig. 9-26. A cutting diagram for beef, showing the relationship of the primal cuts to the bone structure.

159

these directions should prove quite useful. But don't forget to use your eyes, and your common-sense as well. You've seen cuts of beef in the supermarket for many years. This is really not a totally new topic for you.

I will attempt here to describe verbally how to cut up a beef. Photos of John Taylor cutting beef, plus detailed line drawings, supplement the text. But I would much prefer that you use these instructions along with some help from a friend who has cut meat before. The best way to cut meat is to learn by watching and helping in a real-life situation.

I do think it is best to learn to cut your meat into conventional pieces, the same type of pieces that you see in the supermarket. I have seen beginning instructions for farmers that advise boning out the entire beef as a sure-fire method. Obviously anyone could do this—meat is meat, after all. But I think you should try to learn how to cut meat, not cop out by boning everything out. Try to look at the bones and learn the basic anatomy of your steer. The bones are your reference points that help you understand where to make your cuts.

Figure 9-26 shows the relationship between the bones of the steer and the primal cuts of beef. Study the drawing carefully. It will definitely help you understand exactly where to make your cuts.

If you learn how to cut meat properly, you will have a selection of boned and rolled roasts, as well as steaks and roasts that contain bones. And of course you will have hamburger, also. It is this balance—the differences between various cuts—that makes growing a steer worthwhile. To bone out the entire carcass would destroy the variety inherent in the meat. And frankly, isn't your favorite part of meat eating chewing on the bones? I can't imagine throwing out the bones, that would seem highly wasteful to me. But, of course, the choice is yours.

Some words about tools: Cutting beef requires more tools than you have used previously. Of course you can get by with minimal supplies—a large bladed breaking knife (or steak knife) and a smaller boning knife, a steel, a sharpening stone, a meat saw, and a hand grinder. You will also need a boning hook—an inexpensive tool that will help you pull sections of beef off the seams. This hook is essential for proper cutting of beef. If you've never seen one before, it resembles an alfalfa hook.

Now, just for fun, let's take a look at two other pieces of equipment you could use—a wish list that could modernize your beef cutting operation immensely.

A band saw could really come in handy when cutting beef (or veal, lamb, pork, deer, and goat for that matter). In case you aren't familiar with the term, a band saw is an electric meat-cutting saw. A band saw is to meat cutting like a table saw is to carpentry. In other words, you can get along without one, but it sure could be beneficial, especially for certain types of cuts.

With a band saw, you can cut steaks and chops rapidly and evenly. In using a band saw, you do get bone dust on the surface of your meat. Therefore, you use a small tool called a bone dust remover to scrape the surfaces of your chops before you package them for the freezer.

An electric grinder would also come in very handy—especially for beef, when you might want to grind up about 150 pounds of meat for hamburger. Power grinders can chop right through all types of sinewy fat and stringy meat. When you grind by hand, you have to trim meat much more carefully or you can gum up the works very easily.

You can survive without either of these pieces of equipment; in pre-electricity days, everyone did without power tools. But they do speed up the work, and they would also be two tools that you would want if you ever consider going into home meat cutting as a business. (I'll be discussing all of these butchering tools in more detail in Chapter 10 when I talk about John Taylor's home-butchering business.)

At this point, let's get down to the business of cutting up your own beef. You have killed it, skinned it, eviscerated it, and hung it up to cool.

Hopefully, as the meat aged you have studied up on the terminology presented earlier in this chapter. You know the names for the primal parts of the beef and where these parts are located. Now get your knives sharpened, and away you go.

The Hindquarter. Figure 9-27 shows a large hindquarter. It came from a Charolais steer that was butchered at a whopping 1800 pounds. This is an unusually large hindquarter containing more fat than the norm.

You should keep your hindquarter hanging up while you make the first cuts. Your first step is to cut off the flank. As you recall (I hope), the flank is the triangular-shaped section under the belly where the leg connects with the body of the steer. It will probably help you to look back at Fig. 9-26 to understand clearly where the flank is located.

To remove the flank section, make a cut starting beneath the udder fat (where the udder would be). Figure 9-28 shows John Taylor making this cut. You catch the edge of the round, and cut straight downward until you reach the thirteenth rib. Saw through the rib and remove the flank. This cut should not be more than 10 inches into the body of the steer.

The flank is a rather unusual primal cut—it is almost all fat! You are now going to search in this fat for one steak, called the flank steak. This is a flat, oval-shaped muscle which is embedded in the inside of the udder end of the flank, within membranes.

To trim the flank, lay it on your cutting surface, fat side up. About 40 percent of the flank is fat, and this should be thrown away. To find the single flank steak that is hidden inside this fat, you can pull off the fat with your boning hook. That way you don't risk cutting into the steak. You'll want to trim up the steak evenly, so that it has an attractive, squared-off appearance. The trimmings, plus any remaining meat from the flank section should go into your scrap pan for hamburger.

Your next job is to remove the sirloin tip. You begin by loosening the knuckle (knee), as

in Fig. 9-29. (Figure 9-30 is a close-up of the knuckle). Holding onto the knuckle with your hook, you cut with your steak knife about 2 to 3 inches into the leg, until you hit the round bone (upper leg bone). Then cut downward, letting your knife follow the round bone until you reach the **H** bone (hip bone). Now cut back towards yourself to remove the sirloin tip (Fig. 9-31).

The sirloin tip makes a good roast. If you want smaller roasts, you can cut it in half. Figure 9-32 shows the two sirloin tip roasts cut from the Charolais steer.

Your next step is to remove the kidney, which was left inside the beef carcass as it aged. The kidney is located on the backbone, between the sirloin tip and the loin end (or head loin). It is surrounded by fat called kidney suet. You will have to remove some of this fat to get at the kidney, but leave in the fat that protects the loin (Fig. 9-33).

You can now separate the sirloin from the round-rump, which will give you two large primals to work with. To separate the round from the loin, saw through the ball and socket hip joint. No more than two tail vertebrae should be included in the round.

Figure 9-34 shows John Taylor separating the round from the loin. The head loin and short loin are on the hook. In Fig. 9-35 he cuts the round off the bone, and carries it over to his cutting table.

Place the round on your cutting surface. Remove the rump (rear end) by sawing across (below) the **H** bone (rump bone), through the round bone, and then cutting at right angles back out through the **H** bone and backbone. Remember to refer to Fig. 9-26 to help you understand these instructions.

The rump can be boned (which is quite a job as it has plenty of bones), and then rolled into a rolled rump roast and tied with strings. Or you can cut it in half for two rump roasts with bones.

The round is usually divided into three parts: top round, bottom round, and eye of round. But first you should remove the heel and shank

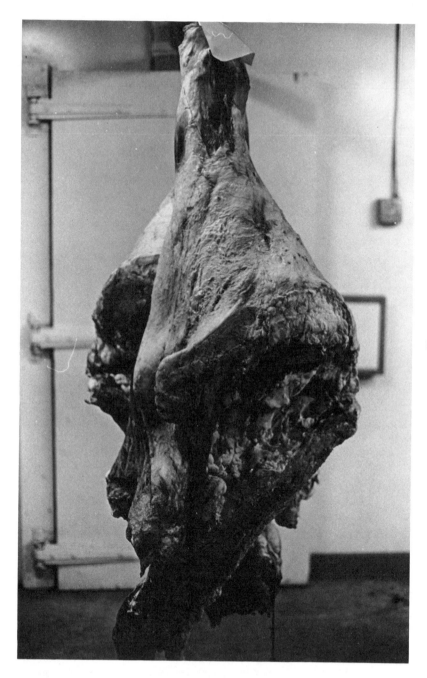

Fig. 9-27. Hindquarter of beef.

(back leg) by sawing through the round bone. You can bone out the heel and shank for hamburger. Or you can saw across it for soup shanks.

Now you can bone out the round. After you have taken out the leg bone (round bone), look carefully at the round. You can see seams that separate the top, bottom, and eye. You need to follow the seams with your boning knife, and gently cut these sections apart, as John Taylor

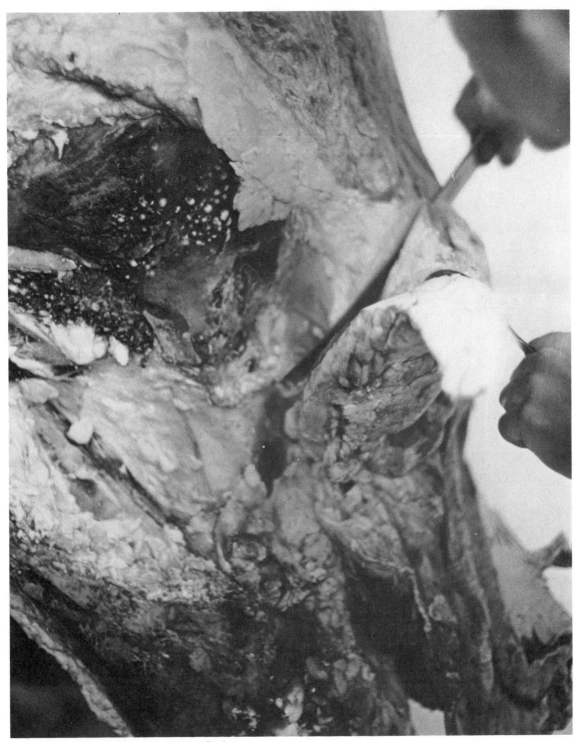

Fig. 9-28. Making the cut to remove the flank.

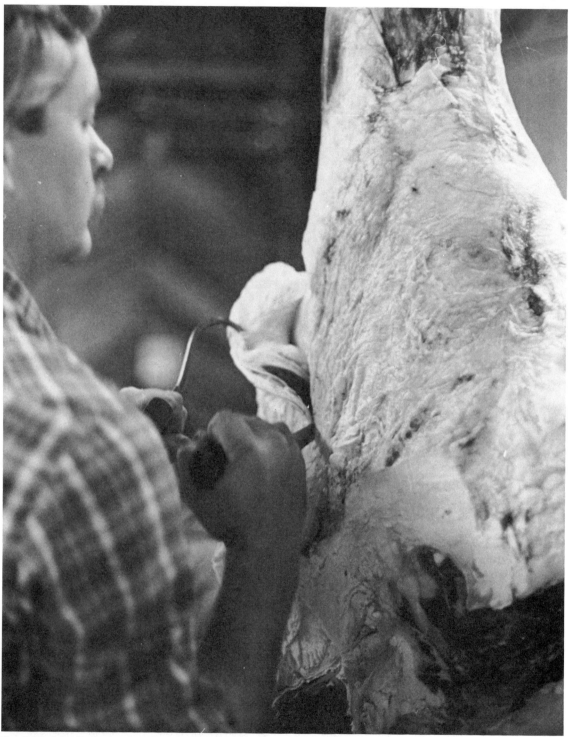

Fig. 9-29. John Taylor loosens the knuckle, as a first step toward removing the sirloin tip.

164

Fig. 9-30. The knuckle, or knee of the steer.

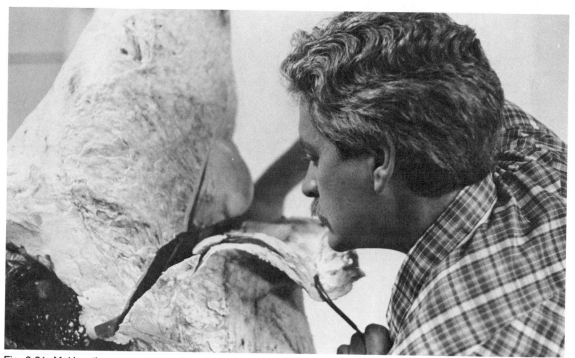

Fig. 9-31. Making the cut to remove the sirloin tip.

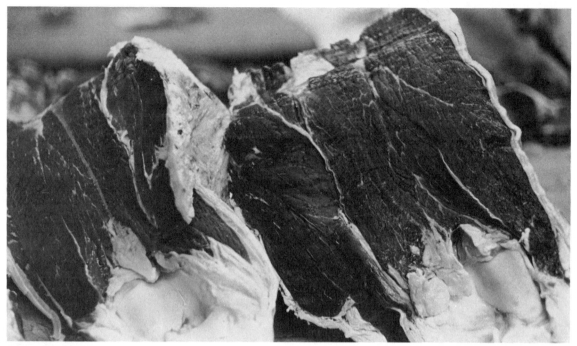

Fig. 9-32. The sirloin tip roasts.

Fig. 9-33. The beef kidney imbedded in fat.

Fig. 9-34. Separating the round from the loin.

Fig. 9-35. Cutting the round off the bone.

does in Fig. 9-36. These are three separate muscles, and you can see them if you look. You can cut each of these sections of the round into steaks or roasts, according to your preference. In Fig. 9-37, John Taylor points to the eye of the round.

Another approach to the round (especially if you have a band saw) is to cut across the face of the entire round, making large round steaks that include bone.

Now we come to the best part of the hindquarter, the loin. The loin can be cut into the short loin and loin end (head loin) by cutting in front of the hip bone with your saw. If you look carefully, you can see a dimple that tells you where to start your cut. The loin end has the **H** bone (hip bone) in it.

Although you could cut roasts from the loin, you will probably prefer steaks. (This is where

a power saw comes in handy.) In Fig. 9-38, John Taylor separates the head loin (on the left) from the short loin, using his band saw. You can cut the steaks whatever thickness your family likes. You will get sirloin steaks from the loin end.

Starting from the rear of the loin end, you will get the butt end sirloin, then the wedge bone sirloin, the round bone sirloin, and last but not least, the flat bone sirloin and the pin bone sirloin. All of these are sirloin steaks but they differ slightly in the formation, or cross-cut appearance, of their bones.

Moving on to the short loin section, you can cut steaks again. Starting from the rear of the short loin, you will cut porterhouse steaks, **T** bone steaks, and then club steaks. Looking at a porterhouse steak, you can see that it is a steak with a bone through the middle, and meat on both sides. The large lefthand section (or eye)

Fig. 9-36. Following the seams with a knife to separate the parts of the round.

Fig. 9-37. The eye of round.

Fig. 9-38. Using a band saw to separate the head loin from the short loin.

Fig. 9-39. The **T**-bone steak.

of the porterhouse is from the tenderloin muscle. The **T**-bone has a slightly smaller tenderloin muscle, see Fig. 9-39, and the club steak only has meat on the right side, or sirloin side.

If you aren't totally addicted to porterhouse steaks, you could bone out the entire short loin. (This is one case in which boning out might be just what you want to do.) Then you would remove the entire tenderloin muscle whole, which is called the filet mignon. Besides this tenderloin strip, you would get a loin strip. You can cut the loin strip into thick steaks, called New York strip steaks. To cut porterhouse steaks or to pull out the filet mignon—this is a toss-up. Both cuts are absolutely delicious. Luckily, your carcass has two halves. You can cut one half one way, and cut the other differently. Be creative.

We have now completed the hindquarter; but in a sense we have just begun. John Taylor spent two years learning to cut beef before he felt he had totally mastered the cuts on a steer. Thus, in the professional sense, cutting beef is quite technical. Each cut is supposed to be a number of inches from "here" and include just so much bone, not more. In the commercial world, meat cutting is an exact science.

Here, however, we are concerned with cutting up your own steer at home. If you didn't cut exactly how I told you, or if you couldn't understand my instructions, that is really quite all right. Your meat will still taste just like it should. As you learn to cut meat—and make mistakes—you can never really destroy the finished product. So relax now, and let's move on to the forequarter.

The Forequarter. Please refer back to Fig. 9-26, which shows the relationship between the bone structure and the primal cuts. Cut the forequarter between the fifth and sixth rib, as illustrated in Fig. 9-40. This will expose the blade bone cartilage, as the shoulder blade ends at the fifth rib. You will have to saw through the backbone, and also through the breastbone. This will divide the forequarter into two sections: the chuck and brisket, and the ribs and plate.

Within the chuck-brisket section you have two main bones: the bladebone (scapula) that runs parallel to the backbone, and the arm bone (humerus) that runs at right angles to the blade bone.

Your first cut will remove the shoulder clod (with the arm bone) from the front of the chuck-brisket section. This shoulder clod is the large outside muscle lying between the elbow and front end of the blade bone.

Taking the chuck section (which can either be hanging, or be put on your cutting surface), run your boning knife from the fifth rib alongside the blade bone, and follow straight down to the fore arm knuckle (front knee) at a 45-degree an-

gle. Pulling outward with your hook in one hand to help pull the meat off the seams, cut on one side, then the other. Then as you pull the clod out, cut behind it. This removes the shoulder clod (separating the arm bone from the blade-bone), along with the fore shank (front leg). Figure 9-41 shows John Taylor removing—or pulling—the shoulder clod. You can now saw off the fore shank, either cutting it crosswise for soup shanks, or trimming the meat off the bone for hamburger.

Remove the arm bone from the shoulder clod to make a boneless roast. After taking out the bone, trim the meat square and pound it into shape as you roll it up into a crossrib roast. Tie it up with strings. This is a fine cut for pot roast, and it also can be baked as a rare roast.

After you take the shoulder clod off, put your hook in the brisket fat and pull the brisket off the brisket bone (breast bone). You peel it off, by

Fig. 9-40. Cutting the beef forequarter between the fifth and sixth rib.

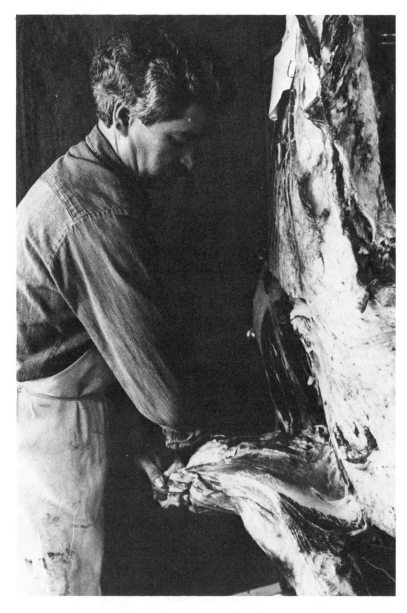

Fig. 9-41. Removing the shoulder clod.

running your knife straight down the brisket bone. To loosen the brisket bone from the brisket meat, pull outward and let your knife follow through on the seam.

Just like the fatty flank section yielded the flank steak when we worked on the hindquarter, the brisket section is also fatty; but within it is a lean cut of meat, which is simply called the brisket. Just separate it completely from the

fat and square if off into a nice shape. It is a marvelous piece for cooking. (See recipes at end of this chapter.) Figure 9-42 shows John Taylor sawing off the chuck, short rib, and brisket bone. He has already pulled off the brisket meat.

You can now place the chuck on your cutting surface. Cut off the neck first. You can bone it and roll it (called a rolled neck), or you can trim it off the bone for hamburger.

173

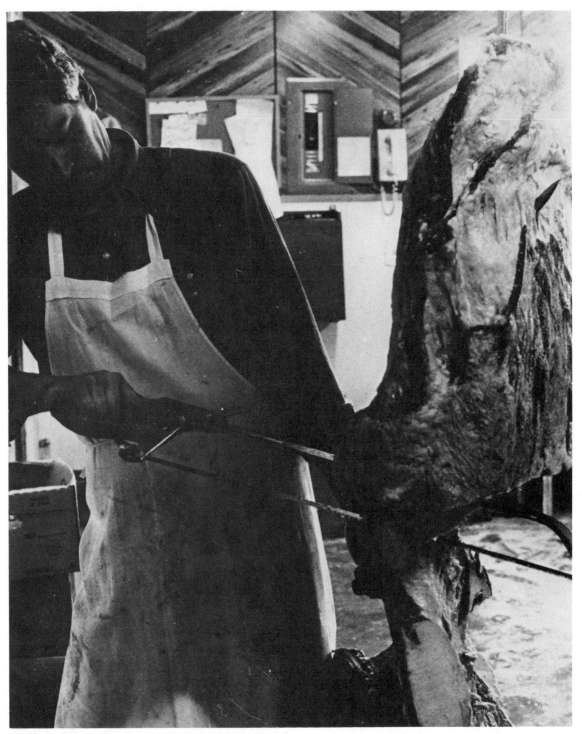

Fig. 9-42. Sawing off the chuck, short rib, and brisket bone.

174

In cutting the chuck into slices, which are called roasts or steaks according to their thickness, it is really handy to have a power saw. Starting from the neck end, the first steaks (or roasts) here are called 7-bone steaks because the bone inside them looks like a 7. The next are called blade chuck steaks. Figure 9-43 shows John Taylor cutting chuck roasts on his power saw. (The trash can holds all the throwaway bones; however, if you cut your steer at home, you might try to use everything.)

If you don't have power equipment to cut these chuck steaks easily through the heavy blade bone, you will probably prefer to bone them out, and make a top (inside) chuck roll and bottom (outside) chuck roll. You make this division into top and bottom along the blade bone. (Always remember that blade bone refers to shoulder blade.)

We now complete the forequarter section by cutting the tenderest section, which is called the rib. You can separate the rib from the short plate (short ribs) by sawing across the ribs about 3 inches from the ribeye. Or you can also leave longer bones on your steaks or roasts. In any event, you will separate the spare ribs (ribs number 13 through 6)—which are called the plate— from your meaty rib section by cutting across the ribs at about a mid point. In Fig. 9-44 John Taylor is separating the plate from the short rib. He uses his band saw, which makes the job go very rapidly.

When you cut up the rib section, you will cut rib steaks, or standing rib roasts, according to your personal preference. If you have a bandsaw, rib steaks might be a good idea. If you are cutting by hand, I'd suggest sticking with standing rib roasts, or you could bone out this section for rolled roasts, or boneless steaks. The short ribs are rather self-explanatory. If you are a spare rib fan like I am, you will want to save the plate intact, and not trim these spare ribs up for hamburger. Some butchers cut little steaks, called rib lifters, from the short ribs, but I am for keeping the bones intact whenever possible. I think bones improve the flavor of meat im-

mensely. But then, I am a gnawer.

Figure 9-45 shows some of the cuts you might get from your forequarter: the boned rib roasts at the far right, the rolled shoulder clod at the right center, the various chuck roasts to the left. And that completes how to cut up your steer. I sincerely hope that these instructions make sense to you, that they contain just the right blend of simple and complex ideas so that they can guide you clearly, but without too much confusing detail.

The same directions apply to cutting veal— but it is so much smaller in comparison to a steer that you will be able to cut it up in no time at all, and wonder what the fuss was all about. (Because of its lack of fat, you won't age veal. You'll want to cut it up after it has cooled for a day or two.)

I appreciate that you have tried to learn how to cut up a steer by reading these directions. To teach yourself through reading is not necessarily the easiest way to learn. I think you should congratulate yourself for your patience and perseverence.

I am sure that you have realized that when a butcher teaches an apprentice to cut up meat, he simply points to a spot on the carcass, and says "cut here." If we were together, I would certainly use that approach, as it is a lot easier (and probably clearer) to grunt and point, than attempting to describe meat cutting in words. I trust you were very successful cutting up your steer. Now enjoy your steaks!

RECIPES FOR BEEF

There are hundreds and hundreds of wonderful recipes for beef and veal. Below I have given a few favorites from family and friends.

Mother's Brisket

Rub brisket all over on both sides with seasoned salt. Put it in a pan covered with heavy duty aluminum foil. Roast at 225 degrees F., for 5 to 7 hours. Let stand as long as possible before slicing. Make gravy from pan drippings.

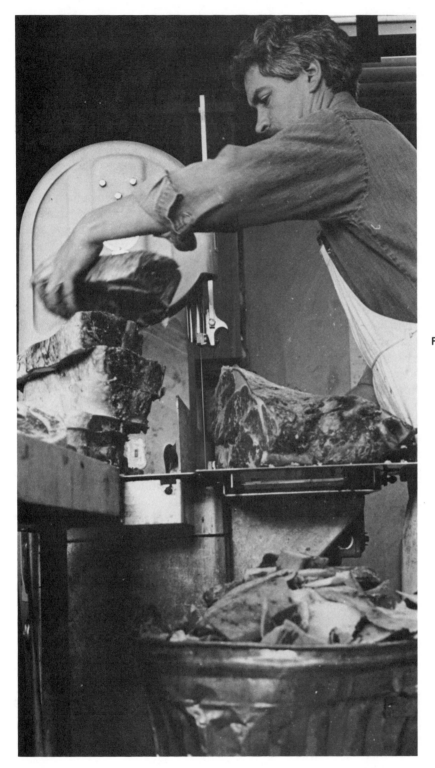

Fig. 9-43. Cutting chuck roasts.

Fig. 9-44. Separating the plate from the short rib.

Fig. 9-45. The cuts from the forequarter.

Aunt Marilyn's Brisket

5 pounds brisket
1 package onion soup mix
8 ounce can tomato sauce
3 tablespoons peach or apricot preserves
garlic
salt
pepper
paprika
barbeque sauce

Season brisket with spices and mix together soup mix, tomato sauce, and preserves, and pour it over the top. Cover. Bake 4 hours until tender at 325 degrees F. Pour off gravy and skim off the fat.

Add barbeque sauce to gravy. Slice brisket.

Pour barbeque gravy over it and reheat. There should be a lot of sauce. This resembles barbequed beef.

Robyn's Fresh Tongue

Robyn says that there are a million tongue recipes, one for every blab of the mouth.

Put the tongue in a pot and add onion, celery, carrot, parsley, black pepper, salt, cloves, a pinch of allspice, and cover with water. Put on a lid and boil under tender, about 1 1/2 hour. (You can put in a fork; if the fork comes out easily, it is tender.) Then take the tongue out, and drain and cool.

Take off skin of tongue and remove membranes underneath. Slice tongue thin.

You can serve the tongue hot with a gravy made from the reduced (boiled down) strained broth. Reduce and add raisins, ginger, grated lemon and thicken with flour.

Robyn prefers to serve the tongue cold, with lemon juice, vinegar and soy sauce. She says her children won't eat tongue hot.

Samantha's Steak Tartar

ground lean beef
chopped onion
egg yolk
salt
fresh ground pepper
worchester sauce
parsley

Basically, steak tartar is seasoned ground steak—served raw. Samantha has always loved it. Mix it together to taste. The egg holds everything together. You can spread it on crackers or rye bread. Serve it in an attractive lump, decorated with parsley. If you want to be real fancy, add capers over the top.

Dad's Delicate Flaming Veal Kidneys

2 kidneys
4 tablespoons margarine
1/4 cup brandy
salt
paprika
white wine

This a recipe for kidney lovers. Do not overcook it. Remove all membranes and other filaments from kidneys. Soak in salted water with a little lemon juice for an hour or two. Drain and dry. Cut kidneys into bite sized pieces.

Saute kidneys lightly in melted butter, until just done. In a separate pan, heat brandy to the simmering point, then pour it over kidneys and light it with a match. After the flame dies down,

add salt and paprika and 1 Tb. flour. Stir. Add about 1/2 C. white wine to make a thin gravy.

Easy Pot Roast

chuck roast
grease
salt and pepper
flour
1 cup water
1 cup red wine
carrots
onions
potatoes

Season roast with salt and pepper, dredge it in flour, and sear it in hot fat in a cast iron pot until brown on both sides. Then add water to the pot and red wine, plus carrots, onions, and potatoes. You can substitute tomato juice for the wine if you wish. Cover the pot tightly, and simmer slowly until done, about 2 1/2 to 3 hours. If you need more liquid, add it. You can add any other seasonings you like, such as thyme, rosemary, hot peppers, garlic—it is your pot roast.

Straight A Brains in Cream Sauce

1 1/2 pounds calf brains (from a calf that was
**   not shot in the head)**
salt
water
lemon juice
1/4 cup butter/margarine
1 onion, minced
1 garlic, minced
2 stalks celery, chopped
1 cup chopped mushrooms
2 tablespoons chopped parsley
1/4 cup flour
1 cup stock (from cooking brains)
1 cup milk
3 tablespoons cooking sherry
1/4 cup grated cheese

Simmer brains in water with salt and lemon juice for 20 minutes, or until done. Drain and reserve brain stock. Remove membranes from brains. Cut into small pieces.

Saute brains, onion, garlic, celery, mushroom, and parsley in butter until slightly brown, stirring often. Sprinkle on flour, salt, pepper and paprika, and add milk and stock, and cook until the sauce thickens, stirring constantly. Add sherry, and cover with cheese. Put on the lid, and let cheese melt for a moment. Serve. You can make the same recipe with sweetbreads—the thymus gland of the calf.

Chapter 10

Making Your Living as a Home Butcher

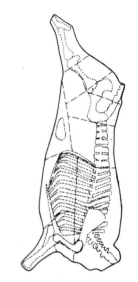

"**I**NEVER REALIZED HOW MANY PEOPLE WERE raising their own meat," shouts John Taylor over the drone of his band saw as he cuts a neighbor's home-raised pork into thick, succulent chops. After cutting the chops with his power saw, John trims them at his work table. He throws the trimmings—the tails of the pork chops—into a plastic pan.

"Julie," he calls to his wife. "Can you start up the grinder. We need to grind these scraps into sausage." Julie Taylor, John's wife, stops wrapping pork in neat, labeled packages, and walks across the room to turn on the powerful grinder. "Custom-ground sausage is really tasty," says Julie. "The customers can have it seasoned exactly as they want."

John and Julie Taylor operate a husband and wife home meat-cutting business that has tripled in volume each year since its beginning. They now turn away customers, the demand has been so large. Their successful experience proves that there is money to be made in home meat cutting. It's a ripe home business opportunity for country folks wanting to make that extra cash.

In rural areas, more and more people are raising animals at home in order to provide their families with healthy, chemical-free meat. Yet most of these people don't have the time or the inclination to cut up their own meat. They prefer to hire a home butcher who has the equipment and expertise to do the job well. In my area they call John Taylor who, in Fig. 10-1, is pictured with a side of pork.

If you live in an area where people are growing meat, there will always be a demand for the services of professional home meat cutters like John Taylor. If you have been enjoying cutting up your own animals, you probably have the talent and knowledge to consider starting your own home meat cutting business.

Of course, as is almost always the case, before you can earn money you are going to have to spend (invest) money to get started. And home meat cutting does require some expensive equipment. But don't let these expenditures

Fig. 10-1. John Taylor carries a side of pork.

frighten you. John and Julie Taylor made their investment back within two years, and they only worked part time. Because your capital outlay for home meat-cutting equipment will reap you many years of profits, let me give you some idea of the facilities you will need.

THE BUILDING

You will want to build a separate building for your home meat-cutting business. Once you begin working on other people's meat, you will want to move out of your kitchen into more professional quarters. Figure 10-2 shows John and Julie working together in their shop.

The shop, which is located behind their house, is a basic rectangular structure, measuring 24 × 26 feet. Figure 10-3 gives a detailed floor plan for the structure.

John likes a spacious environment, so this building is actually larger than necessary. You could get by with less square footage. If you don't mind working in cramped quarters, you can have your walking around space (traffic flow space) be as small as you like. However, you do have to provide adequate square footage for some essential aspects of the business. The building needs to contain the following spaces:

The Cooler. Your building must have a cooler or walk-in refrigerator where you can hang meat until you cut it up. The proper temperature for the cooler is 36 to 38 degrees Fahrenheit.

John Taylor's cooler measures 8 × 16 feet, and can hold up to 10 beef carcasses. (It can hold more carcasses of deer, lamb, or pig, but I am using beef as a measurement.) As a rule of thumb, you will need approximately 12 square feet of ceiling space per beef carcass. I mention ceiling space because you will be hanging up

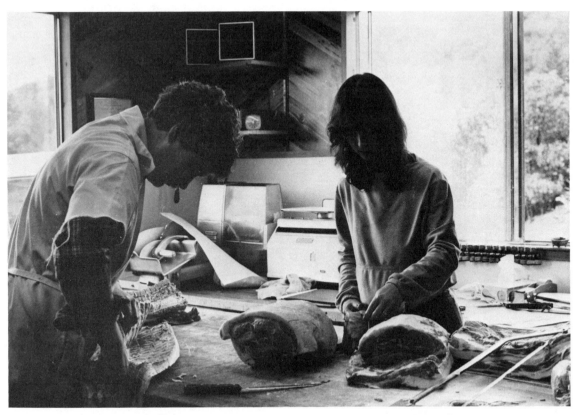

Fig. 10-2. John and Julie Taylor working together at the cutting table in the home butcher shop.

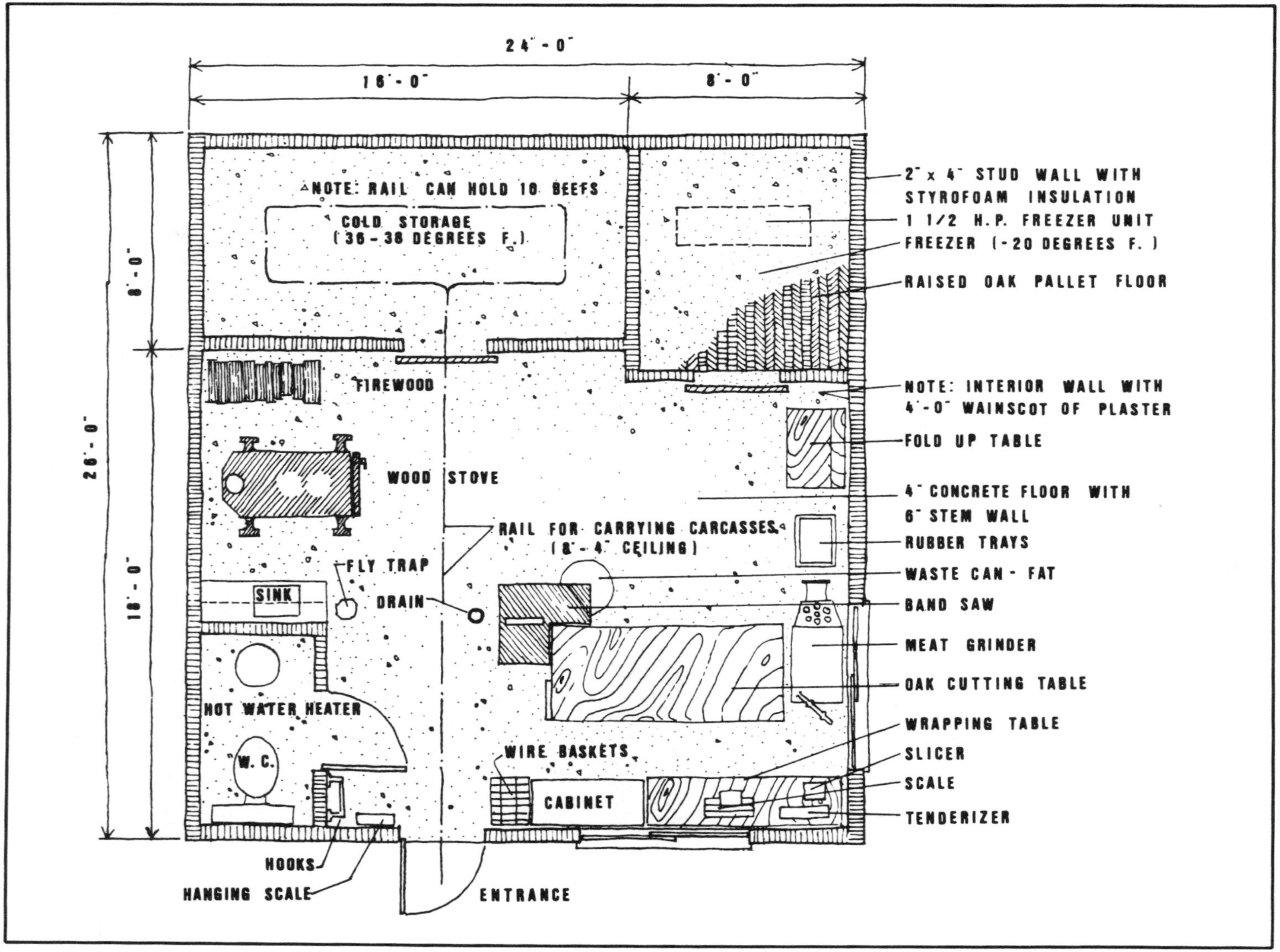
24'-0"
16'-0"
8'-0"
26'-0"
8'-0"
18'-0"
NOTE: RAIL CAN HOLD 10 BEEFS
COLD STORAGE
(36-38 DEGREES F.)
2" x 4" STUD WALL WITH
STYROFOAM INSULATION
1 1/2 H.P. FREEZER UNIT
FREEZER (-20 DEGREES F.)
RAISED OAK PALLET FLOOR
FIREWOOD
NOTE: INTERIOR WALL WITH
4'-0" WAINSCOT OF PLASTER
FOLD UP TABLE
WOOD STOVE
4" CONCRETE FLOOR WITH
6" STEM WALL
RAIL FOR CARRYING CARCASSES
(8'-4" CEILING)
RUBBER TRAYS
WASTE CAN - FAT
FLY TRAP
SINK
DRAIN
BAND SAW
MEAT GRINDER
OAK CUTTING TABLE
HOT WATER HEATER
WRAPPING TABLE
WIRE BASKETS
SLICER
W. C.
CABINET
SCALE
TENDERIZER
HOOKS
HANGING SCALE
ENTRANCE

Fig. 10-3. Floorplan for John Taylor's home meat-cutting shop.

these beef from the ceiling. Each carcass will require a separate hook. Figure 10-4 shows the cooler full of quarters of beef.

Remember that whatever number of carcasses you wish to hang, you need to be able to space them apart from each other. If they hang too close bacteria can build up, especially in meat that was recently slaughtered.

You might wonder whether you could get started cutting meat without a cooler. Theoretically you could simply insist that your customers cool and age their meat at home. Unfortunately, this is an unrealistic idea. Many folks who raise meat have problems finding a cool spot to hang it. That's one reason for hiring a home butcher to cut your meat. For the price of the meat cutting, you get "free" use of the cooler! And because proper aging and cooling is very important, a butcher with a large, sanitary cooler will be much in demand. You don't want to scrimp here.

The Freezer. You will also need a walk-in freezer so that you can quick freeze your customers' wrapped packages of meat to a temperature of minus 20 degrees Fahrenheit. The size of the freezer depends on the amount of meat you wish to freeze at one time.

John Taylor's freezer measures 8 × 6 feet and 8 1/3 feet high. It can hold eight beef. On that basis, I can give you a rule of thumb: an average beef requires 50 cubic feet of freezer space.

Julie Taylor places each customer's labeled packages of meat in a strong wire basket in the freezer. The baskets (which stack, one on top of the next) permit maximum air circulation and even weight distribution.

Because freezing units are expensive to buy and have installed, the Taylors initially started with a chest-style freezer. From their experience, they suggest that you don't go this route. "A chest freezer doesn't freeze quickly enough," explains Julie. "We'd put a half steer in there, but it would take so long to freeze that the blood would leak out of the packages. You can't give customers packages covered with pink ice.

That's not professional at all."

John seconds Julie's viewpont. "I wouldn't recommend starting out with a chest freezer," he says. "It's too small. You can't do volume with it. And when you place all that heavy meat, package on top of package, it ruins the shape of it. The packages on the bottom get mashed."

Therefore, you will want a walk-in freezer, but you may not want to make it excessively large. As a walk-in freezer increases in size, it gets increasingly expensive. A small unit is the most economical. The basic rule is to install what you need, but nothing extra.

The Cutting Room. This area is absolutely essential. Here you will cut your carcasses, wrap them up, and grind hamburger and sausage. How much space you will need is a personal preference. The cutting room where John cuts meat and Julie wraps it measures 24 × 18 feet. John says that he built the cutting room extra large because he doesn't like to cut meat in cramped quarters.

John Taylor's cutting room contains large windows. "I like to look outside occasionally. I hate feeling claustrophobic," explains John. However, he was careful not to have any windows facing south. Solar heat is the last thing you want in a meat-cutting room.

The wooden cutting table measures 8 × 3 feet. Here he breaks (cuts) carcasses into primal pieces, and then divides the primals into the cuts requested by the owner of the particular animal. Figure 10-5 shows John breaking down a hog carcass at the cutting table.

Julie has her own 8- x -1 1/2 foot table for packaging meat. Julie wraps each package of meat using a tissue and two sheets of freezer paper. She has a supply of stamps that neatly print the contents of the package right on top. Julie wraps according to the customer's directions. "Some people want two chops in a package, others want ten," she explains. "It all depends on family size." Figure 10-6 shows Julie working at her table packaging and labeling meat.

She places each customer's packages in

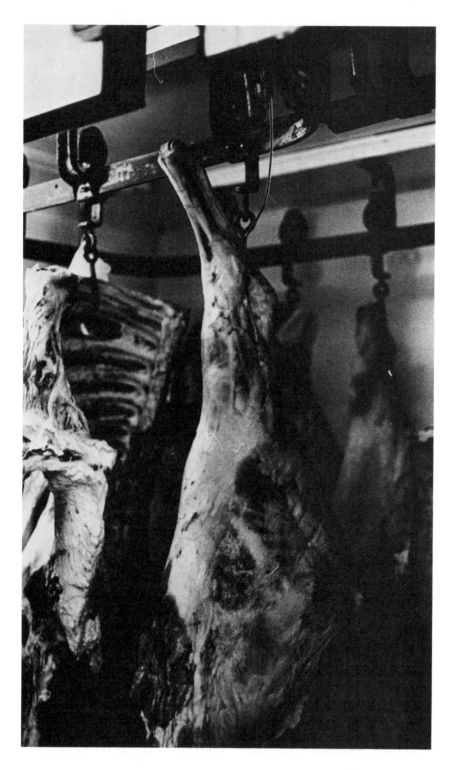

Fig. 10-4. Hindquarters and forequarters of beef hanging on the rails in the cooler.

186

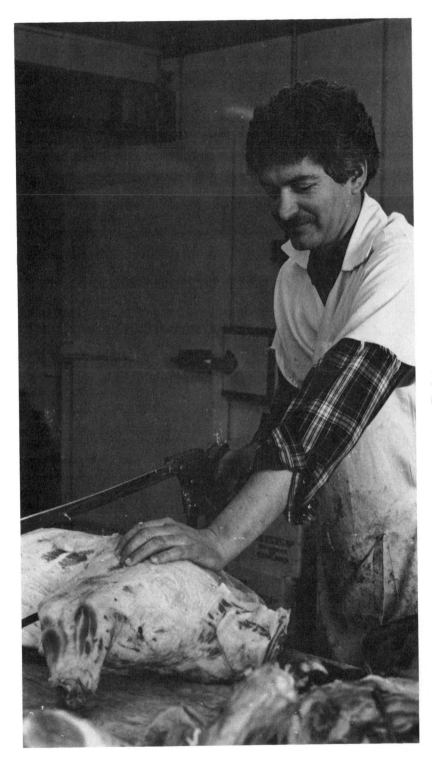

Fig. 10-5. Working at the cutting table with a meat saw to cut the pig into primal pieces.

Fig. 10-6. Wrapping and labeling meat at the work table.

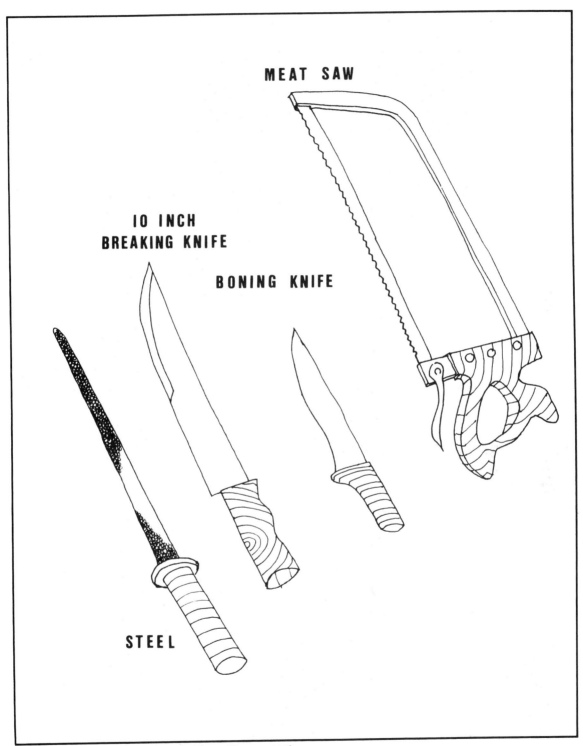

MEAT SAW

10 INCH
BREAKING KNIFE

BONING KNIFE

STEEL

Fig. 10-7. A basic set of tools needed for cutting up meat.

one or more metal baskets bearing the customer's name, before carrying the packages to the freezer. "When dealing with someone else's food," says Julie, "you must be extremely careful and well-organized. You can't risk losing meat that they have spent 18 months raising."

When dealing with other people's meat, you will also want to be very conscious of sanitation. Your state will probably have certain minimum requirements for your meat-cutting building (California does). You would want a sanitary establishment, rules or no rules.

The building should be built in a sturdy manner. The roof rafters need to be strong enough to carry the weight of numerous carcasses. The materials used for the floor (a cement slab) and walls and ceiling must be able to be kept thoroughly clean. A concrete stem wall might be required so that dirt can't get stuck in cracks between the floor and the wall. There must also be a potable water supply of hot and cold running water.

When the state inspector visits John and Julie Taylor's meat-cutting shop, he checks that all facilities and equipment are clean and free of build-up, scaling paint, and rust. He notes whether ceilings, walls, floors, doors, windows, and equipment are in good repair. He checks that all equipment is clean and that there is no sign of flies, rats, mice and the like.

Obviously, you will want to check with your own local and state authorities on the laws pertaining to establishing a home meat-cutting business. Most likely, the regulations will be basic, common-sense laws, the type of rules you would want to follow because of your own interest in health and sanitation. Your customers will deliver their carcasses to you, and pick up their frozen packages of meat. They will see your operation. If the shop isn't ultra-clean, they will take their meat elsewhere.

"How clean your shop is gives the first impression of whether or not you are a good meat cutter," says John Taylor, who keeps his shop impeccable. He is proud that he remembered to build his floor with a slant towards a large 4-inch-

diameter drain to permit easy washing. Little building tricks like that make a big difference when you begin working in your shop.

GETTING STARTED

You might be wondering if you have enough experience to go into professional home butchering. You really shouldn't measure yourself against John Taylor. He was ultra-experienced before he went on his own. John started working in a meat shop at age 13. His job was cleaning up the floors. At 21 he became an apprentice meat cutter and joined the union, working in supermarkets for 12 years.

Says John, "Don't let my experience scare you out of considering meat cutting as a home business. I think anyone can go into home meat cutting and make a success of it as long as they know the basics." The basics include knowing how to cut up a carcass of beef, as well as a pig, lamb, goat, and deer.

Your best bet in perfecting your meat cutting skills is to learn from another professional. John says that when he was learning to cut beef, his teacher actually held his hand and led him through the difficult cuts. "It was just like learning to dance or play golf," explains Taylor. "Until I got the *feel* of it, I couldn't do it properly."

John doesn't think you should envy his supermarket training, because some of the things he learned aren't even relevant to home meat cutting. "At the supermarkets, you cut meat so that the store makes the most money," explains John. "For example, in cutting pork, when you cut the ribs off the bacon, you must be extra careful to keep your knife close to the ribs or you will lose some of the bacon. With bacon selling retail at a much higher price than ribs, cutting meatier ribs and smaller bacons costs the store money."

In cutting meat for a home customer at a flat fee per pound, you don't have to play the percentages in this way. "At the supermarket, we were taught to leave the tails on the steaks to add extra weight, but in my own home shop I

190

just trim them off for hamburger," explains Taylor. "As a custom butcher, your meat cutting style is pro-consumer."

EQUIPMENT

When you start your own meat-cutting business, your first present to yourself will be top quality knives. The most popular knives among butchers today seem to be the Forschner knives made in Switzerland. Other well-known brands are Dexter and Sani-Safe.

John Taylor cuts his meat with Forschner knives. Figure 10-7 shows the equipment he uses most often—a curved 5-inch boning knife and a 10-inch breaking knife, plus a steel and meat saw. These are absolutely essential in meat cutting.

John also uses a cleaver, a hook, a threading tool, and several other knives. Figure 10-8 is a display of his basic non-power equipment.

John makes extensive use of an electric band saw. He uses a Biro, model Number 22. Other power saw brands are Hobart or Butcher Boy. With a power saw, John cuts a stack of steaks or chops in only a few minutes. It's hard to imagine a person cutting a great deal of meat without having this type of power equipment. Figure 10-9 is a close-up of John cutting pork chops with his power saw.

Taylor claims that a person can get by with a hand meat saw and cleaver and get similar results, but it is clear that he prefers his electric band saw for speed and efficiency. As a professional, it is something you will want to buy as soon as you can afford it. It might be expensive (Taylor found his saw used), but it will make money for you.

Actually, that's the bottom line for all the

Fig. 10-8. John Taylor's meat cutting tools.

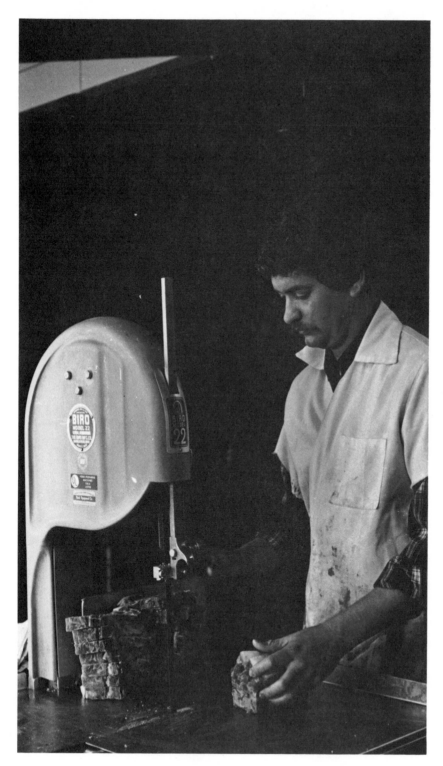

Fig. 10-9. Cutting chops with the band saw.

equipment—from the building, to the freezer, to the electric grinder, to the meat scales. It's all expensive, but it will all make money for you. With good business practices, you will make back the money you spend on the building and equipment. If you can afford to invest in your own home meat-cutting operation, you will reap profits very shortly thereafter, probably within a year or two. Figure 10-10 shows an array of equipment you will need.

With the focus of the business seemingly on cutting meat, it is interesting to note that John Taylor feels that that most important aspect of a home operation is having the right hanging and cooling facilities. When a carcass arrives at the shop, it is hoisted onto a hook right at the front door (Figs. 10-11 and 10-12). Pigs are generally in halves, and steers are in quarters. The meat then travels down the hook and rail system toward the cooler. All John Taylor must do is give the carcass a slight push to get the hook rolling down the ceiling rail, through the meat cutting room and into the cooling room. The hooks on which the carcasses are hung travel on attached wheels (Fig. 10-13) down a rail in the ceiling that runs from outside the front door right into the cooler. Figure 10-14 shows the interior of the shop with hooks and rail running to the cooler door at the far left.

Other necessary equipment includes wrapping paper, tissue, tape, sausage seasoning, sawblades, and meat stamps. You will need a grinder for making hamburger and sausage, a tenderizer to score minute steaks, hanging scales for weighing carcasses, table top scales for weighing finished packages, and a bug zapper to catch the elusive and annoying flies. And when considering expenses for equipment, you shouldn't forget large monthly bills for electricity, plus those annual tax bills.

THE WORK LOAD

The volume of work required in a home meat-cutting business varies with the seasons. Spring is the slowest time of the year because the grass is green and people like to fatten their animals on the free feed.

"When the grass starts turning brown and getting useless, that's when we get business," laughs Julie. "In August business really picks up, and October, November, and December are our busiest months of all. During the holiday season, when everyone else is relaxing, we are working like crazy."

John admits that sometimes the volume of work puts him under a bit of stress (something you'll need to watch out for). "You have to cut up meat fast because it can spoil," he explains. "Beef takes four to six hours to cut up, and if you have a cooler full you really have to hustle. Meat cutting is not the type of job you can put off until next week."

Every year Taylor cuts approximately 50 beef and 100 hogs, plus 30 mid-size animals (lambs, goats, and deer). This amount of cutting keeps the Taylor's part-time home business in the black. Figuring beef at an average of 500 pounds, pigs at an average of 150 pounds, and lambs at 50 pounds, this comes to 41,500 pounds of meat. If we choose an arbitrary price per pound of 25 cents, the gross income from such an endeavor would be $10,375.00.

Of course, you might want to spend more time at this business (the Taylors only work evenings and weekends), and thus make more money. You will make the going rate per pound times the number of pounds you cut each year. Remember, too, that the price you receive is the price per pound times the hanging weight of the carcass, not the packaged weight. When you are finished cutting, the finished packages of meat will weigh quite a bit less (about 25 percent less). That's why you must have a hanging scale on a hook. You need to weigh the carcass when it arrives, so that you can know the amount of money you will make.

Another way to think about money is to determine what you will make per hour's work. At 25 cents per pound, you will make $125 on a 500-pound steer ($.25 × 500 = $125.00). Here's where speed and efficiency will help you make money. If you can cut up the steer in five

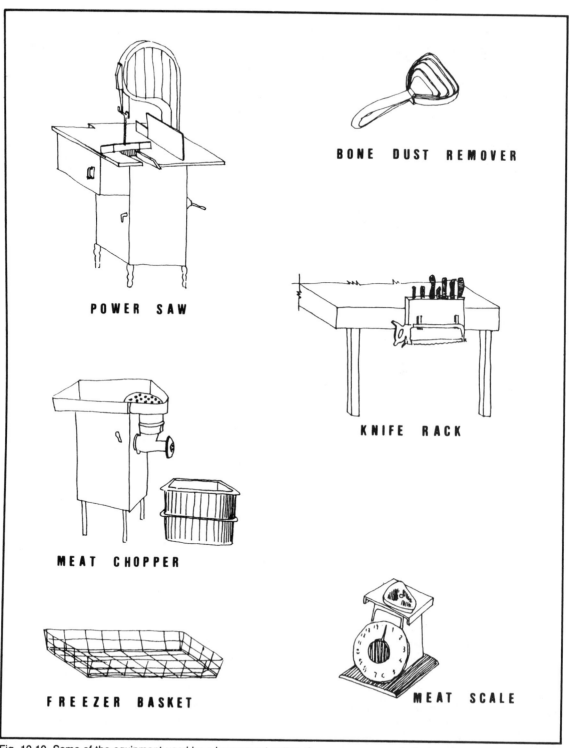

BONE DUST REMOVER

POWER SAW

KNIFE RACK

MEAT CHOPPER

FREEZER BASKET

MEAT SCALE

Fig. 10-10. Some of the equipment used by a home meat cutter: the power saw, meat chopper, meat scale, and more.

Fig. 10-11. Hoisting a half hog onto the hook at the front entrance to the meat shop.

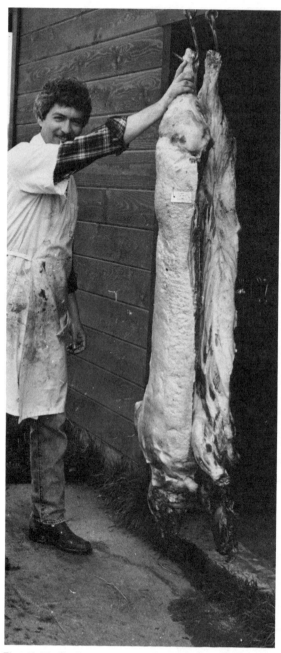

Fig. 10-12. Getting ready to push the carcasses into the shop.

can definitely help pay your other homestead bills.

Moreover, you can make even better money on deer. Here the normal business procedure is not to charge by the pound, but to charge by the deer—a flat fee. The flat fee covers extra time you might have to spend to trim out the blood-shot meat from the area where the bullet entered the deer. By the pound, the fee will run approximately double what you would charge for a lamb.

In fact, because cutting up deer is such a potential money-maker, you might want to consider developing a part-time business that specializes in handling deer during the hunting season. Many hunters who come out to the country from the city, know how to shoot deer, but have no idea how to cut it up. The hunters will be pleased to discover that they can hire someone to solve their dilemma for them. They will think your flat fee is a bargain, and come back to you year after year.

IS HOME MEAT CUTTING FOR YOU?

You have learned the basics of custom meat cutting, but only you can decide if you will be happy with this type of work. Is home meat cutting the right business for you? John Taylor warns that you must be ready to go to work and work real hard. "If you think it is just easy dollars," exclaims John Taylor, "you're wrong. It is labor intensive."

Besides being willing to work hard, a home meat cutter has to be able to get along with people—at least the people who bring in their carcasses to be cut up.

You can advertise for customers, but you will probably end up building your business by word of mouth. Satisfied customers will tell their friends about you, and your business will build up slowly, but steadily. Thus, one of your main objectives will be to keep your customers satisfied. According to John Taylor, this takes a lot of patience, because people who have raised their own animals can be quite fussy. (I suppose that refers to you and me.)

hours (this is approximately how long it takes a trained butcher), then you've made $25.00 per hour. Thus you can see how, once you have paid for your major equipment, this home business

196

"Some people become discouraged when you tell them the hanging weight of their beef," says Taylor. "They insist that their animals must have been larger and that you have made a mistake in weighing them. You'd think they would be happy that the price was less, but they aren't concerned about the price, they are concerned about the status involved in raising a huge hunk of meat.

"Other customers occasionally insist that I

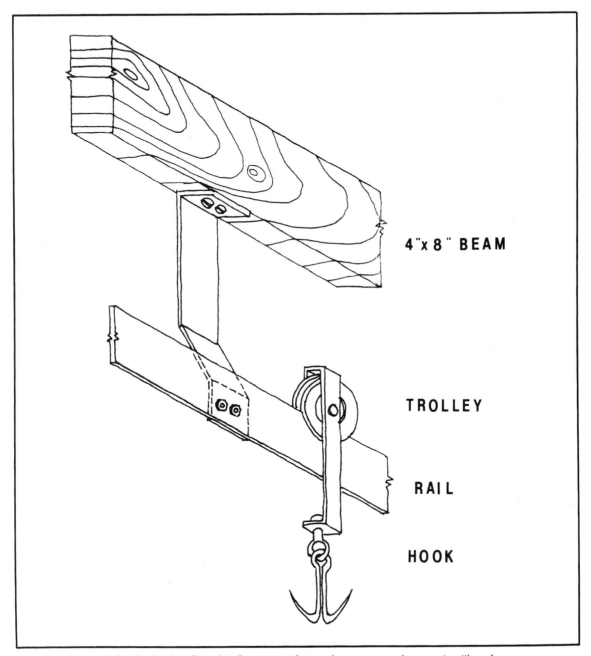

4"x 8" BEAM

TROLLEY

RAIL

HOOK

Fig. 10-13. The plan for the hook, rail, and trolley system for moving carcasses in a meat cutting shop.

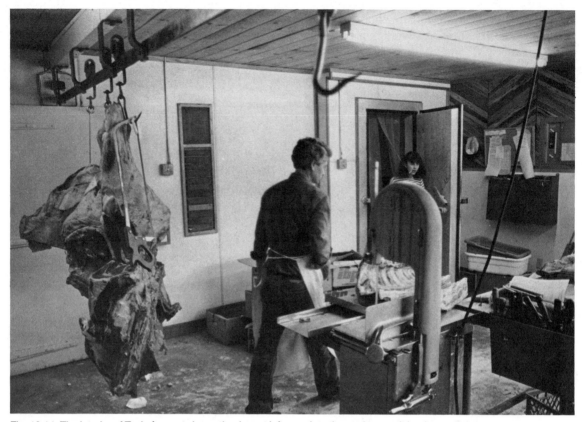

Fig. 10-14. The interior of Taylor's meat shop—the door at left goes into the cooler—and the door at right goes into the freezer.

switched beef on them. If their meat is tough, they will actually assume that it couldn't be their own meat. Everyone who raises their own animals thinks they will get the best meat in the world. You have to know how to appease these people who are unhappy about the quality of their own meat.

"Still another type of customer doesn't trust you and insists on sitting and watching you cut up their animal. I just let them sit there. Usually they will get bored and leave you alone after a while.

"And some customers make you tape every package with tape from a supermarket so that their kids will think the pork is store-bought, and not their favorite pet piggy. We try to keep all of these people happy, but I must say that this customer relations is one of the hardest parts of our work."

From the looks of their home business, John and Julie Taylor keep their customers happy. They truly go out of their way to give the customers whatever they want. If customers want their beef aged three weeks, John complies, even though he has to then cut up meat that is full of green slime and gray fuzzy mold. As a meat cutter, you will undoubtedly have to silently endure customers with a wide range of idiosyncracies.

Occasionally, like any other business person, you, too, might make mistakes. For example, one time the Taylors forgot to read the cutting instructions prepared by the customer, and cut a pork loin into chops before reading that the customer requested a roast. And on another occasion, John completely misunderstood the instructions (mine!). I had written for him not to add any extra fat to my goat hamburger, and

198

John misread the message, and ground the entire goat into hamburger. We had a good laugh over that one, and he dealt with the error by not charging me any fees, and offering to replace any meat I felt I had lost in the process.

Other possible mistakes: One time John seasoned sausage by guesswork without reading the directions on the package of seasoning. The 30 pounds of sausage ended up tasting like a salt block. Luckily the customer was his own sister.

By far the worst mistake occurred the day Julie caught her hand in the power grinder, severing her thumb and a finger tip, and flattening the rest of her fingers. The pain was excruciating and she has had to have repeated surgical treatments to re-construct her hand. Since that terrible mishap, the Taylors have purchased a new grinder with a safety feature which would not permit such an accident to happen. The lesson for you is clear: be careful when buying equipment to check out all safety aspects.

A final comment on home meat cutting: It definitely will work best for you as a two-person, or even a family business. In the Taylor's home operation, John does all the cutting, but Julie works right with him, scoring chops, wrapping and labeling packages, keeping the records, and communicating directly with the customers. In the busiest seasons, Julie's dad also helps out with all aspects of the business. As I mentioned before, when you get a cooler full of meat, you have to get it cut up within a certain time frame—*fast*! When it is slaughtering time in your area, as a popular home meat cutter you should be ready to work around the clock if need be. The more helpers you can muster, the more meat you will be able to handle.

And a final tip . . . don't ever forget the old meat-cutting adage: If you wouldn't want to eat it yourself, don't package it for someone else. Treat your customers like you would want to be treated, and you will undoubtedly have a great success in this very promising home business.

Chapter 11
Professional Slaughtering

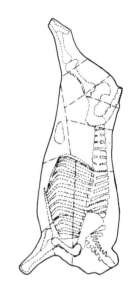

IN MY COUNTY, THERE ARE ONLY A HANDFUL OF people who still kill their own mid-sized to large-sized farm animals. Instead, most folks prefer to hire the local professional slaughterer to do their farm slaughtering for them. "I don't mind raising pigs and eating them," explains one of my neighbors, "but I just can't kill them." Another neighbor puts it this way, "Paying someone else to do your slaughtering is money well spent. A professional does the job cleaner and faster."

With this move away from a total do-it-yourself philosophy, farm slaughtering has become a viable home business opportunity. Although becoming the local animal slaughterer will not attract every reader looking for extra sources of cash, there might be some of you who are well-suited for this challenging job.

In this chapter I will cover all aspects of professional farm slaughtering. If you live in a rural area where many people are raising beef, pork, and lamb, this could be a fine way to work either full-time or part-time at a farm-related oc-

cupation. It's not a job for everyone—but then, what job is?

BILL DOWLING: LOCAL PROFESSIONAL SLAUGHTERER

Bill Dowling, the professional slaughterer, drives his white pick-up truck into Arlo Acton's meadow. Today is the day Bill will slaughter Arlo's two steers. The steers seem to become uneasy when the truck pulls near them. "My truck has the smell of blood and death," explains Bill, as he gets out with his .22-magnum rifle. "Animals know there is something wrong when I drive up."

Arlo, a farmer in his fifties, greets Bill, but immediately says he has to leave to go tend to his crops. "A lot of my customers disappear before I do the kill," says Bill. "They don't like seeing their animals die, and I can understand that."

I stay to photograph Bill for the series on slaughtering beef which you saw in Chapter 9. It is a thrill to watch a person who treats slaughtering as an art. His manner of working is totally smooth and self-assured.

Bill Dowling has been in the business of professional home slaughtering since 1974. The sign on his truck says "RANCH SLAUGHTERING" which means that he comes out to your farm and kills, skins, and eviscerates your animals. And then he takes the carcasses to the local meat cutter of your choice, where they are cooled and cut up. The price for this entire process—the drive to your farm, the kill, skinning, evisceration, and the delivery to the custom butcher shop—is a standard flat fee per animal. (In 1986, Bill's prices were as follows: $25.00 per beef plus the skin, $20.00 per pig, and $15.00 per lamb or goat. For customers with two or more animals, he offered a small discount.)

Bill's local popularity attests to the fact that the farmers in our area find his services indispensable. Nine out of ten people who raise meat in this area hire Bill Dowling to do their kills for them.

If you hold stereotypes of slaughterers as being coarse, blood-thirsty people who hate living creatures, you'd be really surprised to meet Bill Dowling. Bill is mild-mannered and well-spoken. He got into slaughtering because he likes animals and grew up around them. He perfected his abilities to kill and cut animals by reading books and by trial and error experiences. Besides learning his trade on his own, he has designed much of his equipment—from the big boom to his leather apron.

Judging from Bill Dowling's example, the prime qualifications for a job as home slaughterer are an interest in animals and the ability to do some hard work. If you have experience in commercial slaughtering, that certainly couldn't hurt. But as Bill puts it, the main qualification is a willingness to kill animals.

"It's a dirty job," says Bill, "and it has some bad connotations. I get a little harassment from the public. People even make wisecracks to me that slaughterers drink blood, and that sort of thing. But I've made good money at it, and it really isn't bad work at all. But I can't get sad over every animal I kill. I have to keep an aggressive attitude in order to do the job properly." Of course, only you can know if home slaughtering is a job opportunity that sounds appealing. If you have been killing, skinning, and cutting up your own animals successfully, you might want to consider doing some slaughtering for money. In the beginning, you could take on a few slaughtering jobs for a fee, and see how it felt. If you enjoyed the work and the money, then you could gradually expand into a true home business. You know whether there is a customer base in your area. If so, you might want to gather the equipment that you will need, and advertise yourself as a ranch slaughterer.

EQUIPMENT FOR RANCH SLAUGHTERING

Bill Dowling has designed his own equipment through 10 years of ranch slaughtering. Although you could get by slaughtering with less equipment than Bill uses (as you know from experience, a knife and a rope can suffice at the bottom line), proper, heavy duty equipment offers speed, neatness, and efficiency.

The Truck. The first item you will need is a four-wheel-drive truck. The truck will support your boom and winch system for hoisting animals so that they can be skinned and eviscerated. You also need the truck to haul carcasses to the custom butcher.

The four-wheel aspect is essential, unless you enjoy getting stuck in farmer's muddy fields. Raining or not, when it is slaughter time you will be called to do your work. It will be just your luck that the pigs or steers are located on the back forty, off of a road that now looks like a creek. Your chances of getting stuck will be high. Of course, you can have a winch on your truck to winch yourself out of these messes, but four-wheel drive is a real bonus here.

In terms of hauling the carcass to the custom butcher, some states might require a refrigerated truck. Other states, including California, have no such requirements. You might want to check on requirements within your own state. Bill Dowling says he has to register with the state of California as a slaughterman, but that registration requires no permits and no fees.

The Boom and Winch. The boom is mounted in the bed of Bill's truck. It works in conjunction with the electric winch. After Bill has killed a steer, he attaches the cable of the winch to the steer, and pulls the steer up to the truck. The winch contains 150 feet of 1/4-inch cable, which runs through the boom and wrap around a spool that is also mounted on the truck bed. The winch runs off a 12-volt battery located in the engine area next to the truck battery. Bill's inch has an 8000-pound rating, which means that it can hoist a 2000-pound animal off the ground.

Bill's boom has extra chains with which he adjusts its height. The larger and heavier the animal, the higher Bill sets the boom (and the shorter he sets the chains). Bill welded the boom from square, heavy gauge metal. It can support carcasses weighing up to 2000 pounds. Before he made this heavy-duty boom, he used a portable tripod with a 1 1/2-ton jack hoist. Figure 11-1 shows the truck bed with the boom in it. In Fig. 11-2 you can see how the boom works to hold up the steer.

Slaughtering Supplies. As a professional slaughterer you will carry all of your supplies with you and arrive on the site ready for work. Because slaughtering, skinning, and eviscerating can be quite messy jobs, especially if the site is wet and muddy, you will want to come dressed for the occasion. Bill Dowling wears high rubber boots called irrigation boots. "Don't underestimate the muck you might find on various farms," he advised. "You can step real deep inside those pig pens."

Bill also wears a leather apron he made himself. "The apron can be made from naugahide, leather, heavy canvas, or rubber," explains Bill. "But it needs to be waterproof, and you should be able to wipe it off."

Bill wears a belt over his apron. His knife

case (a regular butcher's sheath) hangs from the belt on his right hip, and his steel hangs from a chain on his left hip. Figure 11-3 shows Bill dressed for slaughter.

Bill uses only two knives for slaughtering: a skinning knife with a wood handle for skinning the animals, and a 6-inch boning knife for sticking and eviscerating. He keeps his steel attached to his belt for good reason—he steels his knives before every single cut. "A steel keeps the edge up on the knife," says Bill. "In skinning, if the knife is sharp, then you don't have to push with it. With a sharper knife, you don't hurt yourself, and you don't damage the hide."

Bill carries his remaining equipment on his truck. He has a rifle for stunning cattle and pigs (he doesn't use a gun with sheep or goats), a meat saw for splitting the brisket bone (breastbone), and a reciprocal saw for splitting the backbone. As the name implies, a reciprocal saw cuts with a back and forth or reciprocal motion. It resembles a chain saw, yet it is different. "Most chain saws are too dirty for meat cutting because they have automatic oilers," explains Bill. "Also, chain saws can splinter the backbone because they make too wide a cut."

After he has completed splitting the backbone, Bill rinses the carcass with water to remove any hair or dirt. He also cleans off all his equipment. Because Bill likes to keep his entire operation as sanitary as possible, he carries a 40-gallon water tank on the truck, along with a 12-volt pump that works off the truck battery.

When he first began slaughtering professionally, he relied on other people's water, using a bucket and a brush to clean up the carcass. "Having my own hose and pressurized water system is a great improvement," says Bill. "Anyone who is serious about going into slaughtering as a business, should carry their own water system. Cleanliness is one of your most important features of running a good business. My customers are always very surprised and pleased that I do such a neat, clean job. They expect to have blood scattered all over, but I never leave a drop." Figure 11-4 illustrates all

Fig. 11-1. Bill Dowling's son sits in the back of the well-equipped truck that Dowling uses in his ranch slaughtering business.

the equipment needed for a custom slaughtering business.

THE BUSINESS OF SLAUGHTERING

Let's assume you are interested in going into ranch slaughtering as a profession. How can you decide if you will find enough business in your area? "You need to be near a rural area, where people own 10 to 50 acres and raise their own animals," explains Bill Dowling. "But don't confuse the large ranchers with the small ones. The former take their animals to stockyards. It's the latter group—the people who raise animals for personal consumption—who will hire you."

Fig. 11-2. The carcass hangs from the boom that is mounted in the bed of the truck.

One way that Bill Dowling feels you could increase business would be to handle the cooling, aging, cutting, and packaging of the meat, as well as the slaughtering. Says Dowling, "I've often thought that I could make even more money if I handled the entire business, rather than dropping off the carcasses at the home butcher shop. A person who could perform both aspects of this business (killing and cutting up), would be totally independent. They wouldn't have to count on the custom butchers for referrals.''

Nevertheless, Dowling still makes plenty of money at custom slaughtering. And his capital investment and monthly bills are much less than those for a home butcher shop. Your biggest expenses, once you have bought your equipment, will probably be gasoline for your truck, plus truck maintenance. Dowling doesn't charge farmers for his gasoline, though it seems like he could add on extra charges for people who live at great distances from his home. Interestingly enough, because the rendering company (for offal) is 50 miles from his home, he simply takes the innards to the dump. At only a few dollars per beef innards (the current price is 2 cents per pound), he doesn't feel it is worth the drive to sell them. Moreover, if you intend to sell offal,

Fig. 11-3. Bill Dowling dressed for work as a custom slaughterer—in his handmade leather apron and wearing a belt carrying knives and steel.

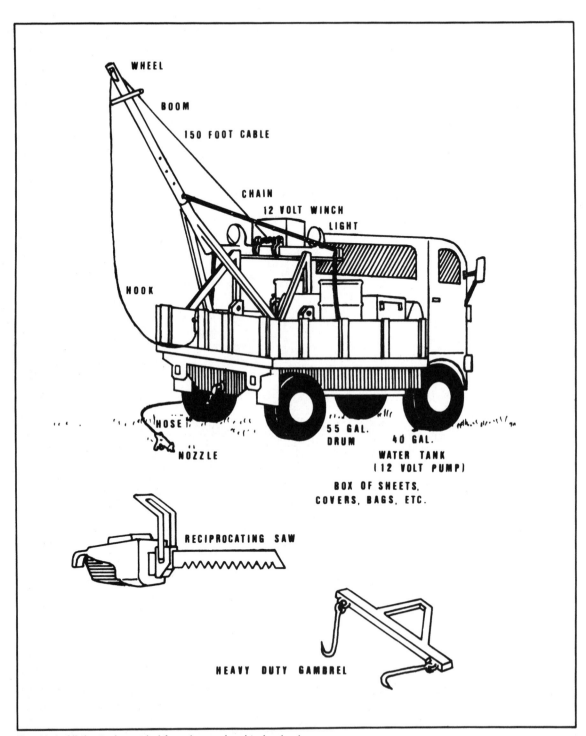

Fig. 11-4. All the tools needed for a home slaughtering business.

206

you must keep it refrigerated until it is sold.

Therefore, whether or not you can make extra money on the intestines is debatable. You will want to sell your skins. Bill Dowling takes his skins home, salts them, and sells them to "the hide man." Skins have a floating market value, but good, unnicked skins from cattle will make you additional money.

One thing you should realize is that custom slaughtering is seasonal work in many areas of the country. Fall is typically the busiest season, the time when people decide to slaughter animals rather than purchase feed for them over the winter. Bill says his work normally runs from July to November. If you are looking for a part-time income supplement, custom slaughtering might be just the thing. And in warmer areas you can slaughter over a longer season.

The price you can charge for slaughtering also varies in different areas of the country. At the bottom line, you will have to stay competitive. If a slaughterer in a neighboring county charges $15 per pig, you can't charge $25. Folks will always hire the cheaper person. Moreover, even if you have no competition, you can't raise your prices so high that it becomes uneconomical for the farmer to hire you. One of the main reasons for raising meat on the farm is a cost incentive. If the price of slaughtering (or butchering) sky-rockets, that would force people to quit raising their own animals. You'd be putting yourself out of business.

CUSTOMER RELATIONS

You might be wondering what problems to expect if you become a ranch slaughterer. I asked Bill Dowling what mistakes a person could make, and he mentioned a few worst case scenarios. He has had a cable break on his winch. As you know, such a mishap could drop a half ton of meat right in the mud. Luckily, when Bill's cable snapped, the hide was still on the meat, and the carcass fell onto grass.

Bill also told me about some of the wild kills. If you shoot the animal in the head, but not the brain, the animal can run like crazy. Bill had to chase a half-killed animal for an hour once, before he was able to down him with a long shot.

There is always the risk that you can kill the wrong animal. That wouldn't endear you to the owner one bit. Bill's advice here is simple: If you are called out on a job and you aren't sure that the animal you see is the animal the owner wants killed—don't shoot! Such identification problems do arise, because owners are often absent for the kill. In fact, one of the main reasons people hire custom slaughterers is to avoid being involved in the kill. It is this aversion to killing that creates the demand for custom slaughtering in the first place. "Most people just don't like to kill animals," says Dowling. "That's what makes my business so good."

Dowling tries to kill six to ten animals per day during his busy season. Although word of mouth from satisfied customers is his best form of advertising (as in custom butchering), Bill Dowling suggests that you still advertise several ways. First, you should contact the surrounding butcher shops to let them know that you are available to do ranch slaughtering. Second, you can advertise in the local paper under the animal section. Third, you can make your own business cards and pass them out at feed stores, hardware stores, the local cafe—anywhere the farmers in your area hang out.

If you go into custom slaughtering, will you be successful? The answer is probably yes, if you are good at it. One reason for your success is that you will become much more accomplished at slaughtering than the average small farmer. Most farmers, like you or me, can't really practice much slaughtering. If we kill two or three large animals per year, that's a lot. Consequently, we aren't working with enough volume to become truly proficient. Custom slaughterers, on the other hand, kill several hundred animals each season. They soon gain the speed and efficiency that impresses customers. Inevitably, their names become popular around the local farms.

Everyone in our area calls Bill Dowling to do their slaughtering for them. But occasionally, he will tell a customer "No thanks." Bill won't slaughter animals that have been chewed up by dogs, nor will he work on sick or dead animals. "Why take chances with your health?" he says. "It's just not worth it."

Chapter 12

Freezing

WHEN I LIVED AMONG VILLAGERS IN THE ISTHmus of Tehuantepec in Mexico, we ate meat (goat, pig, chicken—and also iguana) the day it was killed. The weather was hot, and there was no refrigeration.

The Tehuanan villagers had a feast or famine attitude toward meat. When they killed an animal, we all partied. The bigger the animal—the more people brought in on the festivities. In the long stretches of time between kills, we ate beans. No one expected meat on a regular basis. It was a treat, not a staple.

Wherever preservation techniques are not practiced, meat remains a "kill it-eat it" commodity. Meat spoils so rapidly that you have to eat it immediately, unless you have adequate methods for storing it. If you've ever smelled meat going bad, you know what I am talking about!

Of course, even on the most modern homesteads, if you yearn for an old-fashioned chicken dinner, you can still grab a live chicken from the coop, chop its head off, scald it, pluck

it, draw it, and eat it within an hour or two. You can also enjoy fresh rabbit or duck in this "kill it-eat it" mode.

In our hi-tech era, most homesteaders favor advanced home preservation techniques. Most of us find it more efficient and easier to raise our meat chickens for only eight to ten weeks. It may take us a full day to kill, clean, wrap, and freeze the entire lot, but when we are done, we feel content. After all, do you really like going out in the rain/snow to begin preparation for a chicken dinner? Moreover, when you hunger for **T**-bone steak, you really can't run out and shoot the steer. As you know, it takes 18 months to grow a steer, several hours to kill it, a week or so to age it, and a day or two to cut it up.

The only way we can be spontaneous with regards to our urge for a **T**-bone, is to rush to the freezer and thaw out the package of steaks as we begin to salivate. Here's where our modern preservation techniques come in very handy. And I suppose you could say that we are all quite spoiled by being able to hunt for our meat in the freezer. Those neatly wrapped and labeled, squared-off little packages in the shiny, white enamel freezer—well, they aren't as romantic as a buffalo with an arrow in its heart—but then, what is?

BEFORE YOU FREEZE YOUR MEAT

One of the most compelling reasons for freezing meats is that the nutritional value does not deteriorate with this preservation method. The second reason: freezing is exceedingly fast and simple. You can prepare a drawn chicken for freezing in a few minutes. It would take several hours to can it (time spent watching the canner), and one chicken would give you only 1 quart of canned meat!

I suppose I shouldn't put down canning (I'll be teaching you all about that preservation technique in the next chapter), but for speed and nutritional value, nothing beats freezing. Also, the meat comes out tasting like the fresh (real) thing. Actually, because of the tenderizing effect of freezing, meat often tastes slightly better after being frozen.

Ideally, every homestead should have a freezer (the second most important purchase after the pick-up truck). And even if you don't own one—lack of electricity, lack of finances, lack of space, or whatever—you can always find a friend with excess freezer space to lend, rent, or trade you. Interestingly enough, freezers freeze better when they are full, so don't feel guilty about letting your neighbors know that you'd like to share their freezer space. Unless their freezers are already chock-full, you will be doing them a favor. If it weren't for your meat, they would be filling their freezers with cartons of water!

Quite naturally, many people have a fear concerning the electricity going out, and everything in the freezer thawing simultaneously in a large pool of slush. Because such disasters happen rather infrequently, don't let your fear deter you from freezing. If you have a back-up generator, a rather typical piece of equipment on most farms, your chances of losing all of your food are quite minimal.

Moreover, even without the ability to generate your own electricity, chances are 99 out of 100 that your frozen meat can survive a temporary loss of power. Most freezers will keep meat frozen for several days, even with the electricity off. Just cover up the freezer with blankets, and don't open the door. In extreme circumstances (more than two or three full days without power), pack the freezer with dry ice. In these worst case scenarios, a chest freezer is preferable over an upright. Because all of the food is piled up, it will stay frozen longer.

Of course, the worst possible situation is that your freezer breaks down (or someone pulls the plug) and you don't know it. There is probably more chance of losing your meat this way than from power outages. The solution here is to keep your eye on your freezer (a daily check) or have a freezer with an alarm that goes off if the temperature rises to a dangerous (thawing) level.

Even if your meat should begin to thaw, you have no need to fret. As long as there are still ice crystals in the meat, you can refreeze it without any problems. Frozen meat is much less perishable (or much more refreezable) than frozen fruits or vegetables. And at the bottom line—you can have a much better party with 500 pounds of thawed beef, than 25 pounds of soggy stringbeans.

HOW TO FREEZE MEATS

There are several keys to success in freezing your farm-raised meats and poultry. First, you should only freeze high quality, fresh meat. If you have any questions at all about your meat's freshness, do not freeze it. The old adage here is: When in doubt, throw it out. Please, do not wrap it up and put it in the freezer. You will be wasting space, if not endangering your health.

Moreover, even though I said previously that freezing tenderizes meat, even 12 months in the freezer will not change tough meat into tender meat. So, don't kid yourself that a carcass that is canner grade will magically turn into a choice carcass in your freezer. Such improvements cannot happen.

The second important point in freezing meat: wrap properly. If you are worried about having adequate freezer space, you might want to bone out your meat and cut poultry and rabbits up into parts. If your packages can be small and symmetrical, you'll get the most efficient use from your freezer. However, small packages have a shorter freezer life—a trade-off here!

Many experts on freezing advise bone removal. However, I have been pushing for you to leave in the bones during this entire book so I can't suddenly tell you to remove bones in order to have smaller, neater packages for your freezer—even though boning could save you about 25 percent of your freezer space. You'll have to decide about bones yourself. If you do wrap packages with bones, watch out for sharp edges that could rip open your packages. A trick here is to surround protruding bones with crumpled paper inside the package.

Even if you leave in the bones, you should remove excess fat from your meat. Fat can turn rancid very rapidly, so don't leave on more than you need to flavor your steaks or roasts when you cook them. The less fat on your meat, the longer its life in the freezer.

Bones and fat aside, the main criteria in proper wrapping are the type of wrap you use, as well as the method of wrapping. You need to use moisture-proof and vapor-proof materials to ensure that your meat will not get freezer burn.

We've all tasted food that has had freezer burn. You can still eat it if you are starving, but it tastes pretty lousy, and looks unattractive to boot. Freezer burn is definitely a state of affairs you want to avoid. The money spent on high-quality freezer wraps is your insurance against this nemesis.

There are numerous papers, plastics, and foils on the market for freezing. You can buy a high-grade freezer paper with a polyester coating in large quantities (1100 foot rolls in 15-inch, 18-inch, and 24-inch widths) from supermarket supply houses. You double the freezer-life of your meats by using proper wraps. The longer you intend to freeze the product, the stronger (more expensive) wrap you need.

In general, a freezer wrap should be heavy enough to protect your meat from freezer burn. It should also be odorless, water resistant, and pliable. It should not stick to the meat. Please do not cut corners here.

Years ago a friend brought me a roll of blue butcher paper. He had found it at a yard sale, and it was definitely worth about 100 times more than the 25 cents he paid. Even though this paper isn't technically freezer paper, I use it successfully for freezing my meats in the following manner. I first wrap my meat tightly in Saran wrap. Then I rewrap it in two layers of the blue butcher paper. My point: you can get by without buying traditional "freezer" paper, but you should be sure to use a combination of paper and plastic that works. Always overwrap, rather than underwrap. Don't take chances.

How you wrap is also important. Your goal is to exclude as much air as possible. The reason is that air causes oxidation, which then causes rancidity. In freezing meat, you want to keep that air out of your packages.

Wrapping meat is something like wrapping gifts. Cut a large rectangle of paper, about three or four times the size of the meat you want to wrap. Put your meat—chops, roast, ground meat, whatever—in the middle of the freezer paper. Lift up the two long sides of the paper, and bring them together. Now (and this is the important part) fold these edges over in one direction, making a 1-inch fold. Turn this fold downward a second time to make a double "locking seam." Keep folding this edge downward, until the paper is completely secure around your meat.

Now fold the short ends tightly. You can make "hospital corners," the same folds you make when putting sheets on a bed. Press out any remaining air pockets. Tape the ends shut with freezer tape (tape that won't come off in the freezer).

Figure 12-1 shows you how to wrap meat in the rectangular style. Another method, which

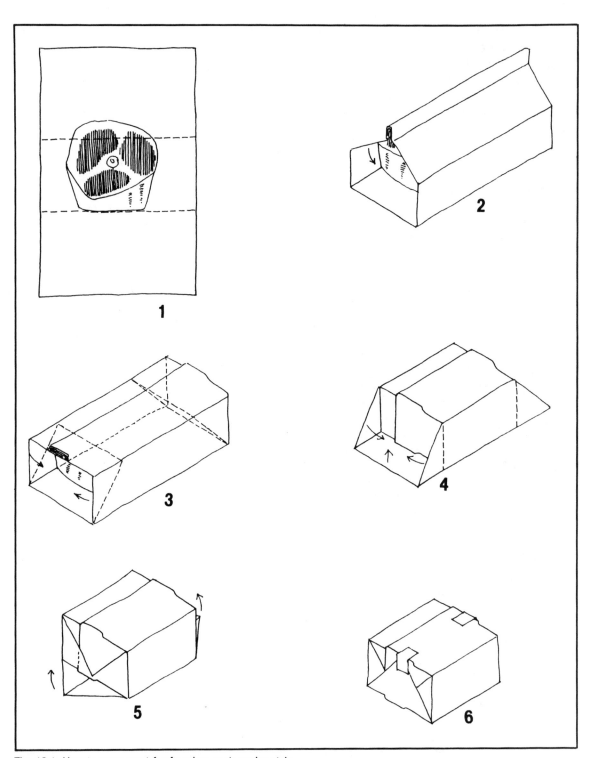

Fig. 12-1. How to wrap meat for freezing, rectangular style.

Julie Taylor uses, is to wrap meat on the diagonal. You put the meat on the paper diagonally, and basically roll it up in the paper. Perhaps you might find this method easier. Figure 12-2 shows Julie wrapping meat.

If you package several steaks or chops together, you can put paper between them (as in Fig. 12-2), so that the pieces don't stick together. You can use your freezer paper for this purpose, or you can buy special tissues or polyester meat sheets, which are pre-cut to 8 × 10 inches, and pull out of their carton like Kleenex.

Stop! Don't put anything into the freezer until you have labeled it with the following information: the name of the meat, the cut, the number of pieces or pounds, and most important, the date. An example: ''beef, rolled rump, 6 lbs., 12/13/85.'' Obviously, it is convenient to know what is inside those packages without ripping them open. And the date is crucial. Different meats have different freezer lives, and none keep forever. You need to eat up your meat before its due date. Don't ever trust your memory; instead, label those packages.

Once your meat is packaged, you will want to freeze it promptly. If you have large quantities of meat, you need to realize that a freezer can't freeze more than 5 percent of its volume at one time. You should only attempt to freeze as much meat as your freezer can freeze solid in a 24-hour period.

If you have a small freezer and a lot of meat, you should cut and wrap it over a period of days to avoid heating up your freezer by putting in too much fresh food at one time. A beef forequarter fills about 3 cubic feet. So plan ahead.

The advantage of having your meat quick-frozen by the custom butcher comes in handy here. You can put any amount of pre-frozen meat in your freezer. In dealing with large quan-

Fig. 12-2. Wrapping meat for the freezer, diagonal style.

tities, even if you cut it up yourself, you might need to pay someone with a walk-in freezer to quick-freeze it for you.

Quick freezing is ultra-important if you want your thawed meat to come out tasting as good as the fresh product. If meat freezes too slowly, breakdown of tissues and loss of juices results. Meat quality is drastically lowered.

FREEZER SHELF LIFE OF MEATS

Once your meat is quick-frozen, how long can you store it before it begins to lose quality? Each type of meat varies in its freezer life. There are scientific reasons why certain meats (fats) go rancid (oxidize) faster than others. In general terms, lean meats like beef have a longer storage life than fatter meats like pork. Other variables that shorten storage life are salting and aging.

Table 12-1 gives approximate recommendations for maximum storage of large, properly wrapped cuts at zero degrees Fahrenheit. It can be possible to enjoy frozen meat that has been stored longer than these recommended limits.

Table 12-1. Approximate Freezer
Shelf Life of Various Meats.

MEAT	MONTHS
beef	6 to 12 months
pork	3 to 6 months
lamb	6 to 9 months
veal	6 to 9 months
goat	6 to 9 months
deer	6 to 9 months
ground sausage	2 to 4 months
ground beef	2 to 4 months
ham	2 to 3 months
bacon	2 to 3 months
chicken	6 to 12 months
turkey	6 to 12 months
ducks	6 to 8 months
geese	6 to 8 months
rabbit	6 to 8 months
liver	2 months
tongue	4 months
heart	4 months
kidneys	4 months
poultry giblets	3 months

But why risk eating meat that has a deteriorated quality?

I don't advise waiting until the last possible moment to eat your frozen meats. Freezing is a way to hold meat for eating. It is not a method for hoarding meat! Start using your frozen food now: the sooner, the tastier.

ADDITIONAL BENEFITS OF FREEZING

Freezing inactivates the enzymes and bacteria that can spoil meats. It also kills trichinosis in pork. Therefore, if you wish to make jerky from pork (or eat pork that hasn't been cooked at high temperatures), you can freeze your pork for 30 days and then make it into jerky.

Salted, or cured, meats do not keep well when frozen. If you want to have bacons or hams year around, one option is to freeze some of your pork fresh, and then cure cuts gradually over a six month period. As you can see, freezing thus opens up more options for you.

For example, right now I have several packages of deer meat in my freezer. I intend to use this meat for deer jerky, but I haven't yet had time to cut it up. Sometime in the next nine months, I shall make time. Meanwhile, my meat sleeps safely in the freezer.

When you thaw meat, you can cook it, cure it or even can it. Actually, you don't even have to thaw meat in order to cook it. If you prefer to cook your meat frozen, just cook it longer. In many cases, especially with soups and stews, the results are identical to working with thawed meat.

Do not salt sausage before you freeze it. The salt really decreases the freezer life of your sausage. It is definitely better to salt it when you thaw it. You can spice the sausage before freezing, but watch out for strong spices like sage that could turn your sausage bitter in the freezer. In general, processed meats don't do well when frozen, so eat them up as rapidly as possible. You can always make more from your frozen fresh pork, as mentioned above.

Liver also does very poorly in the freezer. One time I opened a package of liver that I had frozen for a few months. It had completely changed texture. Luckily the dog thought it was delicious.

In preserving meats, experience is your best teacher. If you are not familiar with all the ins and outs of freezing, I hope you will ask some of the "oldtimers" to share their freezing secrets—successes and failures. As I have suggested throughout this text, one of the best ways to learn about meats is to talk with your neighbors who have experiences to share.

Learning how to communicate with the local farmers is an important homesteading task. Don't overlook the obvious sources of freezing expertise. If your neighbors have a hog, two dozen chickens and eight turkeys in their freezer, chances are they know what they are doing. Get acquainted. Ask questions. Network. You'll share freezing tricks that will help ensure your success. And in an emergency, you'll be able to stuff your partially thawed meat in their freezer!

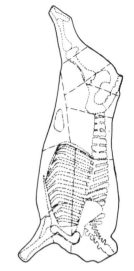

Chapter 13

Canning

O VER MY YEARS HOMESTEADING, I HAVE DEVELoped mixed feelings about canning. In my first years on the farm, during my transformation from city slicker to country cousin, I canned with a zealousness most people reserve for sports.

My canning marathon was a secret contest pitting me against the other fledgling homesteaders in my community. Whenever I ran into neighbors I'd answer their casual greeting of "Well Geeta, what have you been up to?" with "I've canned 400 quarts of food. And you?"

Invariably, I received just what I wanted, a gasp of amazed admiration for any farmer who would stand by a hot stove all day endlessly canning so her darling children could enjoy homegrown food during the long winter. Of course, the conversation ended right there because I had little more to say. Having spent all my spare time canning, I hadn't glanced at a book or newspaper, or entertained an interesting thought in months. My vision was myopic: grow it and get it into a jar by October.

Indeed, visitors to our cabin were always awestruck by my shelves and shelves of colorful quart and pint jars. I kept all my canning out in the open for show, every so often dusting my prized collection, and rearranging it to fill the gaps caused by last week's meals.

I won my own private contest. I awarded myself "best canner" among the younger set, grudgingly realizing that I could never top the retired postmaster's wife, who cans 800 quarts a year and has the temperament of a saint.

And then I slowly began cutting back on my canning for a number of reasons. First, I found better things to do with my time than stand up all day in the kitchen caressing my canner. Second, I learned to be selective in my canning, and only can the foods that everyone ate up ravenously within one season. And third, after seven years on the farm, we brought in electricity, and I began to experiment with freezing, and prefer this method—not so much results or the ends—but the means. With freezing you wrap up the food, label it, shove it in the freezer, and you are done with it. With canning, as you will see, you are going to have to spend much more time. It might come out tasting great, but believe me, you have earned any compliments you get.

WHY CAN MEAT?

After this anti-canning tirade, you might wonder why anyone would consider canning meat. There are actually many possible reasons to pull out the old pressure canner and get to work.

First, you might not have a freezer, and you might not want to borrow freezer space from friends. If you don't have electricity or a freezer, it can be a bit inconvenient driving miles to a friend's house or to the storage locker, just to pick up some meat. In that case, you have no choice but to can your meat.

Second, you might like the immediacy of canned food. Pop the lid off, heat it up, and bingo—dinner is ready. Canning gives farmers instant, pre-cooked, no-thaw meals.

Third, canning does look impressive. Although I am past my maniacal canning phase, I still keep an open shelf full of my glorious canning (I am now down to about 100 quarts a year), and everyone still raves about how wonderful it all looks. ''Geeta, how do you have time to do so much?'' my fans ask. ''Oh, it's nothing,'' I answer with false modesty. ''It only takes me a moment.''

Fourth, canning makes nice gifts. Of course, you could give someone a wrapped chunk of frozen venison with a ribbon around it and they'd probably be thrilled. Nevertheless, a pint jar of cooked venison somehow looks more like a present, more like you took the time to care.

Fifth, canning is a good back-up to freezing. Suppose the electricity did go out and everything thawed (fear of fears), you'd at least have your canning left.

Sixth, canned meat tastes good, especially if you do a creative job in canning it.

Canning meat is not nearly such a popular preservation technique as freezing, or even curing (next chapter). Nevertheless, there's no rea-son why you shouldn't try to do some canning. However, please read these direction carefully before you begin. Canning meat is a very technical project. You have to do it right or you can blow it completely and end up with broken jars, or even worse, a dangerous product that could kill you.

HOME CANNING PRECAUTIONS

There's only one right way to can meat: in a pressure canner at 240 degrees Fahrenheit. If you don't own a pressure canner, buy one—or forget about canning meat. Your relatives might have canned meat in the oven, or in a water-bath canner (at 212 degrees Fahrenheit), but those techniques are now considered **dangerous**.

Why all the fuss about 240 degrees Fahrenheit? The answer: clostridium botulinum, better known as *botulism*. We'll be discussing this nasty bacteria in the chapter on curing as well. Briefly, clostridium butulinum is a bacteria that can produce a toxin (botulin) that causes acute food poisoning (botulism), resulting in nervous disorders or death.

Botulism is commonly found on meat in the spore or resting state, and in this form it is not dangerous. However, it gets dangerous when the spores germinate (seed themselves) in foods in the absence of oxygen. A jar of canned meat is a perfect breeding ground for these dangerous spores. Boiling temperatures will not kill clostridium botulinum as they are amazingly heat resistant; however, temperatures of 240 degrees Fahrenheit demolish these spores.

Therefore, you must always process canned meats and other low-acid foods at 10 pounds of pressure, or 240 degrees Fahrenheit. Moreover, if your finished products show any of the following problems, you must throw them out without tasting them. **Always discard:**

☐ If the can is bulging or if the glass jar has come unsealed.

☐ If the canned food contains gas bubbles or if liquid spurts out when opened.

☐ If the meat seems slimy, mushy, or moldy.

☐ If the meat smells strange, unusual, or cheesey.

In each of these four cases, discard the canned goods. Do not taste them and do not feed them to animals. Presuming your product seems all right, and then you taste it, and it tastes strange, immediately throw it out. Do not continue to eat it.

A final safety precaution to prevent botulism is to boil the food for 15 minutes in an open pan after you have poured it from the jar. If undetected botulin toxin has developed in the jar, it will be destroyed by boiling. Do not taste until the 15 minutes are up.

I hope I haven't scared you so much about botulism that you are turned off to the idea of canning your meat. These precautions weren't intended to frighten you out of this technique of food preservation. The purpose of telling you about botulism is to alert you to a danger that exists if you do not follow proper canning directions.

I've used a pressure canner for many years without fear, worry, or problems. I see no reason to avoid pressure canning low-acid foods. Proceed with caution and you will have excellent results.

PRESSURE CANNING BASICS

There are two methods to can meat: the raw pack and the hot pack. I do not recommend the raw pack method, as I think your end result is not nearly so tasty. Canning is more than a means of preservation. It should taste good when it comes out of the jar.

Before you even begin, read the instructions that came with your pressure canner. It is a good idea to have your pressure gauge checked annually. You need to know that 10 pounds pressure on your gauge is truly 10 pounds pressure.

If you intend to use tin cans, make sure your can sealer is operating properly. You can test it by putting some water into a tin can, and sealing it. Now place the can in boiling water, and look if any air bubbles rise from the can. If so, check your sealer. It needs some adjustments.

Tin cans come in a range of sizes. A Number 2 can holds about 2 1/2 cups, a Number 2.5 can holds about 3 1/2 cups, and a Number 3 can holds about 4 cups.

If you plan to use glass jars (which is what I use), try to buy wide mouth quarts or pints. My pressure canner can hold 7 quarts or 10 pints. Whether to use quarts or pints is a personal question that probably depends on family size. If there's only two of you, pints might be most appropriate.

You might have jars left over from previous years. Be sure to check their rims closely for nicks, chips and cracks. Discard any jars that have any abnormalities. They will not seal properly.

Be sure and buy new lids. Wide mouth lids are often more expensive than narrow or regular mouth. But it will be a lot easier to get your meat in and out of the jars if they are wide mouth. Again, this choice is yours.

The first step in pressure canning is washing your jars with soap and hot water. Rinse well with hot water. Then fill the hot jars up to 1 inch from the top with your hot pre-cooked chunks of meat.

Run a blunt knife into the bottle (being careful not to break the bottle) to let any air bubbles escape. Then add liquid as necessary, to bring the level of the meat juices up to 1 inch from the top. Wipe off the rim (I use paper towel dipped in water for this job).

Wash your lids and keep them in a pan of hot water. Place the clean flat metal lid onto the top of the jar, and screw it in place with the metal screw band. Tighten the band as firmly as you can. Finis!

Using tin cans is a bit more complicated, as you must either keep the food very hot (above 170 degrees Fahrenheit) before sealing the can, or you must exhaust the cans for 10 minutes in hot water before sealing. Read the instructions that came with your cans and sealer for specific instructions.

Now, put warm water in the bottom of the canner. My canner calls for 2 quarts of water. (The water temperature should match the temperature of your bottles. Too hot or too cold can break them.)

Put the rack into your pressure canner and place your filled, sealed jars on the rack. If you have extra spaces—for example, your canner holds 7 quarts and you have only filled 5 quarts—fill some extra jars with water and use them to fill the gaps.

Tighten down the lid of the pressure canner and turn on the stove. Leave the exhaust valve (sometimes called the petcock or vent) open. As the water comes to a boil in the canner, steam will begin to emerge from the exhaust valve. It is very important to let this steam come out for ten minutes before closing the vent. This drives all air from your canner so that it will register the correct pressure.

Close down the exhaust valve. You will see the pressure rising from 1 pound, to 2 pounds, and on upward. You will want to process your meat at 10 pounds pressure. Add on an extra pound for every 2000 feet above sea level. Be-cause I live in the foothills at approximately 2000 feet, I process my food at 11 pounds pressure.

When your gauge reads 10 pounds (or 11 or 12 pounds as the case might be) you start counting canning time. (Even though you've already waited over a half hour, none of that time counts.) Your canning time for meats will be over an hour for the pints, and about one and one half hours for the quarts at 10 pounds pressure (see Table 13-1).

During this period of time, you cannot walk away from your canner. It must stay at 10 pounds pressure, and unfortunately, it is my experience that this takes constant attention.

For example, when my canner reaches the 11 pounds required in my neck of the woods, I'll turn down the gas stove to hold the pressure at that level. Suddenly, the gauge will creep up to 12 pounds, so I will turn the stove further down. Then, just as suddenly it will drop down, to 9 pounds—so I have to turn the gas back up slightly. In all my years canning, I have never been able to find the exact spot on the stove that will hold the canner at an exact 11 pounds. I always have to keep regulating the heat, and in fact, my canning directions tell me to keep regulating the heat. So be prepared to hang out

Table 13-1. Canning Times for Meats (and Veggies) at 10 Pounds Pressure.

MEAT	#2 CANS/PINT JARS	#2.5 or #3 CANS/QUART JARS
beef	75 minutes	90 minutes
pork	75 minutes	85 minutes
lamb	75 minutes	90 minutes
goat	75 minutes	90 minutes
venison	75 minutes	90 minutes
rabbit	65 minutes	75 minutes
turkey	70 minutes	80 minutes
goose	85 minutes	95 minutes
duck	85 minutes	95 minutes
chicken	65 minutes	75 minutes
brains	80 minutes	90 minutes
liver	65 minutes	80 minutes
heart	65 minutes	80 minutes
tongue	75 minutes	90 minutes
kidneys	70 minutes	80 minutes
clear soup	20 minutes	25 minutes
potatoes	35 minutes	40 minutes
corn	60 minutes	85 minutes
kidney beans	65 minutes	75 minutes
carrots	25 minutes	30 minutes

with your canner now, for another hour at least. You want to keep the pressure as stable as possible. Large swings in pressure cause liquid to boil out of the jars.

Finally, when the required processing time is up, you can turn off the heat. The pressure will slowly drop back to zero. After it has been at zero for a few minutes, you can open the escape valve, open the lid, and take out the glass jars. Do not immerse them in water, or let them stand in a draft. Just set the jars on a level surface, with space around them.

If you are using cans, you don't have to wait for the pressure to drop to zero before opening the escape valve. When the processing time is completed, turn off the heat and immediately open the escape valve, and let the steam escape. When the gauge reads zero, you can cautiously remove the cover of the canner, keeping the lid between your face and the boiling water. Cool the tins in cold water. (You can't do any of this with glass, as it will explode on you.)

CREATIVELY CANNING MEAT

As I mentioned earlier, there is a canning method for meats called raw packing, but it is really a misnomer. Basically, you put the raw meat in the jar, and then heat the jars in a pan of hot water until their inner temperature is about 170 degrees Fahrenheit. Because this process takes one and one-fourth hours before you can seal the jars and start canning them, I think raw pack is a misleading term. In other words, you may pack it in raw, but you have to spend a great deal of time cooking the meat (flavorlessly) from the outside before you can proceed. I am therefore only going to tell you the hot pack method, as I think your end product will come out tasting better, and not just like boiled meat.

To can lamb, beef, pork, deer, or goat, cut the meat into convenient sized (boneless) pieces to put into your jar. Heat a little fat in a pan, and sear the pieces of meat, browning them on all sides. Salt and pepper the meat, and add other seasoning that you like—such as onion, garlic, spices, and vegetables (like carrots, tomatoes,

potatoes). Add about 1 cup of water to the drippings in the pan, and roast or simmer the meat covered until it is partly done, but not completely done. Baste as necessary. Basically, cook the meat until it is no longer red at the center. It will get plenty of cooking in the canner.

Pack the hot, partially cooked meat loosely into your hot clean jars up to 1 inch from the top. Add the gravy from the pan. Insert a knife down along the side of the the jar to let all air bubbles escape. The liquid should reach to 1 inch of the top. If you need more liquid, you can always add boiling water. Seal and process. Figure 13-1 shows the steps you will follow using the hot pack method.

You are able to can whole quart-sized roasts in this fashion, or strips and chunks of meat. Each quart jar will hold approximately 1 pound of untrimmed meat. Season according to your family's taste. Canned meat needn't taste like boiled meat. You might want to make stew—meat and vegetables—or perhaps you prefer to focus on meat alone. Sear the meat, season it, add a little water, make a little gravy. Be creative. It will taste much better.

The only thing you shouldn't do is use flour. Flour can turn tough in a canning situation, and also make sterilization difficult. Also, don't use any spices that can turn bitter. You can always add flour to thicken gravy, plus extra spices, when you open your canned food. You could can hamburger, sausage, liver pate, spare ribs, chicken gumbo, duck in orange sauce, ham, corned beef, hash, pork and beans, mincemeat—virtually any meat dish. If you see an interesting canned specialty item in the supermarket, you can make it at home, and can it yourself. Just check the times required for the *type* of meat you are canning. Follow all instructions given here, and you might even invent a new gourmet canned food.

If you are using tin cans, can according to the manufacturer's instructions. Most likely your meat should reach within 1/2 inch of the top, and the liquid can go up to 1/4 inch of the top. If you must exhaust your cans before sealing (because

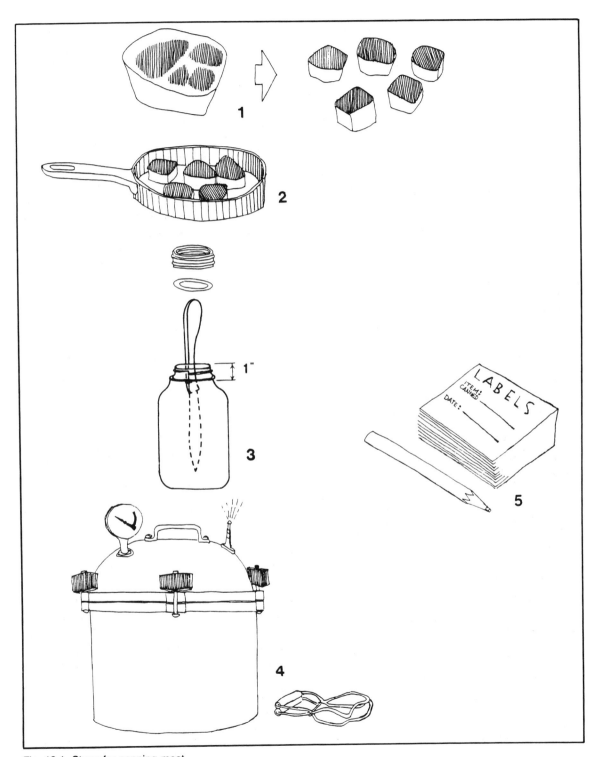

Fig. 13-1. Steps for canning meat.

they haven't stayed hot enough), or if some liquid evaporates, you can add more.

The technique of canning chicken, duck, goose, turkey, or rabbit is similar. Cut it into pieces, salt and pepper it, and sear it (fry it) in hot fat until brown. Pack into jars (with or without bones). Add water to the fat (and other seasonings), and pour this boiling gravy over the bird/rabbit to 1 inch from the top of the jars. Make sure all air bubbles are out. Seal while hot and process. (Do not pack the liver in with the poultry or rabbit; it has too strong a flavor.)

Of course, you can also boil chicken, remove all bones and skin, and then pack the meat in jars, adding 1 teaspoon of salt to each jar. Fill the jar with the broth in which you cooked the chicken to 1 inch from the top. If you are using tin cans, you follow the same instructions, except you fill them up to 1/4 inch from the top.

Canning chicken is an excellent way to use up older birds. After 75 minutes in the pressure canner, they are tender!

In conclusion, I'll state some of my main advice on pressure canning farm-raised meats:

☐ Use only fresh killed meats that have been properly chilled. If in doubt, do not can it.

☐ In canning, you should keep everything hot and clean; put hot, clean meat into hot, clean jars.

☐ You need to take the information about the right pressure and the right number of minutes very seriously. With meats, the pressure will always be 10 pounds. The time will vary according to the animal and the jar size, but it will often be as much as one and a half hours. Canning takes time. Plan ahead.

☐ Once you understand the basic rules of pressure canning, you can vary the recipes in your canning manual. You can make your recipes much more interesting.

Look at your list of ingredients for your own creative concoction. Study the pressures and times required for each ingredient. And then adjust your canning time to the ingredient requiring the highest pressure and the longest number of minutes.

For example, if I can a quart of tomato puree, I only need to process the cooked soup for 15 minutes in boiling water (zero pounds pressure), because this is the amount of time needed for cooked tomato puree. However, if I add carrots to the tomato puree, I have to process the soup at 10 pounds pressure for 30 minutes, because that is what carrots require. Now if I add beef to the soup, I must process these quarts at 10 pounds pressure for 90 minutes, because beef requires an hour and a half. The ingredient requiring maximum time/pressure, rules the soup.

So, you can be as creative as you wish, but you must refer back to the charts for meats (and vegetables) in your canning manual, to make sure you are aware of the maximum requirements of your ingredients.

Your canning should reflect your family's eating habits. If you don't want fat in your foods, don't use it. If you don't want salt, leave it out. Your home canned foods must satisfy your own personal taste. You will spend many hours canning your meats—washing and checking the jars, precooking the food, packing it in the jars, sealing the jars, bringing the canner to a boil, exhausting it 10 minutes, raising the pressure to 10 pounds, holding the pressure at 10 pounds for an hour and a half, and then waiting while the pressure falls back down. You deserve delicious home-canned results!

CANNING TIMES FOR MEATS

Table 13-1 lists canning times for various protein foods. I have compiled the list from numerous official sources. Wherever I found conflicting times, I have chosen to give you the longer (safer) time. In every case, the required pressure is 10 pounds, plus an extra pound for every 2000 feet above sea level.

Always start counting the times after the canner has reached 10 pounds of pressure. Do not can less minutes than the times listed. If you aren't sure about the time, it's safe to add on extra time. But never can for less than the allotted time.

Should you wish to include vegetables, I have added some of the vegetables you might want to use with meats at the end of this list. You can always throw in tomatoes, onions, or garlic to any of your meat recipes, without worrying about their canning times. Good luck with your home canning. Be safe and creative.

Chapter 14

Curing

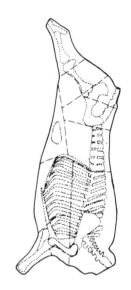

I F YOU ENJOY EATING HAM, BACON, AND SALAMI, then you will probably want to cure some of your home-raised meats. I say "probably," because I am not 100% convinced that curing is a totally safe procedure. By definition, curing is a chemical method of processing—and it is the chemicals used in curing that might be carcinogenic, and therefore dangerous to your health.

Although this chapter contains numerous instructions (with said chemicals) for delicious home-cured products, it would not be fair to teach about curing without including some brief comments on the safety of eating these foods. I think that farmers such as you and I owe it to ourselves to attempt to understand the controversy surrounding curing.

The concern about additives in cured meats is not merely the fantasy of a few health faddists. To the contrary, the possible link between cured meats and cancer is an issue being studied by the United States Department of Agriculture (USDA), the Food and Drug Administration, The

American Cancer Society, the Council for Agricultural Science and Technology, The National Academy of Sciences, the American Meat Institute, the Massachusetts Institute of Technology, the University of Wisconsin, and many other responsible organizations. It is a complex issue scientifically, and it is particularly difficult because cured meats represent about 10 percent of the foods that consumers purchase commercially. In assessing the safety of cured meats, many studies include a risk-benefit analysis based on commercial usage.

In a book on home butchering and home preservation of meat, it is not appropriate to present reams of data concerning what is basically a governmental regulatory issue. After all, you raise and preserve your own meat in order to get away from the store-bought products. Nevertheless, as the government enforces new regulations in an attempt to ensure the safety of commercially-cured meats, home preservers need to follow suit. It would seem foolish for a home-preserver to continue using methodologies which have been deemed unsafe for commercial preservation.

THE CURING CONTROVERSY

Whenever people think of curing, they think of salt. But if you study ancient history, you will learn that impure salt was considered the most desirable curing agent because it gave a pink color to the finished product. This impure salt contained saltpeter, which is sodium or potassium nitrate, as well as the sodium chloride we associate with pure salt.

The term curing, therefore, describes the use of these nitrates plus salt (and perhaps sugar and spices) to preserve meat by applying dry salts or by using a brine. The reason for the addition of the nitrates is threefold: to give meat the delicious cured taste, to give cured meat the popular pink color, and, most important, to prevent botulism. (As you recall from the chapter on canning, botulism is a deadly form of food poisoning.)

As scientists began to study the characteristics of nitrates in curing, they discovered that the nitrate converted to nitrite in the meat. Thus, some cures began to use nitrites directly in the cure, whereas others used nitrates, or a combination of both.

Until the late 1960s, the USDA believed the only potential danger in nitrate or nitrite use was poisoning from overuse. However, in 1970, scientists found that nitrites can form compounds, called nitrosamines, in the human digestive tract. It was later discovered that nitrosamines can also form from nitrites during cooking at high temperatures (such as in frying bacon). Unfortunately, these nitrosamines are considered potent carcinogens. Therefore, since 1970, there has been an aura of controversy surrounding commercially cured meat products.

In 1973, the USDA formed a panel of experts to study nitrates, nitrites, and nitrosamines. After five years of studying the issue, the four major recommendations, published in 1978, can be summarized as follows:

☐ The reduction of nitrite levels for all cures.

☐ The use of chemical inhibitors in bacon cures to minimize nitrosamine formation.

☐ The prohibition of the use of nitrates except in dry-cured products.

☐ The elimination of nitrates from bacon.

In 1978, studies from the Massachusetts Institute of Technology (MIT) linked nitrites with increased cancers in laboratory animals. However, after studying the MIT research, the USDA concluded that there was insufficient evidence to support the conclusion that nitrite causes cancer in test animals.

In 1981 and 1982, a committee of the National Academy of Science (NAS) conducted a study of nitrite at the request of the USDA. According to a letter I received from John C. Prucha, Assistant Deputy Administrator, USDA, the results of the NAS study were as follows:

"The NAS committee concluded that the evidence of the potential of nitrate and nitrite for causing human cancer is 'largely circumstantial' and that studies 'have not provided sufficient evidence' to conclude that these agents cause cancer. But the committee recommended that nitrite in cured meats be reduced 'to the extent that protection against botulism is not compromised.' "

And here's another interesting, authoritative comment on cured meats—just to add to the confusion: In a booklet called "Nutrition and Cancer: Cause and Prevention," put out by the American Cancer Society in 1984, the authors list seven recommendations that "are likely to provide some measure of reducing cancer risk." One of the recommendations is "Be moderate in consumption of salt-cured, smoked, and nitrite-cured foods."

NITRATES AND NITRITES IN HOME CURING

In attempting to examine the issue of whether or not nitrites are safe for home-curing, I have read pages and pages of scientific data, and yet there seems to be no absolute conclusion yes or no, safe or unsafe. Basically, no one denies that there might be some health risks associated with the use of these chemicals, but most studies seem to conclude that the benefits (botulism prevention, proper color, better taste) far outweigh the risks. Advocates of nitrite use also point out that many vegetables have far higher nitrate levels than you would ever get from cured meats. And, at the bottom line, although consumer groups have petitioned the government for the elimination of nitrite as an approved additive, it is at this writing still legal.

For home-preservers who want to delve into the issue further, I have included some resources in the appendix. The best way for you to learn about up-to-date research on nitrites is to contact the United States Department of Agriculture. They have been studying the issue since the early 1970s and are constantly changing their commercial regulations as they gather new information. The USDA is presently considering a further reduction in amount of nitrite used in bacon cures. Moreover, they are actively investigating potential nitrite substitutes, which could one day take potential danger out of home-curing.

I can't possibly advise you whether or not you should cure meat at home. You will have to decide about curing based on your own dietary philosophy.

If you do cure meat, I recommend that you add a nitrosamine inhibitor in any of your curing solutions. My local agricultural agent from the University of California, Davis, suggests that you should use ample Vitamin C in all your cures in order to help reduce any chance that your bacon might contain nitrosamines. (The commercial inhibitors are sodium ascorbate or sodium erythorbate at 550 parts per million, but Vitamin C should substitute quite nicely.)

Finally, for those of you who don't approve of adding nitrites to meats, I suggest freezing your meat fresh, and forgetting about curing altogether. That's definitely the safest approach.

Now that I have probably scared you about the chemistry of curing, accept my apologies, and let's move on to curing hams, bacons, and salamis. If you have raised a pig or two, you probably do want to experiment with making your own cured meats.

HAM BASICS

There are two basic methods (plus thousands of variations) for curing hams. The first method is a dry cure in which you rub the dry-curing mix onto the meat and let it sit on a shelf. The second method is a wet cure, called a brine or pickle cure. In this method you inject the hams with brine, and then soak the injected hams in more brine solution.

The dry cure, which is often called country style, is a slow curing method, which gives you a salty ham with long keeping qualities. The brine cure is typically a faster (easier) method, giving you a ham that keeps only a few weeks, unless it is frozen. The basic advice for all hams is:

☐ Raise lean hams. A lean (or meat-type) hog has no more than 1 1/2 inches of back fat and weighs from 180 to 240 pounds at slaughter. There is much less chance of spoilage in lean hams.

☐ Chill the hog carcass rapidly. The best plan is to slaughter hogs in the afternoon, so that they can be thoroughly chilled by morning. At 30 degrees to 35 degrees Fahrenheit, it takes about 15 hours to chill a 150 pound hog to 40 degrees Fahrenheit internal temperature. If the hogs aren't chilled properly, the hams might sour before curing, or during the cure.

☐ Cut your hams, and begin the cure within 24 hours of the kill—as long as the internal temperature has been chilled below 40 degrees Fahrenheit. When cutting, trim your hams nicely, removing excess fat. If the flesh has been bruised or damaged, do not use it for making hams. For country-style hams, many farmers prefer to use a long cut ham.

226

COUNTRY-STYLE HAMS

To make a country-style ham, I am recommending shelf curing. You will rub a dry cure onto all surfaces of the ham, and then place it on a refrigerated shelf, at 35 to 40 degrees Fahrenheit.

The cure is a mixture of salt, sugar, and sodium nitrate in specific amounts. For 100 pounds of meat, you would mix 8 to 10 pounds salt, 1 to 3 pounds sugar, and 2 to 3 ounces sodium nitrate. You shouldn't vary these amounts beyond the ranges given. Too much sugar could create a slimy ham. And as you learned earlier, too much sodium nitrate could prove toxic. Measure carefully. Let the recipes stand as firm guidelines until you gain more experience.

In case you are curious, here's the reason why sodium nitrate is still permitted in dry curing: As you recall, nitrates turn into nitrites. Because nitrites dissipate rapidly, the use of nitrates lets the cure act over an extended period of time, like a time-release chemical. In faster curing methods, only nitrites are used.

You will need approximately 1 1/2 ounces of cure per pound of ham. You will not apply all the cure at once. Rather, you will rub on one-third of the cure at the beginning, one-third during the first week, and the final one-third during the second week.

Thus, a 20-pound ham would require 1 1/2 ounces of cure per pound, or 30 ounces total, divided into three applications, or 10 ounces per application.

Obviously, if you are only dry curing one 20-pound ham, you only need to mix about 2 pounds of cure, not 10. So be sure that you reduce the amount of salt, sugar, and sodium nitrate accordingly. If you want to weigh out just the right amount of sodium nitrate, you could use a gram scale for additional accuracy. There are 28.3 grams per ounce.

It is very important that you get a uniform cure. Using three applications gives the most even salt penetration. Apply the cure evenly and without a lot of rough rubbing. But be sure and get plenty of cure on the shank end.

Penetration of salt requires seven days per inch thickness. A 14-to-16-pound ham is 4 to 5 inches thick, and requires 28 to 35 days curing. An 18-to-20-pound ham is 5 to 6 inches thick and requires 35 to 42 days curing. A 22-to-24-pound ham is 6 to 7 inches thick, and requires about 42 to 49 days curing.

You can cure the hams in a refrigerator at 35 to 40 degrees Fahrenheit or, weather permitting, in a cold curing room. For every day the curing temperature falls below freezing, you should add on an extra day of curing.

After approximately 40 days curing on the shelf, wash off or brush off the cure, and return the ham to the refrigerated shelf for 20 to 30 days of salt equalization. This resting period is very important, as it allows the salt time to move from the surfaces of the ham equally through the entire piece of meat. This process of salt equalization reduces the chances of later spoilage. After equalization, you can smoke your hams for a day or two, between 70 and 90 degrees Fahrenheit (no higher), until the skin takes on a rich brown color.

After smoking, you can age the country ham from four months to a year. The preferable aging schedule is six months at slightly less than 70 degrees Fahrenheit for the best flavor. During aging, you will have to protect the ham from insects, for obvious reasons. But you still want air circulation around the ham.

The aging is quite a science in itself. In fact, curing country-style hams is a home business possibility for anyone who wanted to study it in detail. If you built a 1000-square-foot building for a home country ham curing operation (and knew what you were doing), you could handle 500 hams every 60 days!

One method of protecting hams from insects is to place the ham in a brown paper bag, that is tied at the top, and then placed in a second bag, that is also tied. In some locales, the ham is first coated with the following substances (per 100 pounds of ham): 1 pound black pepper,

1 quart New Orleans molasses, 1 pound brown sugar, 1 ounce saltpeter and 1 ounce cayenne pepper. I suppose that's an edible insect repellent.

Country hams are a gourmet treat and it might be exciting to experiment with making them at home. But you should realize that the long curing-aging process and rigid temperature requirements offer numerous opportunities for bacterial spoilage and/or insect damage. Moreover, some people find country hams too salty. But they sure would look terrific hanging from the kitchen ceiling. If you feel like taking a bit of a risk, give them a try.

BRINE-CURED HAMS AND BACONS

The farmers in my area prefer to use a shorter curing method called brine curing. Brine curing is really only a partial cure. Your hams and bacons will only keep two or three weeks with this method. Consequently, most people freeze them, and then thaw them when needed.

To brine hams, you mix a brine in a crock and then immerse the hams into the brine or pickle for a number of days. Before immersion, you inject (or pump) the same brine into the hams with a special syringe that has several holes in the needle. Essentially you are pickling them from the inside and from the outside simultaneously.

A basic sweet pickle cure: 8 pounds salt, 3 pounds sugar, and 2 1/2 tablespoons sodium nitrite dissolved in 4 1/2 gallons water. (As you recall, according to government regulations, it is now recommended that only sodium nitrite be used in brined products.)

This recipe is certainly an easy enough pickle to mix up, but interestingly enough, most farmers in my area send their hams out to be cured at "professional" curing shops (another home business opportunity to be sure!)

The professional shop is equipped with refrigerated aging rooms, temperature and humidity controlled smokers, electric powered pumps—the works. The costly equipment en-

sures a cured product that comes out right every time, not just some of the time.

At P.J.'s Meats—the professional curing shop in my area—Mitch Dowling (the son of professional slaughterer Bill Dowling) runs the meat-curing operation. Because Mitch cures hams and other meats all the time and goes to annual conferences to learn ever more of the scientific lore surrounding curing, he has the expertise that separates a pro from a novice.

Mitch practices brine or pickle curing only, and his methods are definitely applicable to a home-preserver if you want to give them as try. He uses a manufactured brine which comes in two parts: Bag A and Bag B. The 3 pound, 11 ounce mixture in Bag A contains 54.2 percent phosphate, 8.8 percent sugar and sodium erythorbate—the nitrosamine inhibitor!—5.3 percent hydrolized vegetable protein, 4.9 percent monosodium glutamate, (MSG), plus flavorings. The 12 pound mixture in Bag B is primarily a mixture of salt, maple sugar, cane sugar, and dextrose, plus .75 percent sodium nitrite, and 2 percent propylene glycol. Mitch dissolves Bag A in 10 gallons of water, and then adds the cure which is Bag B.

You might wonder why I list these ingredients. I must admit I have been an avid label reader ever since I moved back to the land. I think many of us grow our own food because we want to know what we are eating, and when it comes to curing, knowing what is in the cure is quite important. Some brine mixes, manufactured for home use, do not follow federal law. They still contain sodium nitrate, and do not contain nitrosamine inhibitors. Therefore, I would advise against using such pickle mixes, as well as ones that aren't labeled. You should know what is in them. That is your right.

Mitch thinks the maple sugar mix he uses at P.J.'s Meats is a good one taste-wise. And P.J.'s Meats has won prizes for their hams with this mix. It does not contain nitrates, and does have a nitrosamine inhibitor. However, it contains additives to enhance flavor, color, and moisture content, which you might or might not find objectionable.

To cure a ham, Mitch first pumps or injects it with brine, increasing its weight by 20 percent in a boneless ham, or 15 percent in a ham with a bone in it. Therefore, if your ham (with bone) weighs 20 pounds, you should pump it with your syringe until it weights 23 pounds. You'll probably want to use a scale, but Mitch does this by feel. "After you've pumped a thousand hams, you don't need to weigh them," says Mitch.

There are two methods to pump ham. If you can find the artery that runs into the ham (you should remember to leave this intact when butchering), then you can pump into it and the pickle will follow the original arterial system.

Although he is not averse to artery pumping, Mitch Dowling says he feels more secure with the method he uses—known as spray pumping. He inserts a set of spray needles into the hams. The needles are attached to an electric pump, and he literally pricks the ham from all directions, while the needles spurt brine into the ham. He doesn't worry about the small holes the needles make in the hams because he says they close back up automatically.

Most home-preservers will use a hand-operated pump with a single needle. You will want to be sure to inject enough pickle around the bone, because this is the area where the ham is most likely to spoil. Figure 14-1 shows how to pump a ham at home using a syringe with a single needle.

Mitch explains that if the cure isn't injected evenly, sections of the ham will turn green in the smokehouse. "You can still eat hams that get green spots, but they don't look nice and they will only keep for two to three days, whereas properly cured hams keep two to three weeks," says Mitch.

After the ham is thoroughly pumped, it is put in a brine of the same solution. Mitch leaves his hams in the brine for six days. After he removes them, he rinses them off, puts them in a stock-inette bag, lets them dry for an hour, and puts them in the smokehouse. He smokes them to 148 degrees Fahrenheit—eight hours for boneless hams, and ten to twelve hours for regular hams. (More on smoking later in this chapter.) At P.J.'s Meats, Mitch Dowling soaks his bacons in the same maple sugar brine that he uses for the hams, but he doesn't inject the bacons with brine. "If you injected bacons, they would get too salty and too watery," Mitch explains.

After soaking the bacons for six days in the brine, he smokes them for six hours at 110 to 120 degrees Fahrenheit. During the last hour he

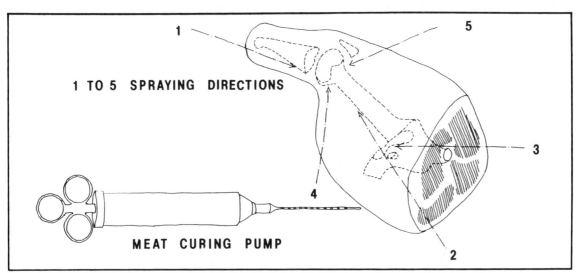

1 TO 5 SPRAYING DIRECTIONS

MEAT CURING PUMP

Fig. 14-1. How to spray a ham with a meat curing pump.

raises the temperature to 128 degrees. Mitch makes bacon from pork, but he says that you can just as easily make bacon from beef. The recipe is just the same.

BRINE-CURING HAMS
AND BACONS AT HOME

If you plan to cure and smoke bacon at home, don't forget that handy tool for hanging bacon in the smoker. It is an official bacon hanger (like a clothes hanger) with prongs, and it is the exact width of a slab of bacon (Fig. 14-2).

I still see a lot of recipes for home-cured bacon that call for a dry-curing mix containing 8 pounds salt, 3 pounds brown sugar, and 3 ounces sodium nitrate. To my way of thinking, this is not a mix you would want to use. First, it has nitrate in it, which is now prohibited for use in bacon. Second, it has no nitrosamine inhibitors as required under the law.

Please try to use a cure for bacon that meets current federal regulations. A brine with nitrite at no more than 120 parts per million, plus sodium erythorbate or sodium ascorbate or Vitamin C at 550 parts per million is essential. As you recall, bacon can form carcinogenic nitrosamines during frying. It is the one cured meat that you don't want to take any chances with. At this writing, the USDA is proposing reducing nitrite levels for bacon lower than ever before. A new processing method, called the "Wisconsin Process" shows promise. It uses lactic-acid forming bacteria along with smaller portions of sodium nitrite (40 to 80 parts per million) to give full protection against botulism.

Hopefully a nitrite replacement will be available in the near future. If you are in doubt about the most up-to-date information on curing bacon, your best bet is to check with the USDA or your local agricultural agent before processing bacon at home.

When brining bacon or hams, cleanliness is essential. The container must be clean and the water must be pure. You can boil water to

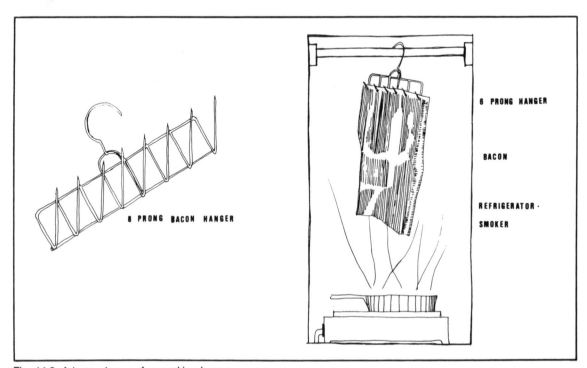

Fig. 14-2. A bacon hanger for smoking bacon.

purify it, but you must cool it to 38 degrees Fahrenheit before the meat is put in the brine. The brine must cover the meat (you can use a weight), but the meat shouldn't be packed so tightly that the brine can't reach every surface of every piece. You can pack bacons skin side down, overlapping them at right angles to each other.

You might want to practice overhauling the meat as a safety precaution. Overhauling simply means taking all the pieces of meat out of the brine, stirring up the brine, and then rearranging the meat in the brine in a different order. If you overhaul, you will have less chances for spoilage.

You want to watch out for mold on the top of the brine, as well as a ropy brine. It's best to skim off the mold, the same as you do in making dill pickles. A little mold probably won't hurt, but you don't want it to get too thick or hard.

Ropy brine is thick like syrup or egg whites. If this happens, you should immediately change the brine. Take out the meat, scrub it off with a bristle brush and warm water, and put it back in a different, clean container, under new brine. However, if the cure was half over, the new brine should only be two-thirds the strength of the original brine. And if the cure was three-fourths over, the new brine should only be half strength.

You can cure bacon and hams in the same sweet pickle brine mentioned earlier: 8 pounds salt, 3 pounds sugar, and 2 1/2 tablespoons sodium nitrite dissolved in 4 1/2 gallons water. You'll want to weigh the meat down, so that it can't float up over the top of the brine. And it should be kept cold, at 36 to 40 degrees Fahrenheit. It's heat that can cause you problems with your brine.

A 10-pound bacon will cure in about 15 days in this brine. Keep accurate records of your brine mix, length of cure—all the details. Then, if your family finds the bacon too salty (or too mild), you can make changes accordingly.

Dennis and Natalie Atkinson use the following recipe for their hams and bacon: 1 1/2 gallons cold water, with 1 pound salt, 5 ounces Prague Powder Number 1 (a sodium nitrite-salt mix), and 5 ounces brown sugar. They inject the hams, and keep them in the brine for seven days. The bacons (and hocks) are not injected. They are kept in the brine for five days.

After curing, Dennis and Natalie smoke the bacons and hams. They let the bacons hang to dry for a half hour and then put them in their smokehouse, pre-heated to 135 degrees Fahrenheit. They leave the dampers wide open to dry the bacons fully, and then close them down to one-quarter open, and smoke the bacons to an internal temperature of 128 degrees Fahrenheit. Then they let the fire die down and leave the bacons hanging in the smokehouse until the color becomes rich and dark.

The hams go into the smoker as the bacons come out. They are smoked for 12 hours at 120 degrees with the draft open. The temperature is then raised to 138 degrees for eight hours, with the drafts half closed. Finally, the draft is fully closed, and the temperature is increased until the hams reach an internal temperature of 152 degrees. This cooks them fully.

HOW TO MAKE SALAMI AND OTHER CURED MEATS

I think you will have great fun making salamis at home from your own meat. Munching a slice of your own spiced, hard salami should give you a stiff dose of self-sufficient ecstasy. Such accomplishments are really what homesteading is all about. Yet, in my area, 99 percent of the pig farmers send their pork out to the professional curers rather than cure and smoke their meats at home. I have no idea why people don't want to make their own cold cuts, except for the fact that it does involve quite a few hours of work.

Dennis and Natalie Atkinson make salamis at home, an impressive example of husband-wife cooperation. Dennis thaws some venison (frozen since hunting season) and some veal (from Little Guy). The night before the great salami stuffing ritual, Dennis grinds up the venison and veal, and mixes them in a 50-50 ratio, along with frozen ground fat (back fat and leaf fat) from the pig he has recently slaughtered. He also adds some soy protein concentrate to hold it all together, plus sodium nitrite, garlic, sugar, and spices. He refrigerates the mix overnight, to let everything mellow together.

The next morning Dennis packs the chilled mix into his sausage press, trying to make sure that he leaves no air spaces. "If there aren't any air spaces in the press," explains Dennis, "then there won't be air spaces in the salamis. Air spaces are a big no-no," he adds, as he fists the ground meat in the press. "They can cause you lots of trouble down the line."

Making salamis definitely takes two laborers. While Dennis huffs and puffs over the manually cranked press, Natalie attaches the 5-inch casings to the press nozzle, and makes sure the salamis get firmly packed into the casings (Fig. 14-3). "This is a great way to use up odds and ends," explains Natalie. "These salamis are made entirely from scraps. But you still have to trim up the scraps very carefully. You can't use any gristle at all. Clogs up the grinder."

"And you should try to use frozen fat," Dennis adds. "If the fat is warm, it sticks to the inside of the grinder and won't pass through. Warm fat can also smear on the sides of the casings, so you need to keep the ground mix chilled thoroughly while you stuff it."

As each casing fills tightly with the chopped meat, Natalie ties it off with a butterfly knot, a type of knot that can't loosen as the salami dries and gets smaller. Next she takes a needle and methodically pops little holes through the casing, wherever she sees air spaces lurking in her salamis (Fig. 14-4). Dennis and his friend Steve Belial proudly take the five salamis to the smoker (Fig. 14-5). These particular salamis are cooked salamis, a soft-textured cured meat available for immediate consumption after smoking.

Dennis' recipe is as follows: 4 pounds lean venison, 4 pounds lean veal, 2 pounds pork fat, 2 tablespoons powdered fructose, 4 cloves fresh garlic, 2 tablespoons nutmeg, 1 tablespoon ground pepper, 2 cups soy protein concentrate, 6 tablespoons salt, and 2 teaspoons Prague

Powder Number 1 (a sodium nitrite-salt mix—if using straight sodium nitrite, the amount would be .9 gram).

Like any good cook, Dennis adjusts the recipe to his tastes and supplies on hand. Because he has both venison and veal available, he creates his own recipe using these two ingredients, with the ratio of meat to fat at four to one. He adds the soy concentrate to help bind everything together. When he is out of soy, he uses dry milk instead. As for garlic, he uses more than some people might want, but he is a garlic lover.

Dennis places the salamis in his smoker (Fig. 14-6). He smokes them at 130 degrees Fahrenheit for half an hour, and then raises the temperature to 165 degrees Fahrenheit for about two hours, until the salamis reach 155 degrees Fahrenheit. In smoking there is about a ten degree difference in temperature between the smokehouse temperature, and the internal temperature of the meat.

Next Dennis plunges the cooked (smoked) salamis in a bucket of cold water, and lets his garden hose run over them to cool them down. He refrigerates them overnight, and by morning the family munches venison-veal salami—that slices perfectly.

Dennis also makes a dry-cured hard salami. He uses 2 1/2 pounds veal, 6 1/2 pounds pork, 1 pound pork fat, 1 teaspoon black pepper, 1 teaspoon ginger, 2 teaspoons garlic powder, 1 ounce powdered fructose, 1/2 cup salt, plus 2 teaspoons Prague Powder Number 2, a nitrate-nitrite-salt curing agent. The reason for the sodium nitrate here is that this salami will be aged three months, and nitrite alone would simply dissipate too quickly.

After grinding and mixing all ingredients, he refrigerates them for three days, and then stuffs them in the casings (Dennis uses storebought sheep casings). He hangs the dry-cured salamis in the house for a few days, and then moves them to the cheese cooler (50 degrees Fahrenheit) for three months. As you notice, dry-cured salami is not smoked, so it is a good recipe for folks who haven't yet built a smoker.

Fig. 14-3. Dennis and Natalie Atkinson work together to make salami.

Fig. 14-4. Removing air bubbles from salami by pricking it with a pin.

Fig. 14-5. Steve Belial (left) and Dennis Atkinson (right) carry the salamis to the smoker.

Fig. 14-6. The salamis hang in the Atkinson's smoker, which they rigged from an old refrigerator and electric hot plate.

As I mentioned earlier, in tying off salamis you should use a butterfly knot. This is a knot that ties off the top of the casing so it cannot come undone, even though the meat has shrunk in size. To make a butterfly knot: when the casing is full, twist it round and round from the top, to force the meat tightly together in the body of the salami. Then tie a knot with string at the base of the twisted casing. Untwist the casing, and take the string and criss-cross it down the middle of the extra casing, so that it divides in two parts like a butterfly. Figure 14-7 shows a sausage tied with a butterfly knot, plus all tools needed for sausage making at home.

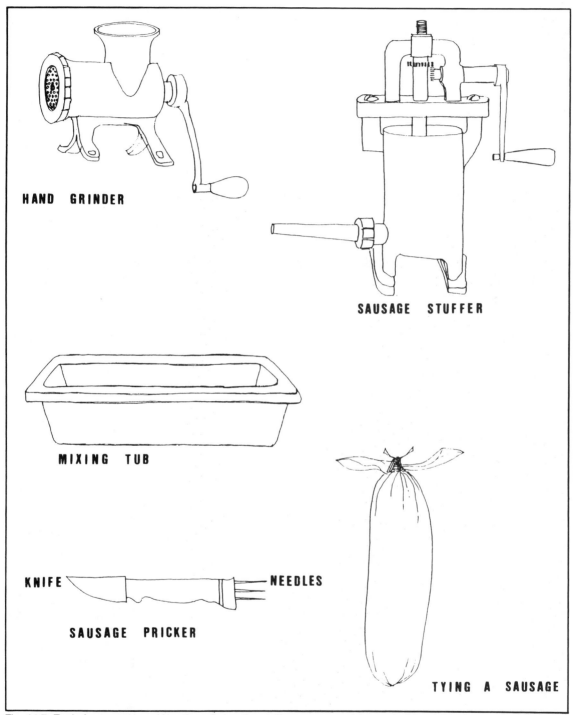

HAND GRINDER

SAUSAGE STUFFER

MIXING TUB

KNIFE — NEEDLES

SAUSAGE PRICKER

TYING A SAUSAGE

Fig. 14-7. Tools for sausage making: the grinder, the stuffer, sausage pricker and mixing tub—plus a salami tied with a butterfly knot.

RECIPES

Before moving on to smokers—how to build your own smoker and how to use it to finish your cured meats—let me give you a few recipes for unsmoked creations that I gathered here in the woods. Please note that none of these recipes call for the addition of nitrates or nitrites.

Basic Fresh Pork Sausage

20 pounds fresh pork trimmings—2/3 lean to
   1/3 fat
1/2 cup salt
6 tablespoons freshly ground sage
3 tablespoons ground pepper
3 teaspoons ground ginger and/or ground
   nutmeg
2 cups ice water

Put the meat through the food grinder twice; add seasonings and put through a third time. Mix it all thoroughly on a large breadboard. You can knead it until the liquid is absorbed and the sausage is doughy. The water is in there to keep the sausage from crumbling when it is sliced for frying.

You can only freeze seasoned sausage for two or three months. However, you can freeze unseasoned ground pork for a longer time, and then thaw it and season it, when you wish.

You can make any type of sausage you wish. You can make it fat-free or salt-free. You can add whatever spices you like, and come up with your own secret recipes. Some possibilities are: cayenne pepper, garlic, onions, oregano, paprika, fennel seeds, thyme, marjoram, and coriander. Of course, you can buy packages of pre-mixed sausage seasonings, but why not be creative yourself? If you wish, you can add liquid smoke.

You can stuff this sausage into casings, make patties, or keep it loose. As long as you are not smoking this sausage in a smoker, you do not need to add sodium nitrite to it. Just grind the meat, mix in the spices, and refrigerate (or freeze) immediately. The variations are endless.

Liver Sausage

4 pounds pork chunks
1 pound liver
2 cups beef broth
2 teaspoons liquid smoke
5 teaspoons salt
2 teaspoons pepper
1/4 teaspoon nutmeg
1/4 teaspoon allspice
1/2 teaspoon ginger
1/2 teaspoon onion powder
1/2 teaspoon cayenne

Cook pork chunks in water, covered, for 2 hours. Grind the cooked pork and liver. Add broth and spices. Stuff into 2-inch casings and simmer in water (175 degrees F.) until it floats. Plunge into ice water and chill for 30 minutes. Refrigerate.

Home-Cured Franks

2 1/2 pounds pork
1 1/4 pounds veal
1 1/4 pounds beef
3 pounds ice
1 cup cracker meal
1/4 cup salt
1/4 cup corn syrup
2 teaspoons pepper

Grind pork, veal, and beef, with half the ice, until the consistency of hamburger. Add remaining ingredients, and grind until a smooth pastry texture is achieved. (Use a food processor.)

Stuff in small casings and link into the length frank you want. Soak casings for about an hour before stuffing, so they will be pliable.

Cook in steam or hot (170 degrees F.) water for about 15 minutes to an internal temperature of 155 degrees F. Rinse in cold running water 5 minutes. Immerse in ice water 10 minutes. Hang at room temperature 15 minutes. Refrigerate immediately. Keep frozen until ready to use because these are very perishable.

Headcheese—a homemade lunch meat

1 large pig head
2 1/2 pounds salt
5 ounces black pepper
1 ounce red pepper
1 ounce ground cloves
1 ounce coriander
2 ounces sweet marjoram

Split the head, remove the eyes, clean the ears and nostrils. Place the cleaned pieces of head, the tongue, the heart, and some lean pork trimmings in water and cook until well done, and the meat easily comes off the bones.

Grind meat and cover it with broth. Add seasonings—the salt, pepper, and other possible seasonings as desired. You can keep tasting to make sure you like how it is being seasoned.

Pack the seasoned headcheese tightly into a loaf pan. If possible, weight it down. Refrigerate. When it is firm, slice and eat.

Headcheese Sausages

Make headcheese as above, and stuff into sausage casings. Cook the sausages in the original broth until they float. Chill in cold water. Refrigerate.

Panhas

Simmer pig's head as for head cheese. Remove meat, discard bones, and grind meat.

Strain broth and skim off fat. Return meat to broth and then thicken the broth with corn meal. Use three or four parts broth to one part meal. (As in making gravy, moisten the meal with a little broth, before adding to the total broth. This prevents lumping).

Season to taste with the same seasonings you use in headcheese. Cook for 30 minutes stirring frequently, and then pour into shallow pans to cool. Slice and serve.

Chorizo—hot sausage

6 pounds pork
1/2 cup vinegar
1 tablespoon oregano
8 cloves garlic
1/4 cup chili powder or paprika
2 teaspoons black pepper
2 tablespoons salt
1/2 teaspoon cumin
2 tablespoons cayenne pepper

Grind pork and mix in all ingredients. Stuff in casings. Hang to dry. Refrigerate. To serve, pan fry. This sausage is hot, but I like it that way. If you want it milder (or hotter), add less (or more) cayenne pepper.

BUILDING A SMOKEHOUSE

There are several types of smokehouses you can build on your farm: a metal drum smokehouse, a shed smokehouse, a refrigerator/barrel smokehouse, or a refrigerator/hot plate smokehouse. The basic design for all four of these smokers is very similar; in fact, all four work on exactly the same principle. They only differ in size and permanence. Once you understand the basic concept of building your smoker, you'll be able to design your own original smokehouse from equipment at hand. And rest assured, if you are not inclined toward do-it-yourself projects this season, there are handy little electric smokers that you can purchase from numerous suppliers.

If you decide to build a smokehouse, it needs to have the four following features: a source of smoke, a place to hold the smoke, a method to hold the meat in the smoke, and a draft-damper near the bottom and near the top. You'll want to operate your smokehouse in a safe location, away from all combustibles. But you won't be raising the temperature inside the smoker above 200 degrees Fahrenheit (like a very slow oven), so you shouldn't have to worry about a melt-down.

Metal Drum Smokehouse with Trench. To build a metal drum smokehouse, find a 55-gallon drum (that is not contaminated) and knock out both ends. Dig a hole in the ground that is 2 feet deep, with a circumference smaller than the circumference of the drum, and place the drum over that hole. Find a lid to cover the top of the drum.

A metal drum can hold about 20 pounds of meat. You need to figure out the best way to hang your meat inside the drum. You can drill holes near the top and run your dowels through them. Or you can run the dowels across the top of the drum. If so, you'll have an airspace left where the lid rests on the dowels, but you can fill that by hanging clean burlap over the top.

Dig a 12-foot-long trench, 6 inches wide and 6 inches deep, connecting the hole under the drum with another 2-foot-deep hole—which will be your firepit. This firepit (and trench) should be dug on the side of the drum from which the prevailing winds come. There should also be a slight slope uphill, from the firepit to the drum. Remember, smoke goes up!

You can line the firepit with fire bricks, and run a pipe down the trench. Or you can simply leave the pit and trench au naturale, and cover the trench with a board topped with dirt. You'll need a metal cover for the firepit, so you can make the fire and adjust the draft. Figure 14-8 (top left) shows a metal drum smokehouse with trench.

A Shed Smokehouse with Trench. If you want to build a fancier—and more traditional—smokehouse, you might want to actually build a little house. You can then store meat in the house as well. The basic principles will be just the same as in a metal drum smokehouse. The house should be air tight, insect proof, and contain a good draft system.

Build a brick or stone fireplace, slightly downhill, and on the side of the house-to-be from which the prevailing wind flows. As always, remember that you want that smoke to travel up into your smokehouse.

Your permanent firepit should have a front door that you can open and close. You'll feed your wood, chips, and sawdust into the pit through the door. The door can also serve as a draft control.

If you wish you can build covered grates into the top of your firebox and turn it into a dual purpose unit—smoker firebox and barbecue pit. You'll need to close off the connection to the smokehouse while barbecuing. A piece of sheet metal that can fit on the back of the firepit should do the trick.

Connect the firepit with the shed-to-be via 6-inch sewer pipe. The pipe will come into the smokehouse in the center of the concrete floor. You'll want the pipe in place (with a bug screen) before you make your pour.

Of course you could get away with a mud floor, but concrete is much nicer for sturdiness, cleanliness, tightness, and permanence. To control settling of the concrete floor, build it on top of four concrete footings, set below the frost line.

Build the shed 6 feet high and 4 feet square. It can be a simple 2- x -4 stud structure. On the sides, nail up horizontal notched 2- x -4s to hold up the sticks on which the meat hangs. If you wish, you can put in shelves, hooks, benches—whatever.

The entire front side of the smoke shed can be your hinged door. Or you can build a smaller door. On one side, near the roof, make a hinged vent with a handle. You'll want to be able to operate the vent from the outside of the building. The vent should also have a fly screen. Figure 14-8 (bottom right) illustrates the shed smokehouse.

Refrigerator/Trash Barrel Smokehouse. If you aren't inclined toward building a shed, you can easily make a smoker from an old refrigerator and attach it to a trash barrel. You could use a trench system as described in the first example (metal drum smokehouse), or you could use an above-ground connection between the metal trash barrel and the refrigerator.

The lid of the trash barrel serves as the

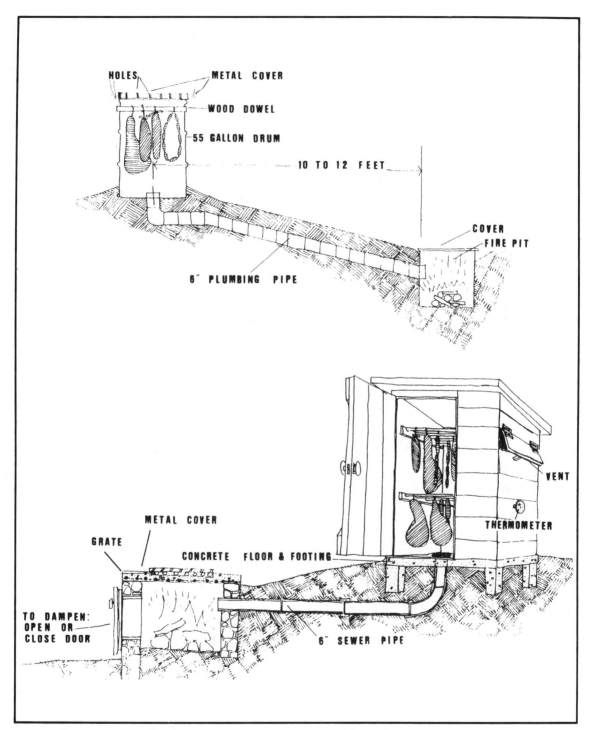

Fig. 14-8. Two types of homemade smokehouses: the metal drum smokehouse (top) and the shed smokehouse (bottom).

lower damper. Put sand in the barrel fire chamber, and use an old skillet for the fire, setting it on the sand.

Place the barrel slightly below the level of the refrigerator smoker, so the smoke will rise. Connect the refrigerator by a 6-inch stovepipe, from 4 to 10 feet long.

Cut a 6-inch hole in the lower side of the refrigerator, and connect the stove pipe there. The smoke enters the bottom side of the refrigerator and rises upward. You can place a perforated plywood shelf (full of 1/2-to-3/4-inch holes) slightly above the 6-inch entrance. This plywood shelf helps spread the smoke evenly in the chamber.

The smoke escapes the refrigerator through a stove pipe in the roof with a damper and cap, just like a woodstove has. You'll want to put screens at the smoke entrance and exit points, to keep out curious insects. The top drawing in Fig. 14-9 illustrates a refrigerator/barrel smokehouse.

This particular smokehouse belongs to another California writer, Neva Beach. There are undoubtedly as many possible smoker designs as there are back-to-the-land folks. What you want is a way to hold your meat in a smoky environment—without burning down the house! It is not all that complicated to build yourself a smoker. You can probably get one together in less than a day, with junk you already have around the homestead.

Refrigerator/Hot Plate Smokehouse. This is really easy—for folks who have electricity. Take an old, broken refrigerator or freezer, and remove the motor from it to make it lighter and easier to handle. Clean it out, and put an electric hot plate in it. You can run the cord out a hole, or simply close the door on it. Put a sturdy metal pan on the hot plate to hold your wood chips.

You should install a thermometer to keep track of the temperature inside your smokehouse. It's best if you can read your thermometer from the outside of the refrigerator. (You could also put a thermometer in the three previously described smokehouses. The sensor should be on the inside, with the recording information on the outside.)

You also need to put in two sets of airholes with dampers, one on the side of the refrigerator to draw in air, and one on the top, to let air out. You'll want to be able to regulate both of these dampers—fully open, half open, and closed. An ultra-simple venting system is to drill a circle of holes and cover them over with sliding or rotating pieces of metal. You can use the shelves that came with the refrigerator, or you can screw hooks into the top to hang the pieces of meat, or both. As you might have noticed in Fig. 14-6, this is the type of smoker that Dennis and Natalie Atkinson use. They keep it indoors, inside a wooden storage structure. The bottom drawing in Fig. 14-9 also shows this type of refrigerator/hot plate smokehouse in more detail.

Nineteenth Century Smokehouse. Essentially smokehouses haven't really changed in the last hundred years. I have a marvelous set of old books called *The Annual Register of Rural Affairs*. The author describes the "fire-proof smoke-house" owned by Honorable George Geddes of Syracuse, New York:

"The left-hand half of the building is occupied with the smoke-house. The ash-pit, surrounded by stone walls and a layer of stone beneath, laid in water-lime mortar and securely coated with the same, keeps the ashes dry, and no water can enter. The ash-pit is entered by an iron door. Over it is a brick arch, containing several holes the size of a half brick, through which the smoke passes into the smoke apartment above—which is entered by the outside door on the left end of the building, by the assistance of a step ladder. This smoke-room is 6 by 10 feet in the clear. The ventilating window at the end, and the ventilating chimney at the top, are both opened when the hams are smoking, and closed shut when the operation is completed. The top of the arch forms the floor of the smoke-room.

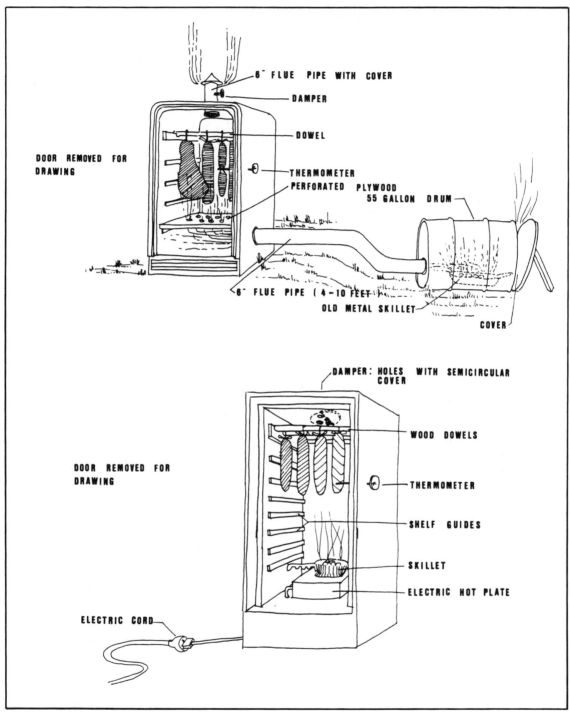

6" FLUE PIPE WITH COVER
DAMPER
DOOR REMOVED FOR DRAWING
DOWEL
THERMOMETER
PERFORATED PLYWOOD
55 GALLON DRUM
6" FLUE PIPE (4-10 FEET)
OLD METAL SKILLET
COVER

DAMPER: HOLES WITH SEMICIRCULAR COVER
DOOR REMOVED FOR DRAWING
WOOD DOWELS
THERMOMETER
SHELF GUIDES
SKILLET
ELECTRIC HOT PLATE
ELECTRIC CORD

Fig. 14-9. Two more types of homemade smokehouses: the refrigerator/barrel smokehouse (top) and the refrigerator/hot plate smokehouse (bottom).

A large number of hams may be placed in this room by the following arrangement: Pieces of hard-wood plank, eight inches wide, and long enough to reach across the room, rest on a ledge or projection from the walls on each side. These pieces of plank have hooks driven in on both edges, far enough apart to receive the hams, so that a row may be hung on each side. When full, each is pushed along to one side, and another filled, and so on till all are in their places. The ventilators above are then opened, and smoke is started on the heap of ashes below. For this purpose cobs are used, or unseasoned maple, or body hickory. The smoking should be slow. By the time the smoke has passed up through the openings in the arch, it has become cold, and cannot heat the hams. Ten or twelve days will usually be enough for the completion of the operation, when the ventilators at the end and in the chimney above are closed shut. The hams being now kept perfectly dark and thoroughly excluded from the air outside, they will keep in good condition; flies will do no injury through the summer with a small fire started once a month, and with the upper ventilator partly open at the time. This obviates the common and troublesome task of encasing the hams in muslin, whitewashing them, or packing them in oats or ashes."*

Figure 14-10 gives a 20th century artist's interpretation of the 19th century smokehouse.

HOW TO SMOKE MEAT

Smoking meat really hasn't changed much in 100 years—or for that matter, since earliest history. Essentially, smoking meat produces colors and flavors that many people enjoy. Smoking also helps in preserving meat to a certain extent. And finally, smoking can be used as a technique to cook meat.

---

*J.J. Thomas, *The Annual Register of Rural Affairs*, vol. 7 (Albany: Luther Tucker and Sons, 1873-1875).

The only proper fuels for smoking are hardwoods, such as hickory, oak, beech, maple, pecan, sweet bay, alder, manzanita, buttonwood, apple, cherry, pear, and other fruit-tree wood. Never use soft woods or woods with pine needles like pine, cedar or fir. Their resinous smoke will give the meat a bad flavor.

Generally, you use sawdust or woodchips from these hardwoods, rather than bigger pieces. Remember, you are looking for smoke, not fire.

Neva Beach chainsaws oak or apple wood into thin wafers. She does her chainsawing over a dropcloth, in order to collect the sawdust. Once she starts the fire, she smothers it with the sawdust to the desired level of smoke. And she tends her fire often.

If you don't have a source of hardwoods, you can purchase hardwood chips and/or sawdust. You can also use dried corn cobs to smoke meat.

Start your fire and let it burn down to embers. Then put on your chips or sawdust to make smoke. You can dampen sawdust to make smoke. You can also squirt fire with a water bottle to get it to smoke.

When you first put your meat in the smokehouse, you want to have an open draft, so there will be a good flow of air that will dry the meat surfaces. Explains Dennis Atkinson, "You always want to have the drafts open wide at first, to let excess moisture on the outside of the meat evaporate. Otherwise, the outside of the meat will cook before the inside does."

Before smoking hams, wash them off to remove the surface concentration of salt. But let all meats dry off before putting them in the smokehouse. A wet surface will not produce a uniform smoked color.

When you hang up your meats, do not let them touch each other or the sides of your smoker. Neva Beach inserts toothpicks in her meats, to keep them from hitting each other. You'll want to use some sort of hangers for bacons, so they won't curl up. You can use commercial hangers or make your own from a

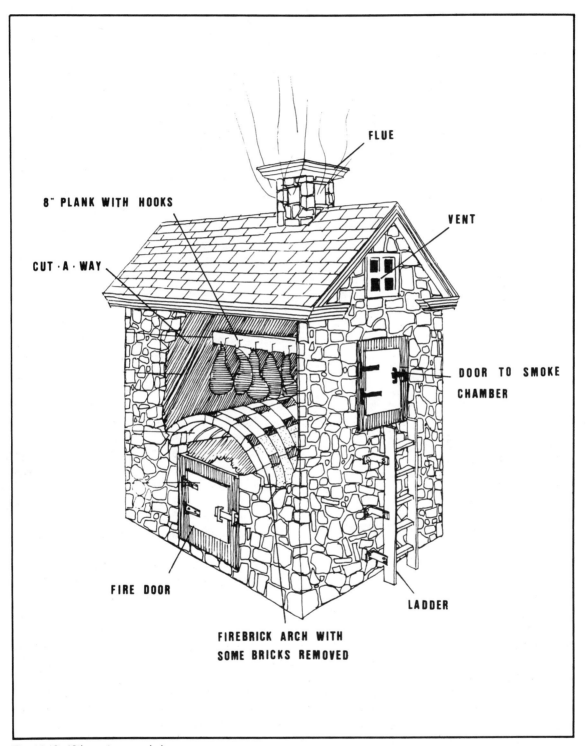

FLUE

8" PLANK WITH HOOKS

VENT

CUT·A·WAY

DOOR TO SMOKE
CHAMBER

FIRE DOOR

LADDER

FIREBRICK ARCH WITH
SOME BRICKS REMOVED

Fig. 14-10. 19th century smokehouse.

non-resinous wood with nails hammered in to hold the bacon.

If you are smoking pork and want to eat it without further cooking, you should be sure to smoke it to an internal temperature of 137 degrees Fahrenheit to make sure you've killed any trichinae. (A friend of mine came down with trichinosis and she was really sick; this is definitely a serious matter.) To test internal temperature of meat, you can use a meat thermometer—just like the kind used for cooking roasts and turkeys.

Another way to determine temperature is to understand that the temperature of the meat in the smokehouse is approximately 10 to 15 degrees less than the smokehouse temperature. So if you raise the smokehouse to 152 to 155 degrees Fahrenheit, you are in good shape.

The USDA gives a suggested schedule for smoking brine cured hams that's somewhat shorter than the schedule Dennis Atkinson follows:

☐ Four hours at 120 degrees Fahrenheit, damper open, smoke off.
☐ Six hours at 140 degrees Fahrenheit, damper one-fourth open, smoke on.
☐ Raise the temperature to 170 degrees Fahrenheit, and hold until the internal temperature reaches 142 to 146 degrees Fahrenheit.
☐ To fully cook the hams, leave them in the smokehouse until their internal temperature reaches 152 to 155 degrees Fahrenheit.

You don't need to smoke bacon to such high temperatures because you are still going to fry it before you eat it. For bacon, the USDA recommends:

☐ Two hours at 115 degrees Fahrenheit, damper open, smoke off.
☐ Two hours at 130 degrees Fahrenheit, damper closed, smoke on.
☐ Raise the smoker temperature to 140 degrees Fahrenheit, until the bacon reaches an internal temperature of 127 to 130 degrees Fahrenheit.

In using your smokehouse, an understanding of temperature is vital. If you generate dense smoke at low temperatures (80 to 110 degrees Fahrenheit) you can really get that smoked flavor onto your meat. This is sometimes called cold smoking. Higher temperatures with less smoke generated (more open draft) speed up the drying process. You can experiment with flavors and speed in your smoker to get the effects that you desire.

As a general rule of thumb, you'll want to keep the draft open initially, driving air past the meat, and thus eliminating the excess moisture that could interfere with the drying process.

You want moisture out before the real drying process can begin. Therefore, don't pack the smoker too tightly, or over its capacity. This would put too much moisture-producing meat in too small a space.

At the end of the smoking period, you'll want less air movement in order to leave in moisture, so that the meat won't shrink so much. It is a little depressing to lose meat to shrinkage in the smokehouse. Once it has shrunk, you can't add weight back on.

You shouldn't raise the heat too rapidly in a smoker. If you do, you can make the meat sweat or exude grease, and this will destroy its appearance. Slow and steady is the rule. You want to smoke the meat to the required temperature, but you don't want to overcook it.

I've been discussing smoking in reference to cured meats, but you can actually use your smoker to cook any meats you like. Essentially, smoking is another method of cooking, and you might enjoy experimenting with smoked venison, smoked tongue, smoked duck, smoked goose—whatever. (You can also smoke fish and cheese.)

You can marinate poultry before smoking for additional flavor. And you can parboil (in marinade and water) tougher cuts like venison or tongue before putting them in the smoker. Part of the enjoyment of having a smoker is being original with how you handle your meats. Your smoker is really just a very slow oven that can give off smoke, along with heat. You can cold smoke—which really doesn't cook the meat, but imparts a smoked flavor—or you can hot smoke and cook the meat as it receives a smoked flavor.

However, don't get so excited about smoking that you replace your normal cooking procedures with this technique. Unfortunately, there are health concerns associated with eating smoked meats. The problem is the smoke. I hate to mention this, but your meat gets that delicious smoked flavor from absorbing smoke, which contains coal tars, which are considered carcinogenic. It is probably wisest to follow a conservative course and eat your cured and/or smoked meats only occasionally, as special treats rather than the daily fare.

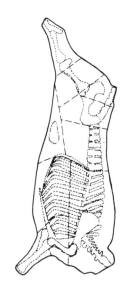

Chapter 15
Meat By-Products

YOUR MAIN GOAL IN RAISING POULTRY, RABBITS, hogs, sheep, goats and/or cattle is to provide healthy meat for your family to eat. I have given you instructions how to grow these meat animals, kill them, cut them up, and preserve their flesh. My work is almost done!

Dead animals, however, contain more than flesh. They have feathers, fur, skin, bones, organs, antlers, fat, blood, intestines, feet—and all of these parts can give you a range of by-products you might enjoy using.

Some of you might want to forego dealing with by-products. If you decide to throw out the head, skin, and intestines, that's your choice. I'm not about to tell you that a back-to-the-land person has to use every conceivable part of an animal to try to prove religiously that self-sufficiency is the best of all worlds. I know better than that. In fact, for many people today, such old-fashioned arts like tanning, soap making, and pillow stuffing have little appeal because they seem to require too much work for questionable rewards. "I would do it, but I just don't have

time," is a common rural lament. Even more frequent is the comment, "I did it once years ago, but I don't remember exactly what I did."

In a book on meat as a farm food, I have no reason to extol the virtues of home crafts. But, if you can squeeze out some extra time, you might end up enjoying the by-products as much as the meat. Sometimes it is important to do things to preserve traditions, to make sure we don't lose track of the total gift that animals give us when we take their lives.

In my daughter's room lies a small floor rug of long white hair. It's the first skin I ever tanned. I gave it to my daughter when she was a young girl and coveted things like animal hair. The brittle goat rug might not look like much, but I am still proud I tanned it. Like the hunters in my area who hang up their deer antlers with pride for all of their family to see, I want my daughter to keep the skin to remind her of her mother's adventures and accomplishments on the homestead.

It's not easy to run a homestead in these final decades of the twentieth century. While most of the population opts for material pleasures and stimulating entertainment, back-to-the-land people focus on the earth, the seasons, the plants, the animals. Your little momentos may be more significant than you realize.

I have the feeling that if you take up soap making, pillow stuffing, tanning—whatever—you will be rewarded with more than a measly bar of soap or a few square feet of leather. Let your children work along with you. The meaning might come in the doing, and the result of your work—well, that will be useful as well.

SAVING RABBIT SKINS

I feel like I left the rabbit raisers stranded, skins in hand, while I killed off and cut up the entire kingdom of domestic farm animals. So please return to the question of how to handle your rabbit skin. As you recall rabbit skins are pulled off like a sweater. The flesh side will be on the outside, and the furry side will be on the inside.

If you want to save skins (and perhaps sell them commercially), you should dry them on shapers, which are also called stretchers. Basically, this is a piece of plywood or a reshaped coat hanger, over which you pull your rabbit skin to dry. The belly will be on one side of the shaper, and the back will be on the other side.

Make your shaper approximately 2 feet long, 7 inches wide at one end and 4 inches wide at the other. Figure 15-1 illustrates this shaper, in wire or plywood. Giant rabbits will require a frame that is 1 1/2 feet long, 4 inches wide at the top, and 9 inches wide at the base. After you gently pull your skin onto the shaper, carefully scrape off any fat that may be clinging to the skin. Note that you are not advised to sprinkle the skin with salt.

You can fasten the skin with clothespins to the edges of the shaper. You want the skin to dry flat and not wrinkle up. Hang the skin in the air, but not in the sun.

You can also dry your rabbit skin flat if you wish. Cut down the belly, and pin it flat onto a board, skin side out, before air drying. If you are storing a rabbit skin in a cardboard box, you should sprinkle it with naphtha flakes (granulated moth balls) to repel moths.

If you wish to try to tan the skin, you can use one of the recipes listed later, for tanning skins with the hair on. But realize that rabbit skins are both small and thin (easy to rip). Therefore, they might not survive the home tanning process, and are better saved stiff and in one piece.

TANNING HIDES AT HOME

The first step in tanning hides from goats, sheep, deer, or cattle is to get the hide off in one lovely piece—without nicks, cuts, blood, or dirt. Before you begin to slaughter an animal, you need to decide: Am I saving that hide or am I throwing it away? If you decide that you want to save the hide, then you must be very careful with it from the start.

Another option is to sell the hide. Properly handled cowhides can make you money. Figure 15-2 shows the proper way to skin a cow if you want to sell the skin or tan it yourself.

Make your cuts on cattle and on all other animals, as described in the slaughtering instructions. In every case, start with the inner hind legs, cut up the center of the belly, and finally cut down the inner forelegs. Thinking of the animal lying on its back, belly up, your basic cutting pattern is like an I. From that basic cutting shape, you need to peel back the skin without slashing it, scoring it, ripping it, or pricking it. Whenever you can fist off the skin, do so. By fisting, you avoid overuse of your knife, and consequently avoid unnecessary damage to the skin.

Keeping the skin clean of dirt and blood is sometimes even more difficult than keeping away knife damage. Frankly, I've had white goats look like pink goats before I realized the mess I was making. I've also had skins fall into the dirt. Luckily, a good soaking in salt water, followed by a wash in water and a mild detergent will clean a sloppy-looking skin.

Your first step in tanning is to look your skin over. You need to trim the edges and scrape off

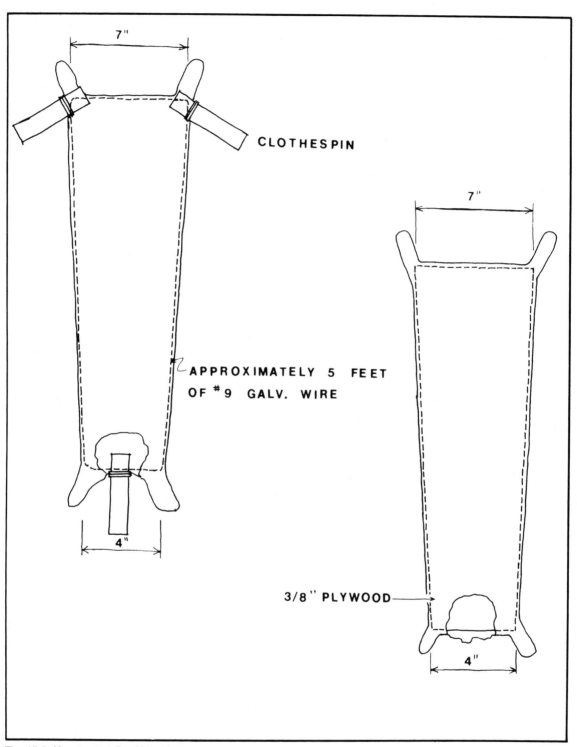

7"

CLOTHESPIN

7"

APPROXIMATELY 5 FEET
OF #9 GALV. WIRE

3/8" PLYWOOD

4"

4"

Fig. 15-1. How to stretch rabbit skins.

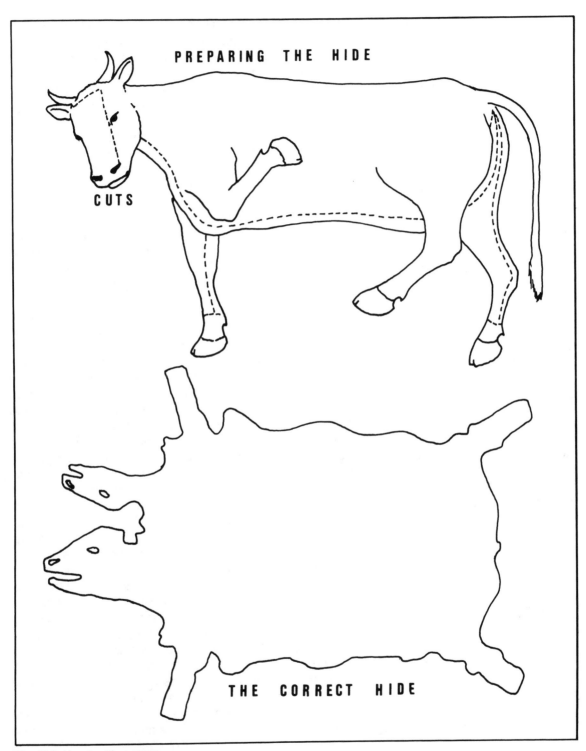

PREPARING THE HIDE

CUTS

THE CORRECT HIDE

Fig. 15-2. How to skin a steer.

any large pieces of meat or fat that have adhered to the hide during skinning. This is not the final scraping (fleshing) you will do later, but just a rough scrape to get rid of any matter that would interfere with the subsequent salting. Even if you plan to send your skin to a commercial tanner, you must do this initial work.

Next you should salt your hide. Salt the flesh side thickly —you can't oversalt. You should leave the salt on for a week or more. You can fold the hide skin side to skin side, roll it up, and put it inside a plastic bag. If you are working with a 60-pound cowhide, you can cut it in four equal sections, running from head to tail for easier handling. However, do not salt hides that you intend to make into buckskin or rawhide. (More on buckskin and rawhide in a moment.)

After the hide has cured with salt, you tan it. You must decide whether you want the fur on (for a rug), or fur off (for leather). Personally, I prefer to leave the fur on; it seems much more unique and a closer memory of the animal.

TANNING WITH THE FUR ON

After salting for two to three weeks, you can resume working on your hide. Or you can keep the salted hide almost indefinitely, until you get around to dealing with it. My neighbor Rex Richardson has a salted hide at home that he's kept for five years. He says it is still in perfect condition, "smells fine and hasn't lost any hair."

If you are intending to store salted hides for any great length of time, you must keep them cold. If they get too warm, they can really start to stink, and it's almost impossible to get that rotten odor back out. They also can get infested with worms, which costs you the hide, and is pretty disgusting to discover.

Therefore, I advise not storing your salted hides rolled up in a ball forever; after all, that has no practical use anyway. Instead, spare some time to work on them (at least within the first year), and you will be proud of your results.

Here's how I approach tanning: When I get started on my salt-cured hide, I wipe off any ex-

cess salt, lay my skin out on the kitchen table, and scrape off all the remaining flesh, fat, membranes, and tissue from the hide. This is called fleshing.

There are special tools for fleshing that have squared off blades or edges. You want to scrape the skin, and not cut it. You can make a fleshing tool from a knife by attaching a handle to the point edge, and filing the edge flat. You can also turn an old garden hoe into a fleshing tool by rounding off the edges so they won't catch on the hide.

There are also special fleshing beams you can make, essentially a barkless log set at a 45-degree angle. Some people find it easier to flesh their hide when it is thrown over such a beam. The top drawing in Fig. 15-3 shows a fleshing beam.

I shouldn't speak so lightly of fleshing. In my opinion, it isn't easy at all. It takes patience and commitment. You must vigorously move your fleshing instrument over the inner side of the hide, without putting any holes in it. You are trying to remove a layer of skin-membrane-flesh, because then your hide will be much easier to soften up through stretching (a later step called staking). You might want to try washing the hide with borax added to the wash water as a preliminary to fleshing. Friends tell me that the borax helps loosen up that top membrane of skin.

When you have completed fleshing (or become fed up with it), it is time to move on to using the tanning agent. I always make an alum-salt tanning solution. I fill a 5-gallon plastic bucket with water and mix 2 1/2 pounds rock salt and 1 pound alum (which I buy at the drugstore). I soak my goat skin in this solution for four or five days, until the inner skin turns completely white. It takes on a slightly greasy feeling, and no longer looks like raw skin.

After taking my skin from the alum-salt-water solution, I rinse it well, wring it out, and then start on the next bit of hard work: stretching the skin. I rub some animal oil on the flesh side of the skin—I use mink oil, but you can also use neat's foot oil or beef tallow. I then pull and

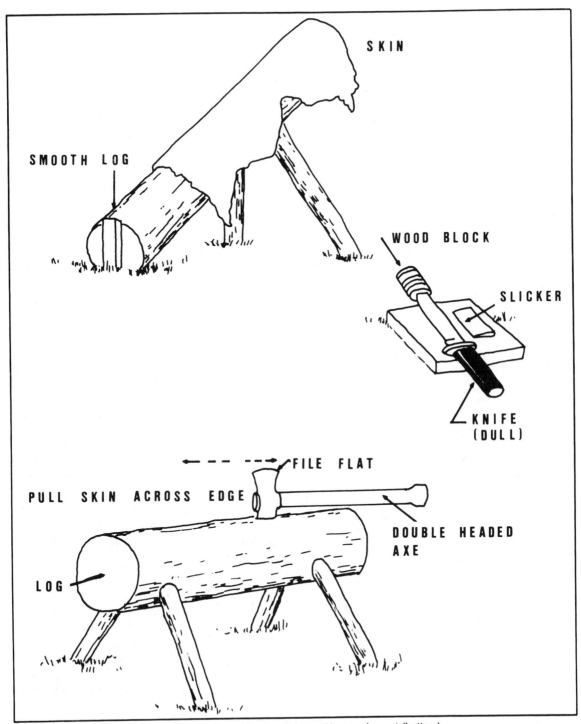

Fig. 15-3. Tools for tanning: the fleshing equipment (top) and the staking equipment (bottom).

tug and stretch, twist and pull some more—for as long as I can hold out. This is staking, or breaking the hide.

If you are staking your skin and your skin starts to dry stiff, then you haven't worked it enough. You can work it over a rail or banister, and you can definitely work it better with a partner than alone. You really can't work it too much.

If you can't find a rail to use for staking, you can make a special staking stand. Mount a log horizontally on legs, and then take a double-headed ax and hit it into the log securely. The side of the ax that is exposed should be blunt. You can now stake your hide back and forth over that mounted ax head. The bottom drawing in Fig. 15-3 shows a staking stand.

My neighbor Rex Richardson has his own staking method. He likes to stretch a rope tight and keep pulling the hide back and forth over the rope. It's a two-person job that applies strong pressure to the hide without damaging it. Rex estimates that it takes a full day to break down a deer hide in this way.

Says Rex, ''The main thing with hides is breaking them down. You must break down all the little channels (fibers) in the hide, or it will get stiff when it dries again. The Eskimos did it with their teeth.''

Sometimes Rex doesn't use any chemicals except salt in tanning his hides. At other times, he uses brains to tan his skins before he works them. It's an easy technique. Just take the brains from the animal you slaughtered, mush them up, and rub them into the skin. The brains work into the skin. You don't have to wash them off.

Essentially, there are many ways to tan skins at home. But if you absolutely must have a soft, supple skin, a perfect skin—a skin to wrap up the baby in the crib—then you should give it a reasonably decent fleshing, salt it, roll it up, and send it out to a professional tanner.

From my experience, you really can't beat professionals at their work. The professional butchers cut meat up a lot better than I do, and skins tanned at commercial tanneries definitely feel a lot softer than my home-tanned skins.

If you want to experiment with home tanning, however, there are a multitude of home recipes you can try. I've seen many variations on my alum-salt recipe. There are alum-salt-sulfuric acid recipes (1 gallon water, 1 ounce alum, 1 quart salt, 1 ounce sulfuric acid); but be careful with the acid. Don't let it splash you. Moreover, after you use a strongly acidic solution like this, you must neutralize the hide by soaking it in baking soda mixed with water.

Another alum soak calls for dissolving 1 pound alum in 1 gallon water, and in a separate container dissolving 1/4 cup crystallized sodium carbonate (washing soda) and 1/2 pound salt in 1/2 gallon water. Pour the second mix slowly into the first mix, stirring hard.

And another acid mix contains 2 gallons water, 2 ounces battery acid, and 2 pounds salt. As always, be careful adding acid to water. Whatever solution you choose, keep the hide immersed in it by weighting it down, and give it a daily stir to make sure all surfaces are receiving the chemicals.

You don't always have to soak hides to tan them. You might prefer using a dry tan or paste tan. You can mix equal parts of salt, alum, and saltpeter and rub this on to the skin and then fold it together. Or you can rub the skin with an alum-saltpeter-bran paste and again fold it skin to skin until it has broken down the hide. Other possibilities include a soap flake-oatmeal paste or a soap flake-kerosene paste. As you can gather, there are numerous tanning agent alternatives for the home-tanner. You can experiment to see what works best for you.

Many tanning agents come from natural sources. Dung and urine have both been used in tanning. You can also use extracts of bark and herbs. No matter what tanning agent you put on the hide, you're going to have to stake it—work it, and stretch it, and work it some more—and this takes muscle and patience. As Rex Richardson says, ''Working hides is no small job.'' And I second that.

TANNING WITH THE FUR OFF

Some people like to remove the hair from their skins. You would do this after fleshing the hide, and before putting it in a tanning solution or staking it.

Lime mixed with water will take off hair. It must be the strong type of lime, called hydrated or slaked lime—not the type you use in your garden, but the type used in outhouses. Soak the skin until you can scrape off the hair.

For sheep skins (when you want to save the wool), you can dehair (dewool) by making a paste of hydrated lime, applying a 1/4-inch layer on the skin side, and folding it up skin to skin until you can remove the wool.

Another dehairing method, and one using readily available materials, is to mix hardwood ashes with water. Soak the hide until the hair comes off. Or make an ashes paste, and apply as above.

Once you have scraped off all the hair, you must delime the skin, or the lime (or ashes) might continue to eat through the skin. To delime, soak the hide in vinegar and water to neutralize its effect. Rinsing well after dehairing is also ultra-important. Now you can continue tanning as already described.

Making Rawhide. When my husband Sam and I and our three children (babies at the time) drove into the Sahara in southern Morocco in 1971, we were taken home by a desert family, a memorable experience that offered us a chance to observe another lifestyle. When we bade farewell to these hospitable people, the wife gave me one of her few possessions, a small, round, hard, yellow-brown box with a fitted lid. Her husband said they had made it themselves from animal skins. I now realize that they made the beautiful box from rawhide.

Rawhide is animal skin that you allow to dry hard into the shape you wish. You can make dishes or drum heads out of rawhide. It is a really exciting crafts material that you have available to you every time you butcher one of your animals.

Because you don't salt the skin, you'll have to make your rawhide immediately after slaughter or you risk losing the skin. Flesh the skin, then dehair it (as previously described). Rinse well. Next, scrape off the hair and outer layer of skin from the hair side, and then scrape the flesh side.

After dehairing and fleshing, wash the hide, and put it up on a stretcher to dry in the shade. You can lace it to a sturdy frame, or tack it on to a wall. Most folks in this area lace their skin on a frame as you can keep tightening up the laces to stretch the rawhide out really flat. Punch holes every two or three inches, and run a strong, thin rope through the holes and around the frame (Fig. 15-4).

The hide will dry stiff. When you need some for a particular project, cut off the proper quantity and soak for a day or until flexible. When Rex Richardson makes drum heads from rawhide, he stretches it over the head of the drum when it is wet and laces it down to an iron ring at the bottom. As it dries, if it begins to loosen up, he laces it down tighter.

Making Buckskin. Buckskin is a close relative to rawhide. Essentially, it is rawhide that has been worked until soft, and then smoked.

As with rawhide, don't salt the skin. Dehair it with ashes in water, rinse well, and then flesh both sides of the hide. You now apply a paste of brains to both sides of the hide, and roll it up for two days to let the brains soak in. Then you begin staking the skin, working it back and forth, stretching it this way and that, pulling it like crazy. You want to break it down completely, to make it totally soft. If you think you are finished and you let it dry and it still has hard spots—wet it lightly, reapply more brains, and rework the hide.

When the skin has dried soft, you smoke it to give it desirable color and keep it from hardening up every time it gets wet. Smoke both sides, but don't burn it. You can use your meat smoker. Traditionalists make a tipi-type frame, drape the buckskin over it, and make a cool fire on the floor in the center.

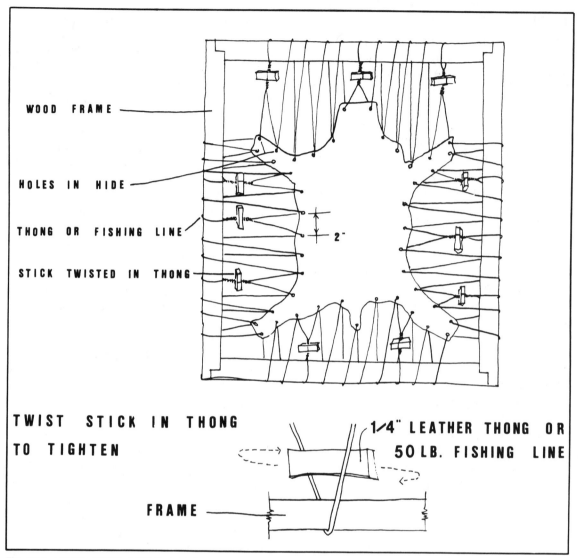

WOOD FRAME

HOLES IN HIDE

THONG OR FISHING LINE

STICK TWISTED IN THONG

2"

TWIST STICK IN THONG TO TIGHTEN

1/4" LEATHER THONG OR 50 LB. FISHING LINE

FRAME

Fig. 15-4. How to stretch rawhide on a frame.

RENDERING ANIMAL FATS

Lard is the fat from hogs, and tallow is the fat from cattle, goats, or sheep. You can use these rendered fats to make soap, candles, and various lubricants. You can also use lard (from hogs) and rendered fat (from poultry) in cooking. Beef, sheep and goat tallow isn't good to cook with, in my opinion. It is far too heavy.

When you slaughter poultry or hogs, don't throw away the fat. You should render it immedi-

ately, so it won't go rancid. You can render it in the following manner: Trim the fat into small pieces of similar sizes and cook them slowly in a stainless steel pan. The fat will begin to melt into oil. Don't let it scorch or burn.

You can also render lard in a slow oven. You'll have less chance of burning the lard if you use your oven. Don't fill the pan too full, and don't forget to stir occasionally.

When you render fat, you get lard and

256

cracklings. You can drain the cracklings on paper towels and eat them salted. Strain the lard through cheesecloth into clean, dry storage containers. You might want to strain it several times until it is perfectly clear. Chill immediately. As it thickens and becomes creamy, stir it. This should produce a firm, smooth lard. Store well sealed containers in a dark, cool place. If you have room in the freezer, you can keep your lard there. Lard can go rancid, so the colder you keep it, the better.

If you want to clarify grease that you have already used in cooking, such as drippings or bacon grease, follow these directions: Melt the grease and strain it. Put the grease in a pan with water, cup for cup. Bring to a boil. Take off the stove, and add four cups cold water while stirring. Let it cool. Skim off the clean fat on top.

You can use lard for deep fat frying. It is certainly the right price, and does the job just fine. You can also saute with lard or rendered chicken fat. Why pay high prices for cooking oil, when you have useful fat that you can render right on the farm? I know that many people look down on the use of animal fats for health reasons, but it seems a waste to throw them out. When Robyn Martin, my neighbor, renders her fat she adds garlic, onion, and various herbs to make a flavored oil. Be creative.

In the Mexican village where we lived for a month, the people considered hog fat a delicacy. They baked marvelous breads from recipes containing tremendous quantities of lard. Never before or since have I tasted such delicious breads. As shortening, lard is superlative.

Besides cooking with your home-raised fats, there are a multitude of other uses. You can use lard mixed with powdered sulfur to make salves to treat sores on your animals. And you can make soap from rendered hog fat.

MAKING SOAP

To make soap, you can follow the recipe on the lye can. This may not seem all that creative, but the recipe on the can works perfectly every time.

Mix one can of lye (13 ounces), with 2 1/2 pints cold water, and 6 pounds clean, sweet, rendered lard. This recipe makes 9 pounds of soap. Considering that the average store-bought bar of soap weighs about 4 ounces, that's quite a bit of soap.

You add the lye very slowly to the cold water in an enamel pan (a water bath canner), and stir it with a wooden spoon to dissolve. Do not use metal containers or implements. Some people like to wear goggles, long gloves, long-sleeve shirts, and jeans for this job, as lye can really burn you if it splatters on you. It makes the water temperature jump near boiling, and gives off fumes—so handle with respect. Let the lye solution cool to 75 degrees Fahrenheit (you can use a candy thermometer). In another pan, melt your lard, and let it cool to 85 degrees Fahrenheit. You want to add the 85-degree lard to the 75-degree solution—or thereabouts.

It is helpful to have a partner help you add the lard to the lye. You have to pour the lard slowly into the lye solution, while simultaneously stirring, very slowly and steadily. It is best to have one person stir, while the other pours. Six pounds of fat renders down to about 11 cups, so the slow pouring, slow stirring takes some time.

Continue stirring until the mixture starts thickening. This takes at least 20 minutes, and sometimes longer. You can see it happen. The rule of thumb is to keep stirring slowly and steadily until the wooden spoon can stand up in the mixture. The mix looks like gravy or honey.

Rapid pouring or stirring can cause soap to separate; the lye and fat never come together to form soap. If this happens, you can stir and stir, but it will never come together. So it is best to be cautious.

At this point, pour the soap into your molds. Natalie Atkinson used to use old (non-aluminum) cupcake pans for molds. She made some lovely round soaps with those pans. Figure 15-5 shows some of Natalie's soaps.

Unfortunately, Natalie ran into a bit of a problem with the round soaps. They ate into the cupcake pans. So, a safer bet is to use card-

Fig. 15-5. Homemade soap.

board boxes or wooden boxes lined with plastic wrap. And always keep your eyes open for boxes that have cute soap bar shapes. You can also pour soap into shallow wooden boxes lined with a damp cotton rag, or glass trays lined with wax paper.

After pouring your soap into whatever molds you choose, let it stand for 24 hours. Do not let it stand in a draft. In fact, it is a good idea to cover it up with a blanket or rug to keep the heat in it while it firms up. In 24 hours, you take it from the molds. If you've used large molds, you cut it into bars with a wire. Let your soap cure several weeks before you use it.

There are a number of variations on this basic water-lye-lard recipe. If you wish to use tallow, it needs to be at 130 degrees Fahrenheit, and the lye-water mix should be at 95 degrees when you pour them together. Half lard-half tallow should be at 110 degrees, with the lye solution at 85 degrees. Natalie Atkinson comes from a long line of soap makers. Natalie's mother makes soap from bacon fat. She filters it after frying her bacon and stores it in the freezer.

When she has 6 pounds, she makes soap from it. Natalie's grandmother's recipe includes 2 tablespoons sugar. The sugar is supposed to make a better lather.

If you wish you can perfume your soap. You could make an infusion of strongly scented plants—pine needles, marigolds, or roses—and substitute homemade pine water cup for cup in your recipe. You can also add in borax (and sugar) if you feel your soap isn't sudsy enough.

Before you start experimenting, I advise you to try out the basic water-lye-fat recipe several times, and get some soap-making success under your belt. Then if you want to experiment with making your own lye from wood ashes, coloring your soap pink with beet juice, or dumping in enticing scents—go ahead.

I think the basic soap recipe comes out very well. The problem with experimenting with soap recipes is that a failure can cause you to lose a great deal of rendered fat. Natalie Atkinson lost 6 pounds of lard when she tried to make "fancy" soap. It separated on her, and she is not sure why. So, she sticks with the recipe on the lye can.

If you want to experiment with original soap recipes, you could make one bar of soap. Mix 5 teaspoons lye with 1/2 cup of water, and add 1 cup lard, and whatever extras you wish. Best of luck.

BLOOD AND FEATHERS,
AND OTHER ODDS AND ENDS

If you've ever made fresh chicken soup, and then refrigerated it overnight, did you notice how it turned to jelly? Something in the bones makes this happen.

You can use the feet and bony segments of various animals to make gelatin. The less water you use, the thicker gelatin you will get. So don't throw away those feet.

Robyn Martin, whom I mentioned earlier, keeps her poultry feet frozen, until she has time to deal with them all. She scalds them, peels off the outer skin, and pulls off the toenails. If you have trouble getting these off, she says you should replunge the feet momentarily in boiling water. "Throw the chicken feet in soup," says Robyn, "but be sure to add salt and some vinegar or wine. The salt and acid pulls out the calcium and gelatin."

If you don't want to make gelatin for salads and jellies, you should at least make soups. Simmer all your bones and feet with water plus garden vegetables, herbs, and seasonings. Strain, cool and freeze for soup stock. Stock is useful in cooking, and excellent broth when you have a cold.

Robyn says there is another, totally different use for animal feet—rattles. She makes rattles from deer hooves. A rattle is an Indian musical instrument, something a shaman might use. Essentially, it is a stick with deer toenails attached to it. Boil deer feet until the toenails come off to get rattles.

Moving around the deer, if you want to save deer antlers, saw them off with a section of the head and mount them on a board. They keep forever. You can do the same thing with horns from a goat. I kept a set over my toolshed for years.

Deer antlers also make nice ornaments, as well as smoking pipes. Years ago a friend cut a 2-inch section of antler, and drilled it out to make Sam a pipe. He left the bottom solid, and drilled a second hole into the side of the antler for the pipe stem. Beautiful.

And don't forget the innards of the animals—deer and all the rest. The organ meats contain more vitamins and minerals than any other part of the animal. Why waste them? If you think you don't like them, learn how to cook them better. Slow cook them in water that includes salt, wine, and herbs. The salt and wine pull out the nutrients.

I included a few organ recipes in the text of the book because of their health factor. After all, when people pay top dollar in health stores for organ extracts, why should we cry "yukkie!" and throw them out? That's really not intelligent.

Robyn Martin, who is a natural healer as well as a farmer, thinks that the organs might be even more important than any of us realize. "They are totally pure," she says. "They are the highest quality foods you can get. I just feel that it is obvious with home-raised animals, that organs present incredible potential for healing people and improving their health. If you have gone to all the trouble to raise your own meat, it seems stupid to ignore those parts of the animal."

The blood is another potent part of the animal. You need to cook the blood, and not use it raw. Catch the blood in a pot as soon as you cut the throat. If you have no idea how to cook it, you can try making a blood-organ pudding from Rex Richardson's recipe: Grind up the heart and kidneys in a meat grinder, and saute with garlic and onions until barely cooked. Mix the blood and organs together and season. Bake in a slow oven until it gets thick.

A friend from Ethiopia taught Rex an interesting way to cook blood pudding. "We killed a sheep, and made pudding from the organs and blood. Then we cleaned the stomach, stuffed in the blood-organ mixture, and closed the stomach with a stick. We threw it in the fire to cook it. Now that is an instant dinner. You don't even need a pan, just an animal and a fire."

Of course, you already know that you can save the intestines for sausage casings and save the brains for tanning. And you probably already save feathers. Feathers are an appealing item to collect.

To save clean feathers you should dry-pick your birds. Have a bag handy into which you can stuff the feathers and down, or it will go all over the place. If you can't get the bird clean dry-picking, you can finish off by scalding the bird and wet-plucking the remaining feathers. But throw away the wet feathers.

You can also pick feathers from live birds, but this might cause them more stress than it's worth. I don't think you should pluck live birds unless you really intended to use the feathers. Pull feathers from the breast, and don't pull them all. You don't want to leave any empty patches of skin. This could make the birds catch cold.

Before storing feathers, you can dry them in the air or in the oven. To air dry, stuff them in old nylon stockings and hang in a warm area. To oven dry, put them in paper bags with a folded top, and have the oven on very low.

The trouble with feathers is that they blow all over the place. They are not easy to handle. If you dry your feathers inside nylon stockings, you might want to keep them there. You can insert the stuffed stockings directly into any pillows or comforters that you decide to make.

I have an easier time handling big feathers. I like to collect large, colorful feathers to use for ornaments and trade. Children especially love feathers. You can make children happy just by giving them some long goose feathers. I'm sure they'd go for some hollow marrow bones strung on a piece of home tanned leather, also.

BACK TO THE LAND

As I have been discussing animal by-products, I have been focusing on ways that you can use them: for food, clothing, soap, and crafts. But a farm is more than the people and animals who use it. The farm is the land, and you can always give your animal by-products back to the land.

There's nothing wrong with throwing any and all of the by-products onto the compost pile. If there is any part of the animal you don't wish to use—blood, bones, skin, hair, intestines, feathers, whatever—be sure to compost it in your pile or bury it deeply in your orchard or garden.

The compost pile is one of the most important aspects of my farm, and satisfying the appetite of the compost pile is ultra-important. The compost pile is a fine place for the animal by-products you don't want to eat or make into crafts projects; animal by-products are rich sources of minerals your soil needs. You should always compost unused parts of your animals. Composting is a positive act, not a waste at all.

Feathers, for example, contain over 15 percent nitrogen. Blood has over 12 percent nitrogen, and hair has about 14 percent nitrogen. These are extremely rich nutrients for your compost. Even bones contain a small amount of nitrogen, plus 15 to 30 percent phosphorous, another necessary garden mineral.

The people, the animals, the plants, the land—all are linked together into an ecological pattern. All rely on each other, all sustain each other, all live and die for each other.

Today I am the keeper of the land. I feed the animal from the food of the land. I kill the animal to feed myself. I return part of the animal to the land. The animal nourishes the land. Raising your own animals keeps you in touch with these cycles, with these principles of deep ecology. The animals, the people, the plants, the land—all are part of the same life force.

If you don't feel like catching the blood and making it into pudding, let it bleed onto the ground. It is all part of the same process.

Be sensitive to your animals, enjoy them when they are alive, take care of them, kill them mercifully—and enjoy as much of their bodies as taste and time permits.

I wish you best of luck with your home butchering projects. Enjoy yourself.

Appendix

Appendix

Sources

Poultry

Hall Brothers Hatchery
222 Cook Hill Road, Box 310
Wallingford, Connecticut 06492
(203) 269-4447

Hockmans, Inc.
Box 7187
San Diego, California 92107-0187
(619) 222-6983

Metzer Farms
26000 Old Stage Road
Gonzales, California 93926
(408) 679-2355

Murray McMurray Hatchery
Webster City, Iowa 50595
(800) 247-4888
(515) 832-3280

Ridgway Hatcheries, Inc.
Box 306
LaRue, Ohio 43332-0306
(614) 499-2163

Sunny Creek Farms & Hatchery
Red Lake Falls, Minnesota 56750
(218) 253-2291

Butchering Supplies

California Butcher Supply, Inc.
451 Los Coches St.
P.O. Box 801
Milpitas, California 95035
(800) 662-6212
(408) 946-2820

Hubert Supermarket Merchandising
1269 Gest Street
Cincinnati, Ohio 45203
(800) 543-7374
(513) 852-6700

Curing/Sausage Making Supplies

The Sausage Maker
177 Military Road
Buffalo, New York 14207
(716) 876-5521

Ham House Plans

Agricultural Engineering Department
North Carolina Agricultural Extension Service
North Carolina State University
Raleigh, North Carolina 27607

Information on Nitrates/Nitrites

The United States Department of Agriculture
Food Safety and Inspection Service
Washington, D.C. 20250
(202) 447-9351

Council for Agricultural Science and Technology
137 Lynn Avenue
Ames, Iowa 50010-7120
(515) 292-2125

The American Cancer Society, Inc.
4 W. 35th St.
New York, New York 10001
(212) 736-3030

Index

Index

A

age, at which to slaughter, 9

B

basic equipment, 38
beef
  breeds, 30
  care, 30
  cuts of, 155, 157
  cutting up, 151
  equipment, 30
beef recipes, 175
bleeding beef, 132
blocking pigs, 106

C

canning meat
  basics, 218
  benefits, 217
  precautions, 217
  times, 222
  tools, 221
canning meat creatively, 220
canning meats
carcass
  health of, 42
chickens
  breeds, 14
  care, 14
  cutting up, 55

conversion ratio
  feed to meat, 11
cost of raising meat, 6
costs
  feed, 10
cured meats
  bacons, 230
  brine-cure names, 228
  controversy, 225
  country style names, 226
  ham, 226
curing meats
  building a smokehouse, 239
  salami, 231
  tools, 237
cuts of beef, 157
  forequarter, 171
  hindquarter, 161
cuts of the pig
  bacon, 122
  ham, 117
  jowl, 113
  loin, 119
  shoulder, 113
cutting up meat
  beef, 151
  deer, 92
  goats, 88
  lamb, 88
  pigs, 113

D

danger, 2
debraining poultry, 47
ducks
  breeds, 17
  care, 15
  equipment, 17

E

equipment
  basic, 38
  fencing, 8
  housing, 8
  knives, 34
  large animals, 38
  poultry, 38
  slaughtering goats, 72
  slaughtering pigs, 8
  slaughtering sheep, 72
  slaughtering veal and beef, 129
eviscerating goat, 79
  pigs, 108
  poultry, 52
  rabbit, 63
  sheep, 79
  steer, 140
  venison, 85

F

feed, 10

fencing animals, 8
freezing meat, 210
  benefits, 214
  shelf life, 214
  wrapping, 212

G

geese
  breeds, 20
  care, 20
  equipment, 20
goat
  eviscerating, 79
  primal cuts, 89
goat recipes, 96
goats
  breeds, 27
  care, 26
  cutting up, 88
  equipment, 27
  skinning, 75
  slaughtering, 72

H

ham
  curing, 226
health benefits, 2
health of carcass, 42
hides
  tanning, 249
  tanning with fur on, 252
hoisting steer, 140
housing animals, 8

J

jerky
  general instructions, 94

K

knives
  sharpening, 36
knives for butchering, 34

L

lamb
  breeds, 29
  care, 29
  cutting up, 88
  equipment, 29
lamb recipes, 96

M

meat by-products, 259
meat cutting
  as a business, 183
meat cutting business
  equipment, 191
  getting started, 190
  the building, 183
  tools, 191
  work load, 193
meat cutting business, 191

meat cutting equipment
  cooler, 183
  cutting room, 185
  freezer, 185
meats
  home curing, 225
  smoking of, 244

N

nitrates and nitrites in home curing,
  225

P

pigs
  blocking, 106
  breeds, 23
  care, 23
  cutting up, 113
  equipment, 23
  evisceration, 108
  how to roast, 125
  scraping, 100
  skinning, 100
  slaughtering, 100
plucking poultry, 47
pork recipes, 124
poultry recipes, 56
poultry slaughtering
  debraining, 47
  evisceration, 52
  removing feathers, 47
  tools, 45
  skinning, 52
pound of meat from each animal, 6
pre-slaughter considerations
  pigs, 100
professional slaughtering, 200
  customer relations, 207
  equipment, 201
  tools, 206

R

rabbit
  breeds, 21
  care, 21
  cutting up, 70
  equipment, 21
  evisceration, 63
  recipes, 69
  saving the skin, 249
  skinning, 59
  slaughtering, 59
recipes
  beef, 175
  cured meats, 238
  goat, 96
  lamb, 96
  pork, 124
  poultry, 56
  rabbit, 69
  venison, 96
rendering animal fats, 256

roasting a pig, 125

S

scraping the pig, 100, 103
sharpening knives, 36
sheep
  eviscerating, 79
  primal cuts, 89
  skinning, 75
  slaughtering, 72
skinning goat and sheep, 75
  poultry, 52
  rabbit, 59
  calf/steer, 134
  pigs, 100, 103
  venison, 85
skins
  rabbit, 249
slaughtering
  as a business, 200
slaughtering beef
  bleeding, 132
  cutting up, 151
  equipment, 129
  stunning, 132
slaughtering equip-
  ment (professional)
  boom and winch, 202
  truck, 201
slaughtering goats
  equipment, 72
slaughtering pigs, 100
  blocking, 106
  cutting up, 113
  evisceration, 108
  scalding and scraping, 103
  skinning, 103
slaughtering poultry, 44
  debraining, 47
  evisceration, 52
  removing feathers, 47
  skinning, 52
slaughtering rabbit
  evisceration, 63
  tools, 59
slaughtering sheep, 72
  equipment, 72
slaughtering steer
  eviscerating, 140
  hoisting, 140
  skinning, 134
  splitting, 140
slaughtering veal
  equipment, 129
slaughtering venison, 72, 85
smokehouses
  building of, 239
  types of, 240
smoking meat, 244
soap making, 257
splitting steer, 140
stunning beef, 132

T

tanning
  with fur on, 252
tanning hides, 249
  buckskin, 255
  rawhide, 255
  tools, 253
  with fur off, 255
tools
  poultry slaughtering, 45

slaughtering, 40
turkeys
  breeds, 19
  care, 19
  equipment, 19

V

venison
  chilling the carcass, 88

eviscerating, 85
skinning, 85
slaughtering, 72, 85
venison recipes, 96

W

weight
  of dressed animal, 6
  of live animal, 6

Other Bestsellers From TAB

☐ **THE GARDENING IDEA BOOK**

Whether you have space for a full-scale garden or only a pocket size backyard, this exciting collection of articles from *Farmstead Magazine* shows how you can grow all kinds of delicious, healthful fruits and vegetables, easily and inexpensively. Whether you're a first time gardener or an old hand at growing your own fruits and vegetables, here's expert advice and guidance that's guaranteed to make your garden more productive, easier to take care of, and less expensive! 208 pp., illustrated.

Paper $10.95   **Hard $15.95**
Book No. 2684

☐ **RAISING CHICKENS—Haynes**

Now veteran chicken handler and hatchery owner Cynthia Haynes puts you in touch with the realities, the rewards, and the potential hazards of raising your own chickens . . . and gives you the kind of practical, "voice of experience" advice and guidance that just isn't available from any other source. From choosing the chicken breed for your particular needs to finding a source for chicks or brood hens, you'll find it here! 272 pp., 274 illus. 7″ × 10″.

Paper $12.95   **Hard $21.95**
Book No. 1963

☐ **MAKING KNIVES AND TOOLS—2nd Edition—Blandford**

Here is the completely revised and expanded new second edition of a guidebook that has become the "bible" in its field. Written by a highly respected metalworking/woodworking craftsman, it shows you how you can make almost any type of edged tool or knife, at amazingly affordable cost! You'll learn how to make pro-quality knives and tools from plain kitchen knives to shaping tools. 256 pp., 187 illus.

Paper $12.95   **Hard $18.95**
Book No. 1944

☐ **PROFESSIONAL CARE AND FINISHING OF GUNSTOCKS—Traister**

Packed with essential information that all gun hobbyists will appreciate, this excellent sourcebook covers selection of gunstock woods, stock design, stock construction, stock inletting, finishing (and refinishing), gunstock repair, and even the fine points of checkering, carving, and accuracy bedding. Adding to its appeal for collectors and woodworkers alike are the 30 photos of finished rifles made by well-known master stockmasters! Here is all the step-by-step direction anyone needs to move from complete novice to skilled gunstock maker. 208 pp., 162 illus., 7″ × 10″.

Paper $15.95   **Hard $21.95**
Book No. 1756

☐ **BEGINNING BLACKSMITHING WITH PROJECTS—Converse**

In this comprehensive sourcebook you'll find all the basic how-to's you need to learn the art of blacksmithing the right way—the first time out! In no time you'll have the essential knowledge and skills necessary to effectively and safely make a wide range of useful products ranging from tools to plant hangers. You'll receive all the practical guidance and over-the-shoulder instruction you need to make shackles, chains, rings, hooks, even a forge weld! 288 pp., 260 illus. 7″ × 10″.

Paper $12.95   **Hard $18.95**
Book No. 2651

☐ **THE COUNTRYSIDE BOOK OF FARMING LORE**

Lush, ripe tomatoes, fresh from the vine . . . fresh-baked bread made from all-natural grains you've grown and milled yourself . . . ALL the pleasures and money-saving benefits of being self-sufficient (*without* the problems) can be yours with the help and guidance provided by this exceptional new sourcebook! Filled with fascinating, informative, time- and money-saving tips from the experts at *Countryside Magazine*, this is an invaluable guide for every backyard gardener, homesteader, or small farmer. It gives organic solutions to common farming problems and shows how to get the most productive use from your available land. 288 pp., 91 illus.

Paper $13.95   **Book No. 1952**

☐ **PRACTICAL LANDSCAPING AND LAWN CARE—Webb**

Make your lawn the envy of the entire neighborhood . . . *without* spending a fortune or putting in never-ending hours of maintenance time! Here's absolutely everything you need to successfully plan, plant, and maintain lawn grasses and groundcovers, vines, and flowering ornamentals . . . annual, biennial, and perennial flowers . . . shape trees, lawn trees . . . even decorative (and delicious) fruits and berries. It doesn't matter whether your climate is cold and damp or hot and dry . . . whether your soil is sandy, rocky, or gummy clay . . . *everything* you need is here! 240 pp., 84 illus. 7″ × 10″.

Paper $13.95   **Hard $21.95**
Book No. 1818

☐ **ATTRACTING, FEEDING AND HOUSING WILD BIRDS . . . WITH PROJECT PLANS—Moorman**

Here is a thorough, up-to-date look at how you can provide a total environment that will attract the most birds—both common and rare varieties. It's also a rich source of project plans for practical and easy-to-construct bird feeders and birdhouses that can be inexpensively built from space age materials. Includes a year-round bird feeding schedule, recipes for custom seed mixtures, and detailed plans for birdhouses and bird feeders. Plus landscaping ideas for making your yard more attractive to birds! 154 pp., 33 illus.

Paper $8.95   **Hard $15.95**
Book No. 1755

Other Bestsellers From TAB

☐ **RAISING GOATS: THE BACKYARD DAIRY ALTERNATIVE—Weems**

Here's a book that shows, in step-by-step detail, how to raise goats as a home-grown source of both dairy products and meat. This book gives you a practical look at the ins and outs of selecting, raising, caring for, and breeding goats. You'll learn how to select the goat or goats that will be best for your purposes and find out about the characteristics of the five major breeds of dairy goats. 208 pp., 120 illus.

Paper $12.95   **Book No. 1534**

☐ **MR. SINGLE SHOT'S GUNSMITHING—IDEA BOOK**

Whether you're a pro or amateur gunsmith, you'll find dozens of easy-to-do projects to help you remodel, repair, restock, rebarrel, rechamber, rebuild, and restore both new and obsolete singleshots. You don't need fancy tools or experience; these step-by-step directions and illustrations show you all the basic techniques of gunsmithing. Soon, you'll be doing pro-quality work! 176 pp., 173 illus. 7″ × 10″.

Hard $18.95   **Book No. 1511**

☐ **COUNTRY WISDOM: THE ART OF SUCCESSFUL HOMESTEADING**

Whether you're homesteading in a remote rural area . . . or you're a city or suburban dweller who'd like some back-to-basics hints for more economical energy-efficient living, this sourcebook is jam-packed with projects and how-to's for just you! From planning your ideal homestead to operating a wood stove, from producing your own solar power to tips on livestock raising, it's all here! 544 pp., 363 illus.

Paper $12.95   **Book No. 1356**

☐ **BIRD TAXIDERMY—Tetley**

Here's a complete step-by-step introduction to the specialized art of bird taxidermy. You'll find clear, easy-to-follow instructions and lots of photographs and illustrations to guide you through every phase of preparing and cleaning game birds and waterfowl, how-to's for choosing mounts and lifelike poses, a complete explanation of the tools and materials used by the taxidermist, how to choose a professional taxidermist, and much more! 112 pp., 94 illus.

Paper $12.95   **Book No. 1313**

☐ **GROWING FRUITS OR BERRIES—Webb**

With the proven gardening methods detailed in this natural method handbook, you'll be able to choose the fruit and berry varieties that will flourish in your particular climate and soil conditions . . . raise productive plants the organic way . . . beat the high cost of supermarket produce . . . get the extra landscaping bonus offered by attractive fruit-bearing trees and bushes . . . even earn extra income by selling your surplus fruit crop! 304 pp., 60 illus.

Paper $12.95   **Book No. 1518**

☐ **BUILDING A LOG HOME FROM SCRATCH OR KIT—Ramsey**

A step-by-step guide to planning, designing, and constructing a modern, energy-efficient log dwelling! Find out how you can *save even more by building your own log house* either from scratch or from a kit! All the how-to's you'll need are included in this exciting new guide that takes you from the initial planning stages right through the final interior finishing. 256 pp., 257 illus.

Paper $12.95   **Book No. 1458**

☐ **COUNTRY KITCHEN—A PROJECT AND IDEA BOOK**

Now, the editors of *Countryside Magazine* have selected the very best country kitchen techniques, recipes, and money-saving ideas for your needs: a range of low-cost ideas for making your own cheeses, making your own homestyle luncheon meats and sausage, ice creams, pickles and preserves, even vinegars, cider, and geletin. You'll be amazed at the variety of ways to stretch your food dollar! 144 pp., 17 illus.

Paper $9.95   **Hard $15.95**

Book No. 1354

☐ **SOLAR GREENHOUSES: *UNDERGROUND***

With the easy-to-follow directions included in this ingenious, do-it-yourself book, you'll be able to design, construct, and use your own underground solar greenhouse to grow fresh fruits, vegetables, and flowers all year long . . . using solar energy as a heat and power source! You'll learn how an energy-efficient, underground greenhouse works to optimize light and radiation and more! It even gives step-by-step gardening techniques. 416 pp., 203 illus.

Paper $12.95   **Book No. 1272**

*Prices subject to change without notice.

Look for these and other TAB books at your local bookstore.

TAB BOOKS Inc.
P.O. Box 40
Blue Ridge Summit, PA 17214

Send for FREE TAB catalog describing over 1200 current titles in print.